DICTIONARY OF ELECTRONICS

WITHDRAWAL

No. 300

$9.95

DICTIONARY OF ELECTRONICS

Harley Carter

SECOND EDITION

FIRST PRINTING—SEPTEMBER 1972

Copyright © George Newnes Ltd., 1960, 1963

Printed in the United States
of America

Reproduction or publication of the content in any manner, without express permission of the publisher, is prohibited. No liability is assumed with respect to the use of the information herein.

Hardbound Edition: International Standard Book No. 0-8306-2300-X

Paperbound Edition: International Standard Book No. 0-8306-1300-5

Library of Congress Card Number: 72-90780

Published in England by George Newnes Ltd.

Reference
TK
7804
C34
1972

AUTHOR'S PREFACE

THE spectacular and rapid development of the science of Electronics during the past two decades has had repercussions in almost every branch of human activity. It has revolutionized the art of telecommunications. It has made available new techniques for industry and, indeed, has made possible many processes and manufacturing methods previously impossible of achievement. It has placed new and invaluable tools in the hands of the research scientist, the physician and the surgeon.

At the same time it has presented personal problems to many individuals who are concerned either primarily or in a secondary degree with electronic phenomena or applications. These problems arise from three main causes.

In the first place, electronic scientists and engineers have found it necessary to add to their vocabulary a large number of new technical terms in order to provide names for newly discovered phenomena or newly developed processes. Secondly, electronic research has resulted in the formulation of new hypotheses and concepts which provide more acceptable explanations of many familiar phenomena.

Thirdly, large numbers of engineers and technicians, originally trained and working in other fields, now find themselves called upon to apply electronic techniques to their own technical activities, or to instal, operate or maintain electronic equipment.

While the necessary knowledge can be gleaned from the many technical books now appearing in rapid succession, and from articles in the technical and trade press, these books and articles often assume that the reader is already familiar with the special electronic terminology—which is not always the case.

In preparing the present volume I have attempted to provide at least a partial solution to these problems. The selection of entries has been made on the basis of terms relating to the fundamental facts of electronic science as first choice. To these have been added explanations of many familiar electrical terms, written in the light of more modern scientific concepts. Finally, a number of

Appendices provide a large amount of tabulated data, in most cases supplementing the information given in individual entries in the body of the book.

The system of cross-indexing by printing key words in small capitals will assist the reader to turn to other entries which may provide additional information relating to a particular subject.

I gratefully acknowledge the kindness of Mr. W. E. Pannett, A.M.I.E.E., and Mullard Ltd. for permission to reproduce or to adapt information and illustrations originally prepared by them. Acknowledgement must also be given to the many other sources, too numerous to list, from which information has been drawn.

In conclusion, I trust that this book will prove helpful to the many engineers, technicians, apprentices and students for whose work or studies familiarity with the science of Electronics, and in particular with its terminology, is essential.

HARLEY CARTER

DICTIONARY OF ELECTRONICS

A

α-Particles. See ALPHA PARTICLES.

A Amplifier. An amplifier immediately following a microphone or other signal source. A PRE-AMPLIFIER.

A Battery. Battery used for heating the cathodes of thermionic valves. A LOW-TENSION battery.

A.B.C. Receiver. Radio broadcast receiver which can be adapted by simple switching, either for operation from dry batteries or for operation from a.c. or d.c. electricity mains.

Aberration. Distortion of an image due to the inability of a system of lenses and/or mirrors to bring all rays to a focus at the same point. The aberrations of optical systems have their counterparts in electron lens systems.

Absolute Temperature. Temperature based on the absolute zero of temperature (−273° C or 0° K) at which a body possesses no thermal energy. The degree absolute is equal to the degree Centigrade.

Absolute Unit. Unit which can be defined completely in terms of the fundamental units of length, mass and time.

Absorber Circuit. Combination of a resistor and a capacitor in series, connected across the terminals of a switch or other circuit-breaking device in an oscillatory circuit. Its function is to damp the circuit and thus to prevent sparking or arcing when the current is interrupted.

Absorptiometer. Instrument for the accurate measurement of the absorption and transmission of light by semi-transparent substances and used for the determination of turbidity, fluorimetry, etc. In one form, illustrated in Fig. A-1, two photocells are connected in a bridge circuit. Light from a common source falls directly upon one cell, and via the substance under examination on the other cell.

The bridge is then adjusted to balance, the ratio between the resistances of the two variable arms being a measure of the absorption of the specimen.

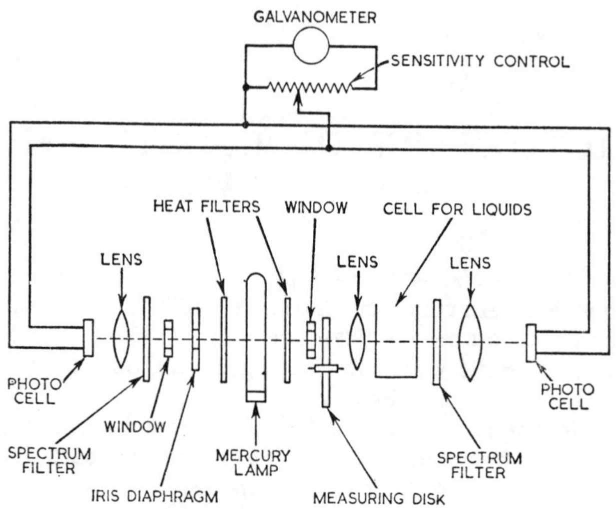

FIG. A-1.—SPEKKER ABSORPTIOMETER.

Accelerating Electrode. An electrode in an electron tube which is maintained at a positive potential with respect to the cathode and any other electrodes situated between the cathode and the accelerating electrode, thus imparting acceleration to electrons in the direction away from the cathode. Although this definition includes the anode of the tube, the term is usually reserved for accelerating electrodes other than the anode.

Accelerating Grid. ACCELERATING ELECTRODE in the form of a grid.

Accelerating Potential. Potential applied to one electrode of an electron tube, positive with respect to the cathode, and therefore exerting an accelerating force on electrons present in the field.

Acceleration. Rate of change of velocity. A free electron in an electric field experiences an accelerating force in the direction of the positive pole. Its velocity therefore progressively increases.

Accelerator. (1) ACCELERATING ELECTRODE (q.v.).

(2) An electronic device for accelerating charged particles to high energies. See PARTICLE ACCELERATOR.

Accelerator Tube. A thermionic tube employed as a particle accelerator.

Acceptor (Acceptor Atoms). Atoms of an element deliberately introduced into the crystal lattice of a semiconductor, and having a lower valency than the semiconductor. An acceptor atom captures or " accepts " an electron from the semiconductor in order to complete its valency bonding, thus producing a positive charge carrier or " hole " and becoming itself negatively charged. See p-TYPE SEMICONDUCTOR and TRANSISTOR.

Acceptor (Acceptor Circuit). Circuit comprising an inductor and a capacitor in series and thus presenting very small impedance to signals of frequencies equal to or very close to the resonant frequency of the circuit. An acceptor circuit may be connected in electronic equipment in such a way as to provide an effective short-circuit for interference or signals of a particular frequency. See WAVETRAP.

Acorn Valve. Familiar name for a form of thermionic valve for use at ULTRA-HIGH FREQUENCIES, in which, by adopting very small dimensions and special constructions, the inter-electrode capacitances, lead inductances and TRANSIT TIME effects are greatly reduced.

Acoustic Feedback. The return of acoustic energy from the output of a sound-reproducing equipment such as a microphone–amplifier–loudspeaker combination, to the input or to an intermediate stage, thereby causing the system to generate sustained oscillations which are manifested as continual howling. See MICROPHONY.

Activation. Process or series of processes in the manufacture of thermionic tubes whereby the cathode acquires its full emissive properties. See AGEING.

Adaptor. Arrangement of electrical contacts on an insulating base, so disposed that it permits an electron tube or similar device to be plugged into a socket designed for tubes having some different arrangement of connecting pins.

Adcock Aerial. Aerial system consisting of two vertical open-spaced DIPOLES with screened horizontal connexions, and therefore responding almost entirely to the vertically polarized component of the wave.

Adcock Direction Finder. Direction-finding equipment employing an ADCOCK AERIAL.

Address System. See PUBLIC ADDRESS SYSTEM.

Adjacent Channel. CHANNEL, the frequency of which is immediately above or below that of the channel to which a piece of apparatus is tuned.

Adjacent Sound Channel. In television, the sound channel, not associated with the television transmission to which a receiver is tuned, but having a frequency immediately above or below that of this transmission.

Adjacent Vision Channel. In television, the vision channel the frequency of which is immediately above or below that of the channel to which a receiver is tuned.

Admittance. (Symbol Y) Reciprocal of the impedance of an electrical system, and thus analogous to the CONDUCTANCE of a purely resistive system.

Aerial. Conductor or system of conductors, usually elevated above ground level, and employed to radiate or to intercept electromagnetic energy of " radio " frequency. Some authorities limit the use of the term to simple systems and employ the word ARRAY to more complex systems having directional or other special properties. In the present work, however, the word aerial is used for both the simple systems and for the more complex arrays.

Aerials can be roughly classified as: (1) those in which the power to be transmitted is applied, or the incoming signal is developed, between an elevated conductor or system of conductors and earth, and (2) those in which the signal is applied or developed between two conductors or conducting systems insulated from the earth.

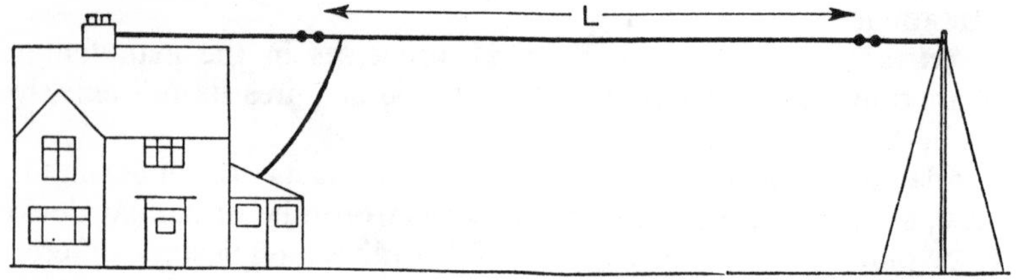

FIG. A-2.—INVERTED-L AERIAL.

Typical of Class (1) are the inverted-L aerial, Fig. A-2, which consists of an elevated horizontal conductor connected to the transmitter or receiver at one end and the T-aerial, in which the horizontal elevated conductor is connected to the transmitter or receiver at or near its mid-point. Aerials are also made with vertical conductors, an example being the mast aerial used in many high-power medium-wave transmitting stations. In this type a steel mast is used as the elevated conductor.

Typical of Class (2) is the dipole aerial, the most usual form of which is a conductor having a length equal to approximately half of

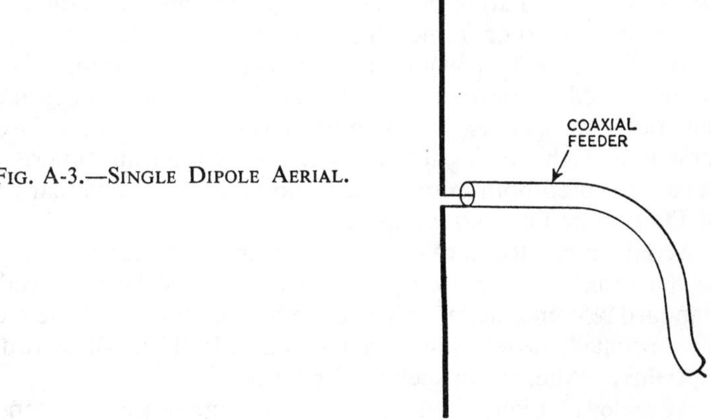

FIG. A-3.—SINGLE DIPOLE AERIAL.

the wavelength of the signal to be received, and divided at its electrical centre by a short air-gap, Fig. A-3. The transmitter or receiver is connected across the air-gap. Such an aerial has little or no directional properties, that is to say, as a transmitter it radiates equally in all directions, or as a receiver it is equally

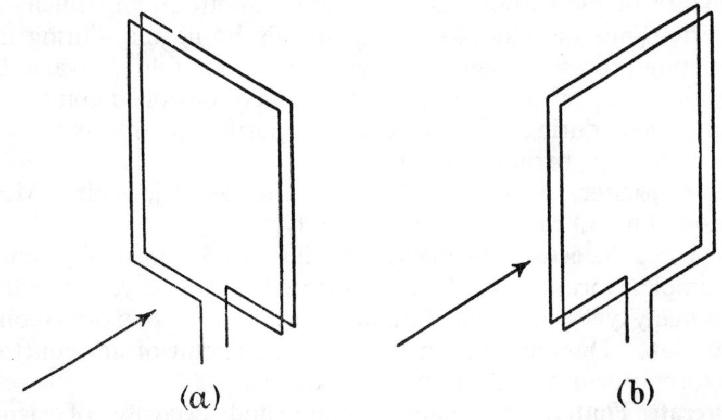

FIG. A-4.—LOOP AERIALS SHOWING AT (a) THE DIRECTION OF APPROACH OF SIGNALS GIVING MINIMUM RESPONSE, AND AT (b) THE DIRECTION OF APPROACH GIVING MAXIMUM RESPONSE.

sensitive to signals arriving from all directions. By the use of one or more REFLECTORS, in the form of vertical conductors suitably dimensioned and spaced, the aerial becomes more or less directive. For point-to-point or BEAM communication, highly directional aerials are necessary, and usually consist of ordered arrays or assemblies of radiating or collecting systems and reflectors.

The loop aerial or frame aerial, Fig. A-4, consists of one or more turns of wire, usually wound on a non-conducting frame, the turns being located in approximately the same plane. It has considerable directional properties, being most sensitive when the axis of the loop is at right angles to the direction of the transmitter. Loop aerials are used both in portable radio receivers and in many forms of DIRECTION FINDING equipment.

Aerial Gain. Ratio of the signal power transferred from an aerial to the input of a receiver to that which would be produced by a standard reference aerial under the same conditions. Unless otherwise specified, the reference aerial is assumed to be a half-wave dipole.

Aether. Alternative spelling for ETHER.

Afterglow. Light emitted from the luminescent screen of a CATHODE-RAY TUBE for a period following the cessation of excitation of the screen material by the impact of the electron stream. See PERSISTENCE.

Ageing. Final process in the manufacture of thermionic tubes whereby the cathode acquires its full emissive properties. In the case of oxide-coated cathodes the cathode is originally coated with a mixture of the carbonates of barium and strontium, which are converted into the oxides of those metals by heating during the evacuating process. Thereafter the cathodes are fully activated by " ageing ", i.e. by operating the tube under controlled conditions for a period, during which a small proportion of the oxides are reduced to pure barium and strontium.

Air Capacitor. CAPACITOR in which the dielectric is air. Most variable (tuning) capacitors are of this type.

Air-cored Inductor. INDUCTOR having no ferromagnetic core. The simplest form is a single-layer solenoid. Multi-layer solenoids are of many types, including PANCAKE COILS and WAVE-WOUND coils.

Air Gap. Discontinuity in the magnetic circuit of an inductor, transformer or other electromagnetic device.

Aircraft Flutter. Alternate increase and decrease of signal strength at a television receiving aerial due to the simultaneous reception of the direct signal from the transmitting station and a signal reflected from a passing aircraft. The fluctuations are the result of rhythmic changes in the phase between the two signals as the distance between the receiving aerial and the aircraft changes.

Aligned Grid Valve. Thermionic valve in which the wires of the SCREEN GRID and of another grid which is at a negative potential are so disposed that the screen current is minimized.

Alignment. Process of adjusting the values of the components in two or more oscillatory circuits so that the circuits are accurately tuned to resonate at a given frequency, and/or can be simultaneously tuned to any frequency within a specified range by the operation of mechanically coupled (ganged) variable circuit elements.

Alloyed-junction Transistor. Type of transistor used as an amplifier or oscillator. See TRANSISTOR.

Alpha (α). Symbol for the incremental current gain in a TRANSISTOR. It is numerically equal to the ratio of the change of output current to the change of input current producing it. In the COMMON BASE circuit the current gain is slightly less than unity, although there is a considerable power and voltage gain. In the COMMON EMITTER circuit there is also a substantial current gain, which is then denoted α'.

Alpha Particles (α-particles). Nuclei of the atom of helium, comprising two NEUTRONS and two PROTONS, and thus exhibiting a positive electric charge.

Alpha Rays (α-rays). Stream of swiftly moving alpha particles. Are capable of ionizing gases and of producing fluorescence in certain substances.

Alternating Current (Voltage etc.). Electric current (voltage, etc.), which changes direction rhythmically, rising from zero to a maximum in the positive direction, falling to zero again and then

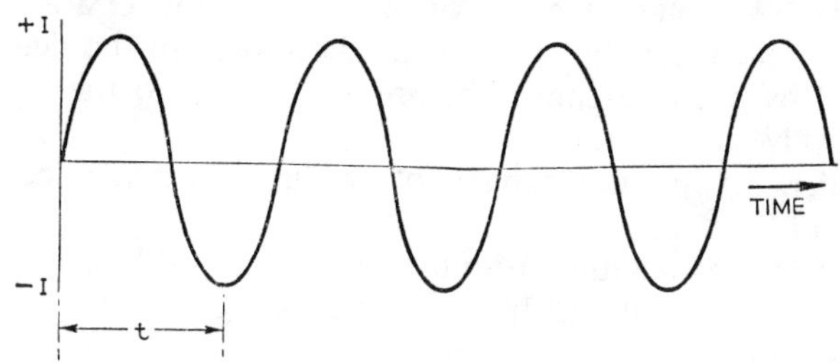

FIG. A-5.—INSTANTANEOUS VALUES OF AN ALTERNATING CURRENT PLOTTED AGAINST TIME.

The interval t is the periodic time, the number of periods in one second is the frequency and the shape of the curve is the waveform.

increasing to a maximum in the negative direction before returning again to zero, after which the cycle repeats. The number of cycles per second is the FREQUENCY of the alternating phenomenon. Instantaneous values of the current, etc., plotted against time show the WAVEFORM, Fig. A-5.

Alundum. A form of aluminium oxide. One of its uses is in thermionic-tube manufacture for insulating the cathode heater from the tubular cathode.

Ambient Light (Illumination). The normal illumination in the space in which a piece of apparatus (such as a television receiver or a photo-electric device) operates.

Ambient Temperature. The temperature of the surroundings in which a piece of apparatus operates.

Ampere. Practical unit of electric current. Equivalent to the flow of $6{\cdot}25 \times 10^{18}$ electrons per second.

Ampere-Turns. Measure of the magneto-motive or magnetizing force, and equal to the number of turns of wire in the magnetizing coil multiplied by the current in amperes flowing through the coil. The c.g.s. unit of magneto-motive force is the gilbert, equal to $10/4\pi$ ampere-turns, symbol AT.

Amplification. Process by which a comparatively small SIGNAL is applied to the input of an AMPLIFIER and appears at the output in greatly magnified form.

Amplification Factor. Figure of merit for a thermionic valve, indicating the maximum voltage gain theoretically obtainable from the valve; symbol μ (see VALVE CHARACTERISTICS).

Amplification Factor (Gas). Factor by which the sensitivity (i.e. the anode current for a given input) of a gas-filled tube, e.g. a gas-filled photocell, is increased by the ionization of the gas filling.

Amplified Automatic Gain Control. AUTOMATIC GAIN CONTROL system in which the control voltage, derived from the detector, is magnified by a d.c. amplifier before application to the controlled valve or valves.

Amplifier. Apparatus capable of producing a magnified version of an input SIGNAL.

Amplitude. Maximum instantaneous value (positive or negative) of a periodic quantity such as an alternating voltage. (See also PEAK VALUE.)

Amplitude Distortion. Variation of GAIN in an amplifier with change of amplitude ot the input signal, the frequency of the signal remaining constant.

Amplitude Limiter. Device for suppressing the peaks of " noise " pulses in amplitude-modulated signals, or for removing variations of the carrier amplitude, including noise peaks, in frequency-modulated signals. In the amplitude-modulated case the limiter may be a diode so connected that a sudden signal pulse of excessive amplitude causes the valve to become non-conductive for a brief period. In the frequency-modulated case the limiter is usually a saturated pentode operated under CLASS C conditions, the self-bias circuit being so designed that the grid bias varies in sympathy with the amplitude of the input in such a way as to maintain constant amplitude of the output voltage. See NOISE LIMITER.

Amplitude Modulation. Method of combining a signal with a carrier wave of constant frequency in such a way that the carrier amplitude is varied in accordance with that of the signal.

Analogue Computer. General name for computing devices in which the variables in a given problem are represented by physical quantities such as lengths, pressures, electric charges, etc., the calculations consisting in the manipulation and measurement of these quantities, the values of which may change continuously. The above very wide definition covers such familiar devices as the slide rule, in which length is used to represent numbers, and also the various electronic analogue computers in which such magnitudes as electric charge or magnetic strength are used to represent variables (cf. DIGITAL COMPUTER).

Ångström Unit. (Symbol Å) Unit of length, particularly employed for the measurements of the wavelengths of light, X-rays, etc. Equal to 10^{-10} m, or one ten-thousandth of a MICRON.

Angular Frequency. (Symbol ω) Since one complete cycle of an

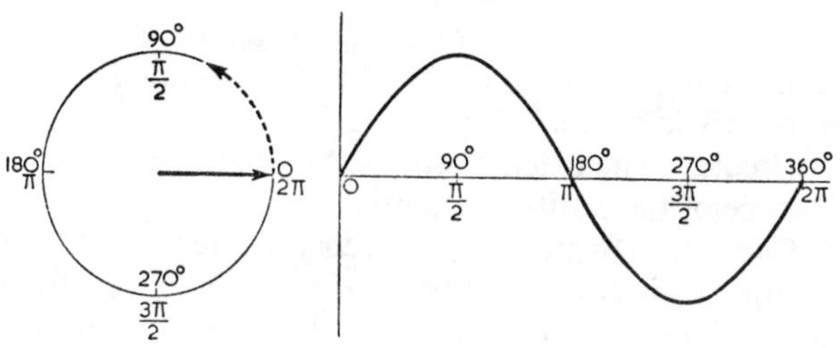

FIG. A-6.—REPRESENTATION OF AN ALTERNATING QUANTITY AS THE ROTATION OF A VECTOR, TO ILLUSTRATE ANGULAR FREQUENCY AND ANGULAR VELOCITY.

alternating quantity (e.g. an alternating voltage, current etc.) is equivalent to the rotation of the corresponding vector through an angle of 360° or 2π radians, the total angular movement of the vector in one second is equal to 2π times the frequency, or $2\pi f$ radians. This quantity, denoted by the symbol ω, is known as the angular frequency. See Fig. A-6.

Angular Velocity. Rate of change of angular displacement. May be expressed in radians per second, degrees per second or revolutions per second.

Anion. Negatively charged ION which, in an electrolyte or in a gas-filled space, travels towards the positive electrode or anode.

Anisotropic. Said of a property of a given material the extent of which is different in different directions. Thus, certain ferro-magnetic materials can be treated to render them more permeable in one direction than in others. Other substances have anisotropic conductivity.

Annihilation Radiation. Energy in the form of GAMMA RAYS emitted when an electron and a positron come into collision and annihilate each other.

Anode. Principal positive ELECTRODE by which the current leaves an electrolyte, electron tube, etc.

Anode Battery. Battery which supplies the anode circuit(s) of a valve or valves. Familiarly known as the h.t. (high-tension) battery, and sometimes as the B battery.

Anode Bend (Bottom Bend). The curved part of the anode current/grid volts characteristic curve of a high-vacuum thermionic valve.

Anode-bend Rectification (Anode-bend Detection). Rectification of a radio-frequency signal which occurs when it is applied between the control grid and cathode of a high-vacuum thermionic valve operated in the region of the bottom bend of its anode current/grid volts characteristic curve. See Fig. A-7.

Anode Circuit. The external conducting path between the anode and the source of the positive potential.

Anode Current. (Symbol I_a) Electric current in the external anode circuit of an electron tube, and represented by the flow of electrons from the region of the cathode to the anode within the tube. That proportion of the CATHODE CURRENT of the tube which actually flows in the anode circuit.

Anode Dissipation. That part of the total power supplied to the anode circuit of a valve which is lost at the anode by conversion to heat as the result of bombardment of the anode by swiftly moving electrons.

Anode Drop (Valve Drop). Voltage drop across the internal anode-to-cathode path of a valve and due to the internal resistance of the valve.

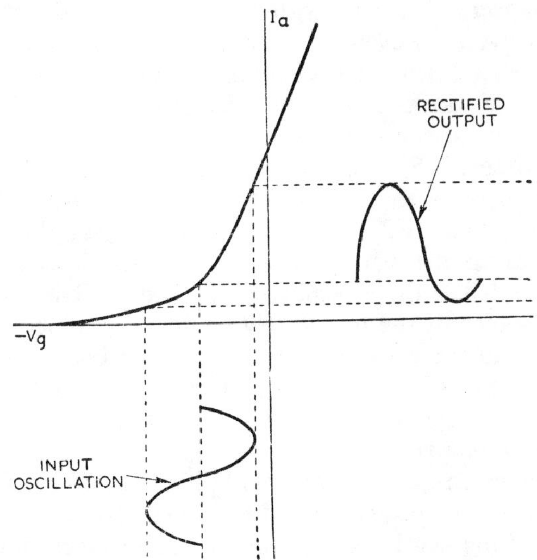

FIG. A-7.—ANODE BEND RECTIFICATION.

Anode Impedance. A complex a.c. impedance of the anode-to-cathode path within a valve, comprising not only the internal resistance (which varies with the instantaneous working conditions) but also the effects of inter-electrode capacitances, lead inductances and other frequency-dependent properties.

Anode Load (R_a). Element or elements possessing impedance and included in the external anode circuit of a thermionic valve. The variations of voltage, current or power in the load resulting from the application of a signal to the control grid constitutes the OUTPUT of the valve.

Anode Modulation. Method of combining the information to be transmitted with the CARRIER by introducing the signal material into the anode circuit of the transmitting valve.

Anode Resistance (r_a). Internal resistance of a valve measured between cathode and anode under specified circuit conditions.

Numerically equal to a small change in anode voltage divided by the resulting change in anode current:

$$r_a \text{ (ohms)} = \frac{\delta V_a \text{ (volts)}}{\delta I_a \text{ (amps)}}$$

See VALVE CHARACTERISTICS.

Anode Stopper. Element included in the anode circuit of a thermionic valve to prevent or to damp out parasitic oscillations. Typical devices are a resistance, connected as close to the anode as possible, and FERRITE BEADS threaded on the wire forming the connexion to the anode of the valve.

Anode Voltage. (Symbol V_a, Anode potential) The voltage between the anode of an electron tube and the cathode. The anode voltage is less than the voltage of the anode supply (V_b) by an amount equal to the voltage drop across the impedance of all elements included in the external anode circuit. These include the internal resistance of the h.t. supply source, the impedance of the anode load, and the resistance of the cathode bias resistor if employed. Variations of anode current due, for example, to the application of a signal to the control grid, cause corresponding variations of anode voltage.

Anode Voltage Drop. The potential difference between the anode and cathode of an electron tube during the period of conduction.

Antenna. Conductor or system of conductors intended to radiate or to intercept radio signals. See AERIAL.

Anti-cathode. TARGET of an electron tube, and particularly the electrode at which Röntgen rays are produced in an X-ray tube. The anti-cathode may or may not be the anode proper.

Anti-interference Aerial. Aerial system in which that part which is intended to intercept signals is connected to the receiver by screened leads, thus reducing the risk of picking-up local interference signals. Sometimes called an anti-static aerial.

Anti-microphonic. Applied to methods of mounting thermionic valves to reduce the risk that mechanical vibrations will be transmitted to their electrode systems, setting up microphonic oscillations. See MICROPHONY.

Anti-polarizing Winding. Auxiliary winding on the core of a transformer or inductor, and carrying a direct current of such value and direction that it neutralizes the effect of a direct current or currents circulating in the normal windings and tending to cause saturation of the core.

Anti-static Aerial. See ANTI-INTERFERENCE AERIAL.

Antimony. Brittle, silver-white, pentavalent metallic element. Employed as the base on which is deposited a thin layer of caesium to form the cathode in certain types of PHOTO-EMISSIVE CELLS.

Aperiodic. Incapable of sustained oscillation under specified conditions. The term is applied particularly to a circuit or network in which either: (1) the DAMPING is sufficient to prevent the build-up of oscillations when impulses are applied to the circuit, or (2) the natural frequency of the circuit is so different from the band of frequencies over which the network is intended to operate that the circuit characteristics are practically constant over the working frequency range.

Aperiodic Aerial. Aerial, the characteristics of which change but little over a specified band of frequencies.

Appleton Layer. One of the regions of ionized air in the upper atmosphere which reflects radio waves. See IONOSPHERE.

Aquadag. Proprietary name for a solution of colloidal graphite. One of its applications is for applying the conductive graphite coating to the internal surface of cathode-ray tubes.

Arc Discharge. Luminous and high-temperature electrical discharge in an ionized gas, the current being carried mainly by the vapour of the electrode material.

Arc Transmitter. A radio transmitter in which the radio-frequency oscillations are generated by an electric arc.

Argon. One of the inert gaseous elements, constituting about 0·8 per cent of the earth's atmosphere.

Argon-filled Noise-source Tube. Cold-cathode diode filled with argon gas and used as a standard source of " noise " signals for testing the noise performance of radio receivers. See NOISE.

Array. Complex aerial system consisting of a number of radiating or receiving elements so arranged as to possess directional properties.

Arsenic. A pentavalent metallic element. n-TYPE germanium for use in transistors can be produced by alloying pure germanium with a small but accurately controlled proportion of arsenic.

Artificial Aerial (Artificial Antenna). A circuit comprising inductors, capacitors and resistors adjusted to have electrical characteristics similar to those of a working aerial, but unable to radiate energy. Used for testing transmitting equipment. Also called a dummy aerial.

Artificial Earth (Counterpoise Earth). System of wires erected slightly above ground level and used instead of or in addition to the earth connexion of an aerial system.

Aspect Ratio. Ratio of picture width to picture height in television. In the British system the aspect ratio is 4 : 3.

Associated Sound Carrier. The carrier wave which is modulated by the sound accompaniment of a particular television programme.

Astigmatism. Aberration of a lens system, whether optical or electronic, due to the focal length being different in two planes.

Asymmetrical. Said of a magnitude the variations of which are not equally (i.e. symmetrically) disposed on either side of a given value.

Asymmetrical Deflexion. Effect in a cathode-ray tube of applying a deflecting voltage which does not vary symmetrically about a fixed value relative to the potential of the final anode. An asymmetrical deflexion voltage applied to the pair of deflexion plates nearer the final anode could result in trapezium distortion of the trace on the luminescent screen. However, tubes are available with deflexion plates specially shaped to compensate for this.

Atmospherics. (Often written X's) Electromagnetic radiations of radio frequency produced by natural causes. The term is also applied to the disturbances thus caused.

Atom. Smallest quantity of a chemical element which can enter into combination or take part in a chemical reaction.

Atom, Structure of. Hypotheses concerning the structure of chemical atoms are in a constant state of flux as the result of further research. The following simplified account, however, includes those conceptions which are most necessary for an understanding of electronic science. It is based on ideas first put forward by Lord Rutherford, as modified by Niels Bohr, since the Rutherford–Bohr atom provides a satisfactory explanation of all electrical and magnetic phenomena.

According to this hypothesis, a chemical atom consists of a central nucleus which exhibits a positive electric charge and, revolving in orbits about the nucleus, a number of particles called ELECTRONS, each of which exhibits a negative electric charge of a fixed amount. The number of electrons associated with a normal atomic nucleus is such that their combined negative charges exactly neutralize the positive charge of the nucleus.

The nucleus itself is of complex structure, and always contains particles called PROTONS, each of which carries a positive charge equal to the negative charge of one electron. Since the normal atom is electrically neutral, the number of protons in the nucleus of a given element must be equal to the number of orbital electrons associated with the nucleus of a normal atom. This number is the ATOMIC NUMBER of the element.

The simplest atom is that of hydrogen, which contains a nucleus consisting of one proton, about which revolves a single electron (Fig. A-8). The mass of an atom resides almost entirely in the nucleus, for the mass of a proton is about 1840 times that of an electron. In addition to protons, the atomic nuclei of all elements

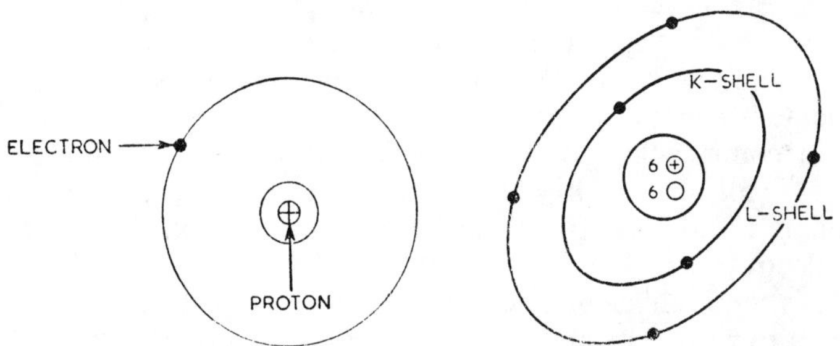

FIG. A-8.—(*left*) REPRESENTATION OF THE HYDROGEN ATOM.
The nucleus consists of a single proton and a single electron is associated with it. Atomic Number: 1, Atomic Weight: 1·0080.

FIG. A-9.—(*right*) REPRESENTATION OF THE CARBON ATOM.
Six neutrons and six protons comprise the nucleus and the six electrons are situated two in the K-shell and four in the L-shell. Atomic Number: 6, Atomic Weight: 12·010.

except hydrogen contain other particles called NEUTRONS, having approximately the same mass as a proton but carrying no electric charge. The number of protons plus the number of neutrons in the nucleus determines the ATOMIC WEIGHT of that element (see Fig. A-9).

Atoms of certain elements exist having slightly different atomic weights. This is due to the fact that some atoms, while having the requisite number of protons, have different numbers of neutrons. Atoms which differ in this way are called ISOTOPES or isotopic forms of the element in question.

The properties of a given element are largely determined by the number and arrangement of the electrons in the atom.

If an atom is deprived of one or more electrons it exhibits a net positive charge, and is termed a POSITIVE ION, while the freed electron is, of course, a negative charge carrier. On the other hand, an atom may acquire one or more electrons in excess of its normal quota, and it then exhibits a net negative charge and is termed a NEGATIVE ION.

The electrons revolving about the nucleus of an atom are considered to be arranged in a number of " shells ", shown in the flat for the sake of clarity in Fig. A-9, the shells corresponding to different energy levels of the electrons. These shells are designated the *K*, *L*, *M*, . . . *Q* shells, commencing with that nearest to nucleus. For each shell there is a definite complement of electrons which can never be permanently exceeded, although a shell may contain fewer than its maximum complement of electrons. The maximum number of electrons which a particular shell can accommodate is equal to $2n^2$, where n is the sequence number of the shell again commencing from the innermost shell. Thus for shell *K*, $n = 1$; for shell *L*, $n = 2$ and so on, so that shell *K* can accommodate up to 2 electrons, shell *L* up to 8 electrons, shell *M* up to 18 electrons, etc.

It is the number of electrons in the outermost shell of an atom which to a great extent governs the properties of an element. For example, metals, which are good conductors of electricity, have in general only one, or sometimes two, electrons in the outer shell. Again, atoms which have eight electrons in the outer shell are chemically inert, e.g. argon, neon, krypton, etc. A full outer shell, or one containing eight electrons represents a stable condition, and all atoms endeavour to attain this stable state, for example by sharing one or more electrons with another atom or group of atoms—the basis of chemical combination.

Since each shell corresponds to a definite energy level, it is possible, by imparting additional energy to an electron, to transfer it from a shell of a certain energy level to a shell of higher energy level. However, since a shell cannot retain more than its normal quota of electrons, the displaced electron immediately returns to its original shell, at the same time giving up, in the form of electromagnetic radiation, the extra energy which had been imparted to it. The frequency of this radiation is related to the amount of energy radiated.

The amount of energy required to move an electron from one shell to the shell of next higher energy level is called a *quantum*, and the relation between the quantum and the frequency of the resultant radiation is that the quantum is equal to the frequency multiplied by PLANCK'S CONSTANT.

Atomic Number. The number allotted to a chemical element in the series resulting from the arrangement of all elements in ascending order of the number of electrons revolving round the nucleus of the normal atom. See ATOM—STRUCTURE OF. The atomic number is NOT the ATOMIC WEIGHT (q.v.).

Atomic Weight. Relative weight of the atom of an element when the weight of an oxygen atom is taken as 16 (more accurately, when the weight of the ^{16}O oxygen atom is taken as 16).

Attenuation. Reduction or falling off of a physical quantity due to: (*a*) natural, or (*b*) artificial causes. An example of (*a*) is the falling off of radio signal strength with increasing distance from the transmitter. An example of (*b*) is the variation of signal input to an amplifier by means of a volume control or other special network. See ATTENUATOR.

Attenuator. Electrical network used to reduce deliberately the input signal to some piece of apparatus, or to reduce the degree of amplification of signals of particular frequencies. The simplest continuously variable attenuator is a POTENTIOMETER or voltage divider connected across the input terminals. Typical networks giving a fixed degree of attenuation are the pi- (π_1) network and the T-network—see Fig. A-10.

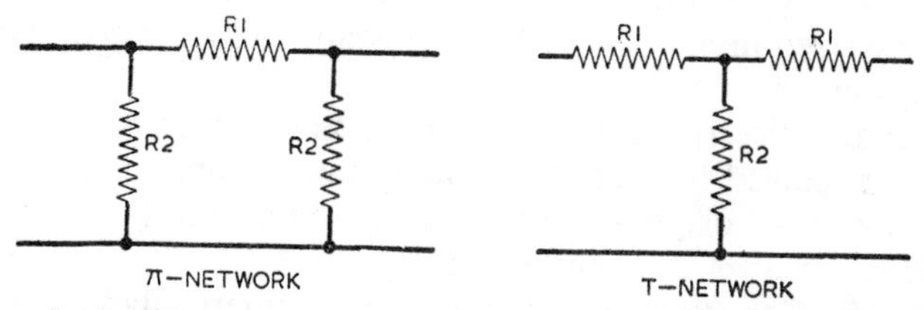

FIG. A-10.—TYPICAL FORMS OF ATTENUATOR NETWORKS GIVING A FIXED DEGREE OF ATTENUATION.

Attenuator Pad. A network included in a circuit in order to introduce a fixed loss, or to obtain impedance matching between two circuit elements as, for example, an aerial and its transmission line.

Audio Frequency. Frequency of an oscillation within the range which, if the oscillation consists of pressure waves, produces the sensation of sound. For practical purposes the audio-frequency band may be considered as 30 c/s to some 15 kc/s.

Audio-frequency Amplifier. A thermionic amplifier designed to operate over the audio-frequency range.

Audio-frequency Transformer. A static transformer the windings of which are located on a ferro-magnetic core, and intended for use as a coupling transformer in networks through which flow currents of AUDIO FREQUENCY.

Audio Output. The output, measured either in volts or in watts, of an audio-frequency amplifier.

Audion. Name originally given to the three-electrode high-vacuum thermionic valve by its inventor, Lee de Forrest. Now replaced by the term TRIODE.

Autodyne Oscillator. A valve employed in an AUTOHETERODYNE RECEIVER, for both generating the local oscillation and for some other purpose, such as amplification or detection.

Auto-emission. Emission of electrons from a cold cathode by reason of the high potential gradient existing at the surface of the cathode.

Autoheterodyne Receiver. A radio receiver employing the principle of BEAT RECEPTION, and incorporating an AUTODYNE OSCILLATOR.

Automatic Bias. See AUTOMATIC GRID BIAS.

Automatic Control. In its widest sense, any system whereby a particular condition, e.g. temperature, or a process, operation or programme of operations, is governed in accordance with pre-determined requirements without constant human surveillance or intervention.

Automatic Direction Finding. Direction-finding system in which the signal received controls servo-motors which operate the rotation of the loop aerial or goniometer, coming to rest automatically at the position of maximum or minimum signal.

Automatic Gain Control. Method of automatically increasing or decreasing the amount of amplification in a radio-frequency or intermediate-frequency amplifier so that, for a given modulation depth, the output remains substantially constant independent of fluctuations in signal strength. Automatic gain control (a.g.c.) is employed in most radio and television receivers to counteract the effect of FADING. The method is illustrated in the basic circuit of Fig. A-11. A part of the output of the final pre-detector amplifier stage is rectified by the diode V2, thus providing a direct voltage proportional to the amplitude of the carrier wave. This voltage, suitably filtered by the network R.C., is applied to the control grids of the r.f. and/or i.f. valves in such a sense that increase of carrier amplitude increases, and decrease of carrier amplitude decreases the negative grid bias of the valves. Since the valves concerned have VARIABLE-MU characteristics, increase of signal amplitude (and hence of grid

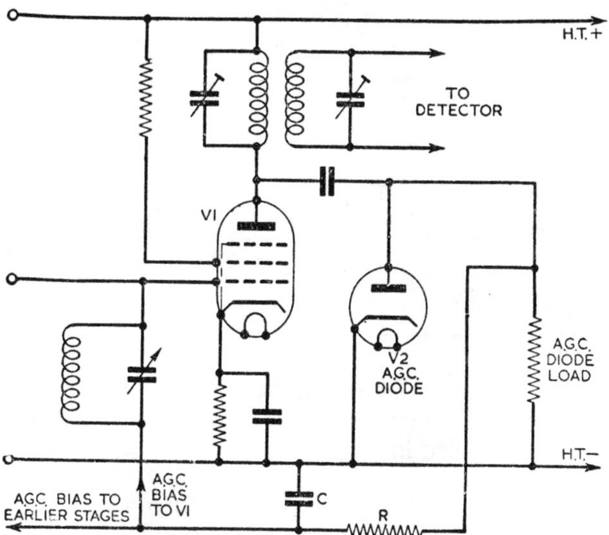

FIG. A-11.—BASIC A.G.C. CIRCUIT.

bias) reduces the gain, and decrease of signal amplitude (and hence decrease of grid bias) increases the gain of the controlled stages, thus maintaining the output constant.

Automatic Grid Bias. Steady potential (grid bias) produced at the control grid of a thermionic valve without the use of a separate grid bias battery or other supply source. It can be due either to the potential drop resulting from the flow of grid current in a resistor connected in the grid circuit, or by the potential drop across a resistor connected between the cathode and the negative terminal of the high-tension supply, in which case the cathode is maintained at a positive potential with respect to the control grid. See Fig. A-12. This form of automatic grid bias is often, and more correctly, termed CATHODE BIAS.

Automatic Picture Control. Form of AUTOMATIC GAIN CONTROL adopted in television receivers to compensate for variations in signal strength such as those resulting from FADING or from reflexions from passing aircraft (see AIRCRAFT FLUTTER). The general principle of automatic picture control is the same as that of automatic gain control in a sound receiver, but the varying control bias is derived from the BLACK LEVEL of the television signal.

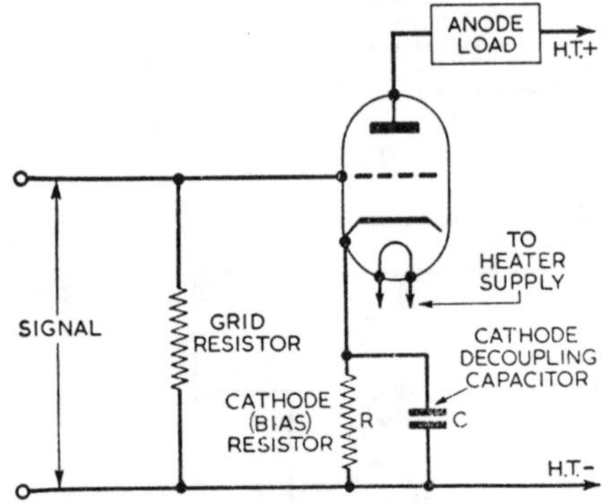

FIG. A-12.—BASIC CIRCUIT FOR AUTOMATIC GRID BIAS BY MEANS OF A RESISTOR IN THE CATHODE CIRCUIT.

The cathode is maintained at a positive potential with respect to the grid by an amount equal to the voltage drop across resistor R, capacitor C decouples the cathode, thus preventing negative feedback from anode to cathode.

Automatic Tuning. Design feature of certain domestic radio receivers whereby any one of a number of pre-selected programmes can be instantly tuned in by pressing the appropriate button on the panel.

Automatic Volume Control. (Often written a.v.c.) Term originally applied to the process now more accurately denoted AUTOMATIC GAIN CONTROL.

Automation. Omnibus term for the automatic control and operation of industrial plant and processes, and covering not only such simple applications as the maintenance of correct temperature and other working conditions but also the complete programming and control of the most complex series of processes.

Autotransformer. Static transformer having a single winding, part of which is common to both primary and secondary circuits (see Fig. A-13).

Auxiliary Grid. Name originally applied to the second or SCREEN GRID of a tetrode.

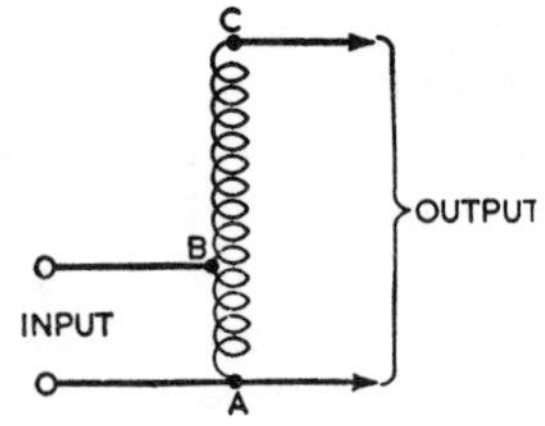

FIG. A-13.—DIAGRAMMATIC REPRESENTATION OF AN AUTOTRANSFORMER.

The part AB is the primary and the whole winding AC is the secondary.

B

β-particles. Abbreviation for BETA PARTICLES.

β-rays. Abbreviation for BETA RAYS.

B Amplifier. Audio-frequency amplifier which follows the A AMPLIFIER in broadcasting studio equipment. Mixers and faders are interposed between the output of the A amplifier and the input of the B amplifier.

B Battery. The battery which supplies the power to the anode circuits of thermionic valves. More usually termed the HIGH-TENSION Battery.

Back Coupling. Coupling in an amplifier whereby energy is fed back from the output to the input. See FEEDBACK.

Back Porch. Period of 6 μsec occurring at the end of each line synchronizing pulse in a television transmission, during which the signal is held at BLACK LEVEL, thus suppressing the picture during the line flyback. See also TELEVISION WAVEFORM (Fig. B-1).

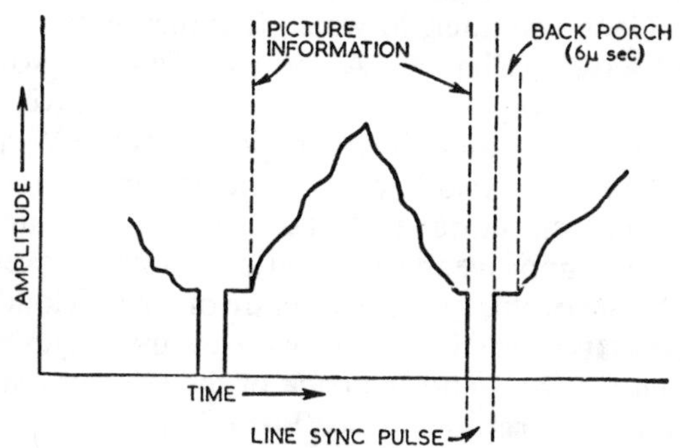

FIG. B-1.—TELEVISION LINE WAVEFORM SHOWING LINE SYNCHRONIZING PULSE AND BACK PORCH.

Back Projection. Method of optical projection in which the image is thrown on to the rear of a translucent screen and is then viewed from the front. The system is largely used in PROJECTION TELEVISION.

Background Noise. The aggregate of random noise in a sound-reproducing system, arising from such causes as radio interference, valve and other circuit noise, record scratch, etc., and not from the signal being reproduced.

Backlash. (1) Term sometimes applied to REVERSE GRID CURRENT in a thermionic valve, i.e. the current flowing in the grid circuit due to loss of electrons by the grid.

(2) Persistence of oscillation in a resonant circuit when the stimulus (e.g. feedback) is reduced to a value less than that which was needed to cause oscillation to commence.

Back-to-back. Two electron tubes are said to be connected back-to-back when an alternating signal is applied to them in such a manner that one tube conducts during one half of the signal cycle and the second tube during the next half cycle.

Back-scatter Method of Measurement. Method of measuring the thickness of a coating as, for example, of lacquer or rubber on steel cylinders, or of tin or zinc on steel plate, or of glaze on tiles. It employs a source of beta radiation and a GEIGER–MÜLLER counter tube. The beta radiation is directed on the coated surface. Part is scattered, part absorbed by the coating and part penetrates the coating and is reflected from the surface of the backing material. Of the proportion re-radiated in this way, part is absorbed, but a part proportional to the weight of the coating material per unit area reaches the Geiger counter, in which it is measured.

Backward-wave Oscillator. A form of TRAVELLING-WAVE TUBE in which the electron beam and the r.f. wave travel in opposite directions. Power outputs in the region of 500 mW are obtained at 2500–5000 Mc/s. Also known as the O–carcinotron.

Baffle. Rigid structure such as a sheet of sound-insulating material, used to improve the distribution of sound waves. In particular, a structure of this type in the centre of which a loudspeaker can be mounted. Its effect is then to increase the length of the sound path between the front and the back of the speaker diaphragm.

Balanced Valve Operation. See PUSH–PULL OPERATION.

Ballast Resistor. Series resistor included in a circuit to ensure that the current flowing is substantially constant. In a d.c./a.c. mains-operated radio receiver, the ballast resistor is usually an adjustable resistor connected in the series heater chain and adjusted to a value which, at the prevailing mains voltage, limits the current

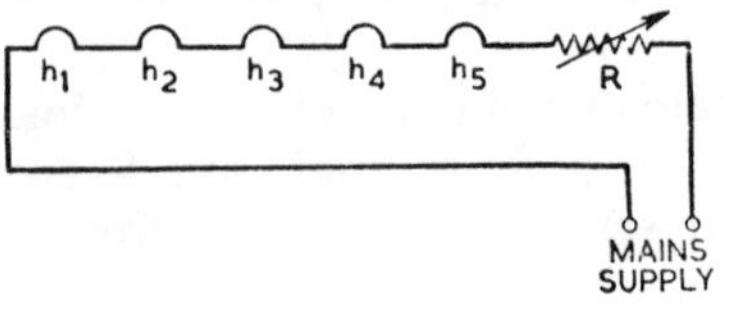

FIG. B-2.—BASIC CIRCUIT OF SERIES HEATER CHAIN FOR FIVE INDIRECTLY HEATED VALVES OPERATED FROM AN ELECTRICITY MAINS SUPPLY.

R is the ballast resistor.

to the rated value for the valve heaters (Fig. B-2). A more elaborate form of ballast resistor is the BARRETTER, which, by reason of its temperature coefficient of resistance, maintains the current constant independent of fluctuations in the applied voltage.

Balun. Shortened term derived from " BALanced-to-UN-balanced transformer ". Balance transformation systems are often used in connexion with v.h.f. aerials to permit an unbalanced co-axial feeder to be correctly matched to a balanced dipole.

Band (Frequency Band). Portion of the continuous frequency spectrum between defined limits. See also BAND WIDTH.

Band-pass Filter. A filter circuit which has a good response to inputs having frequencies between two critical limits, but which severely attenuates inputs of higher or lower frequencies.

Band-pass Tuning. Method of tuning a receiver by employing two resonant circuits, simultaneously tuned to the same frequency, the coupling between the two circuits being such as to give a substantially uniform response over a frequency band which just covers the sidebands corresponding to the signal modulation.

Band Spreading. Reduction of the tuning range of a resonant circuit by connecting a relatively large fixed capacitor in parallel with the tuning capacitor. By providing a number of different fixed capacitors, any one of which can be selected by a multi-way switch, the complete range of variation of the tuning capacitor can be made available for tuning over each of a number of comparatively narrow wavebands, thus facilitating accurate tuning.

Band Switching. Use of a multi-way switch to select different inductors and/or capacitors so that a single tuning dial can be employed for tuning over a number of frequency bands.

Band Width. In general, the frequency limits of a given waveband. More specifically, the term is used to indicate the width of the frequency band occupied by a modulated carrier wave, or the width of a frequency band allotted to a particular service or over which a particular transmitter or receiver can operate.

Bands I to V. Five frequency bands in the v.h.f. and u.h.f. region allotted to broadcasting and television. They cover the following frequencies:

Band I, 41–68 Mc/s;
Band II, 87–100 Mc/s;
Band III, 174–216 Mc/s;
Band IV, 470–585 Mc/s;
Band V, 610–960 Mc/s.

Barium. A metal of the alkaline earth group. Barium oxide is one of the oxides used for coating thermionic cathodes. Barium metal is sometimes used as a GETTER in the manufacture of high-vacuum electron tubes.

Barkhausen Oscillator. High-vacuum thermionic valve and its associated circuit which produces oscillations in the order of 100 Mc/s, its action depending upon the transit time of electrons between cathode and anode.

Barkhausen–Kurz Oscillations. Parasitic oscillations which can occur in a high vacuum valve under certain conditions of electrode potentials. When generated in television receivers, e.g. in the line output stage, they produce irregular white vertical lines on the left-hand side of the picture.

Barrel Distortion. Distortion of an image in such a way that the the sides, top and bottom of a rectangular picture are convex (Fig. B-3). In television reproduction, barrel distortion is usually due to non-uniformity of the field produced by the scanning coils.

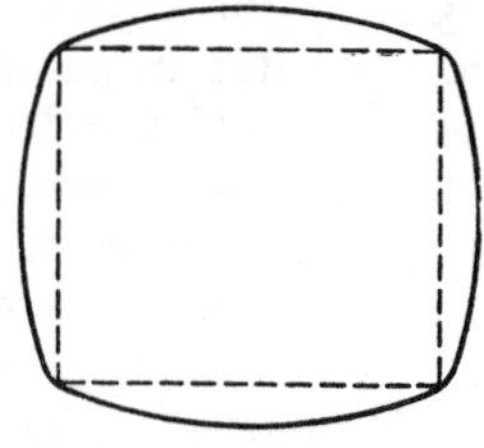

FIG. B-3.—BARREL DISTORTION.

Barretter. Resistor, e.g. of iron wire, having a negative temperature coefficient of resistance, enclosed in a gas-filled glass envelope. Due to its temperature coefficient, its resistance increases if the current tends to increase, and decreases if the current tends to decrease. A barretter is therefore suitable for use as a BALLAST RESISTOR, since it tends to maintain constant current in spite of fluctuations of applied voltage.

Base. In a TRANSISTOR, that zone of semiconductor material which is located between the EMITTER and the COLLECTOR.

Base (Valve). Lower end of the envelope of a thermionic valve or other electron tube, at which are situated the metallic pins or other contacts whereby the electrodes of the tube are connected to the external circuit. For details of various standard bases, see VALVE BASE.

Basic Circuit. A circuit, in diagram form, containing only the essential features necessary for explaining the operation of a system, the refinements incorporated in practical configurations being omitted for the sake of clarity.

Basket Coil. An inductor consisting of a self-supporting spiral winding, adjacent turns being disposed in criss-cross fashion to minimize self-capacitance.

Bass Boost. Increase of low-frequency response of an audio amplifier without sacrificing overall gain, for example by modifying the negative-feedback network.

Battery Eliminator. Apparatus for supplying electric energy derived from the mains to a radio receiver originally designed for operation from batteries.

Battery Receiver. Radio receiver in which the supplies for the anode circuits and for cathode heating are obtained from primary or secondary batteries.

Beacon (Radio). Fixed radio transmitter which radiates signals as an aid to navigation. See DIRECTIVE BEACONS, EQUI-SIGNAL BEACON, MARKER BEACON, RADAR BEACON, RADIO BEACON.

Beam. (1) Electromagnetic radiation concentrated so that it is propagated solely or mainly in one direction.

(2) A similarly concentrated flow of high-energy electrons.

Beam Aerial (Beam Antenna). AERIAL system having pronounced directional properties.

Beam Array. BEAM AERIAL consisting of a number of suitably arranged radiating members.

Beam Current. That part of the electron stream in a CATHODE-RAY TUBE which passes through the aperture of the final anode and strikes the luminescent screen.

Beam-forming Electrodes. Electrodes so located, and maintained at such potentials, that they cause the electron stream to be concentrated into one or more beams.

Beam Modulation. Deliberate variation or modulation of the beam current in a cathode-ray tube by the application of a varying signal voltage between control grid and cathode, in order to produce corresponding variations of the brightness of the image on the screen. Continuous beam modulation is employed in television tubes in order to reproduce the graduations of light and shade in the picture. Rhythmic modulation of the beam is sometimes used in cathode-ray oscilloscopes to indicate time intervals.

Beam-splitting Plates. Electrodes sometimes incorporated in a cathode-ray tube. By applying a potential to these electrodes the electron stream is divided into two beams which can be deflected independently, thus permitting two different traces to be displayed on the screen at one and the same time.

Beam Suppression. Deliberate interruption of the electron beam in a cathode-ray tube by applying a large negative potential to the control grid. Often employed to suppress the trace on the screen during the FLYBACK, or as a safety device in the event of TIMEBASE failure.

Beam Tetrode. Four-electrode thermionic valve in which secondary emission effects are reduced by a negative space charge produced in the region of the anode by beam-forming plates or electrodes, thus giving the valve characteristics similar to those of a pentode (Fig. B-4).

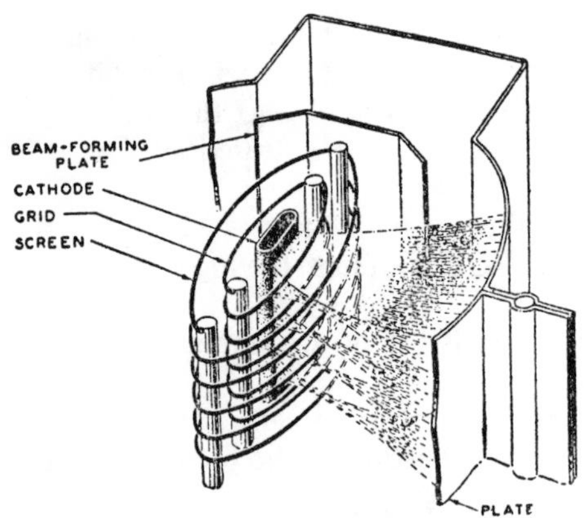

FIG. B-4.—BEAM POWER TETRODE.

Beam Transmission. Transmission of radio signals from a highly directive aerial for point-to-point communication. A similarly directive aerial is required at the receiving station.

Beam Valve. Thermionic valve in which the effects of secondary emission from the anode are minimized by the arrangement of the electrodes.

Bearings. Direction, in degrees of arc from true North, from which an incoming signal arrives, as determined by DIRECTION-FINDING equipment. Bearings are classified according to their probable accuracy as 1st class (accuracy within ±2 per cent); 2nd class (±5 per cent) or 3rd class (±10 per cent).

Beat. Rhythmic increase and decrease of amplitude resulting from the combination of two oscillations of slightly different frequencies. When the oscillations concerned occur in an electric circuit the phenomenon is known as HETERODYNING.

Beat Frequency. The frequency of the resultant amplitude variations due to the combination of two oscillations of different frequencies. The beat frequency is equal to the difference between the frequencies of the original oscillations.

Beat-frequency Oscillator. (Contraction b.f.o.) Device for generating oscillations of approximately sinusoidal waveform by combining two radio-frequency electrical oscillations of different frequencies. A beat-frequency oscillator, consisting of a fixed frequency and a variable frequency valve oscillator, an electronic mixer, the necessary filters and amplitude control, and giving an output of frequency adjustable between, say, 20 c/s and 10 kc/s is a useful piece of service equipment for testing the performance of audio-frequency equipment such as amplifiers, loudspeakers, etc.

Beat Oscillator. Thermionic valve oscillator used for generating the local oscillation required for BEAT (HETERODYNE) RECEPTION.

Beat Reception. Method of radio reception in which the incoming signal is combined with a locally-generated oscillation of different frequency, thus producing a beat-frequency signal. If the incoming signal consists of continuous-wave telegraphy and the difference between the signal frequency and the local oscillation frequency falls within the audio-frequency range, the output signal will be audible.

Becquerel Rays. Name originally given to the radiations emitted by radioactive substances, and now distinguished as ALPHA RAYS, BETA RAYS and GAMMA RAYS.

Bel. Unit used when comparing two amounts of power, voltage or current. If P_1, P_2; V_1, V_2; or I_1, I_2 are the amounts of power, voltage or current respectively, and N is the corresponding number of bels, then $N = \log (P_1/P_2)$ or $2 \log (V_1/V_2)$ or $2 \log (I_1/I_2)$. Voltage and current ratios must be specified with reference to input and output impedances.

Bellini–Tosi Aerial. Arrangement of two large fixed-frame aerials mounted at right angles to each other and used in conjunction with a RADIOGONIOMETER in radio direction finding.

Beta Particles. Electrons travelling at velocities up to 99 per cent of the velocity of light, such as are emitted from the nuclei of the atoms of radioactive materials.

Beta Rays (β-rays). Stream of high-velocity beta particles travelling at speeds approaching that of light.

Betatron. Apparatus for accelerating electrons to very high velocities by means of a periodic magnetic field, thus producing " artificial " beta rays.

Bias. Steady direct voltage applied between the cathode and control electrode of a thermionic tube in order to determine its WORKING POINT. See also GRID BIAS.

Bifilar Winding. Method of winding a conductor, or two conductors carrying the same current, in such a way that the inductive effect is zero. For example, the wire may be doubled back on itself and then wound in a coil as in the non-inductive resistor shown in

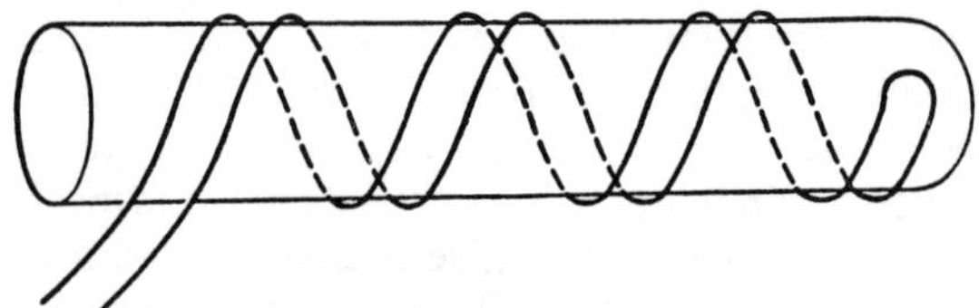

FIG. B-5.—NON-INDUCTIVE BIFILAR WINDING.

Fig. B-5. Heaters of indirectly-heated thermionic valves are often arranged as bifilar windings in order to prevent the transfer of mains-frequency hum to the cathode circuit.

Binary Scale. System of notation based upon two digits only. See SCALES OF NOTATION.

Binode. Name previously applied to the thermionic double diode having one cathode and two anodes.

Black Level. Modulation level of a television signal (Fig. B-6) corresponding to a black area of the transmitted picture. In the

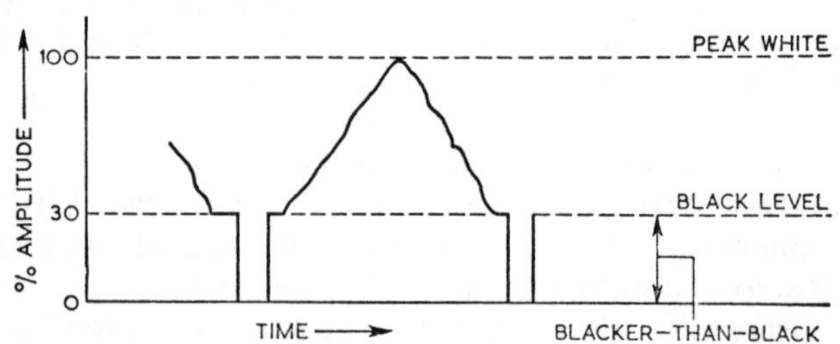

FIG. B-6.—TELEVISION LINE WAVEFORM SHOWING PEAK WHITE LEVEL, BLACK LEVEL AND THE " BLACKER-THAN-BLACK " REGION.

British television system, black level is 30 per cent of the maximum carrier amplitude. See TELEVISION WAVEFORM.

Black-level Clamping. Application of pulses of flat-topped waveform to the television signal before transmission in order to compensate for the disturbance of the BLACK DATUM LEVEL in the video-frequency amplifying system.

Blacker-than-black. That part of a television signal in which the amplitude is less than the black level and therefore carries no pictorial information (Fig. B-6). The line and frame synchronizing pulses are transmitted in the blacker-than-black region. See TELEVISION WAVEFORM.

Blanking. Suppression of the video signal at the end of each line and frame of a television transmission in order to separate the picture information from the synchronizing pulses.

Blattnerphone. Early form of sound recording by modulation of the magnetization along a steel wire or tape. See TAPE RECORDING.

Blind-landing System. Radio navigational aid for aircraft whereby the pilot is informed by radio of his location with respect to the landing ground and is given instructions during his approach so that he can land safely under conditions of bad visibility.

Blind Spot. Position within the normal service area of a radio transmitter at which, due to interference effects resulting from reflexion, the field strength is greatly below the normal value.

Block Diagram. Diagrammatic representation of a circuit or system in which the various parts of the system, e.g. amplifier stages, frequency changer, detector, etc. are represented by a rectangle or " block " or similar symbol and not by a detailed circuit. Fig. C-4 is a typical example of a block diagram, and Fig. C-5 the corresponding detailed circuit.

Blocking Capacitor. A CAPACITOR connected in such a way that it isolates one part of a circuit from direct potentials occurring in another part of the circuit, while permitting the passage of alternating signals (Fig. B-7).

Blocking Oscillator. One of the many types of circuit available for generating SAW-TOOTH VOLTAGES for use, for example, as television TIMEBASES. In the basic circuit shown in Fig. B-8 it must be assumed that at the commencement of the cycle the grid of the triode is at a negative potential beyond the cut-off point, due to a heavy charge on capacitor C_g, so that no anode current flows. Capacitor C charges from the high-tension supply via resistor R, producing the rising part or stroke of the saw-tooth V_0, and also building up the positive potential at the anode of the valve. Simultaneously the charge on C_g leaks away via R_1 so that the grid potential of the valve ultimately rises to a value at which anode current commences to flow. The transformer T is so connected

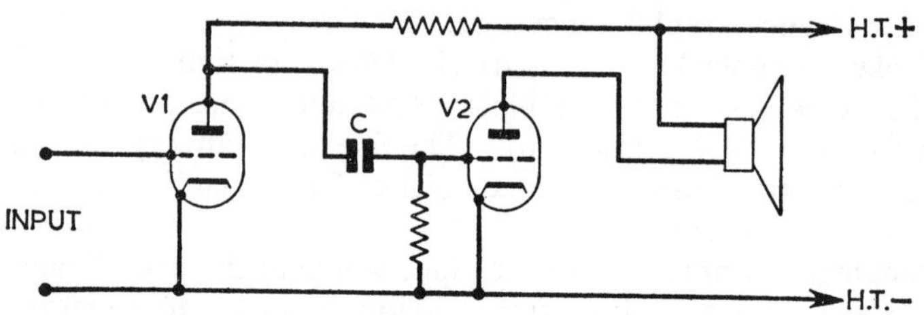

FIG. B-7.—BASIC CIRCUIT OF AN AMPLIFIER.

Capacitor C is a blocking capacitor isolating the grid circuit of V2 from the H.T. supply, while permitting the (alternating) output of V1 to reach V2.

that the reduction of anode potential resulting from the increase of anode current produces an increase of grid potential, thus permitting the anode current to increase further. This action is cumulative, the anode impedance of the valve falling to a low value and thus permitting capacitor C to discharge rapidly through the

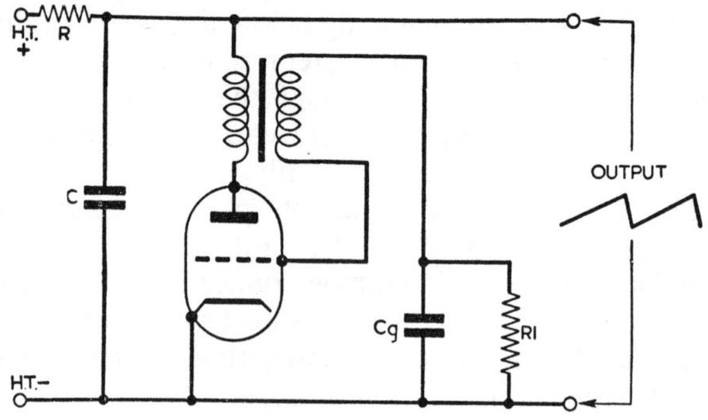

FIG. B-8.—BASIC CIRCUIT OF A BLOCKING OSCILLATOR.

valve, producing the flyback portion of V_0. Ultimately the grid attains a positive potential and grid current flows, charging capacitor C_g in such a sense that the grid is driven to a negative potential beyond cut-off, and the cycle recommences.

Blue Glow. Characteristic luminous effect accompanying conduction in a thermionic electron tube containing gas.

Bohr Atom. Conception of the structure of the chemical atom due to the Danish physicist Niels Bohr. It is, in effect, a combination of Rutherford's conception (see RUTHERFORD ATOM) and the QUANTUM THEORY. The Bohr atom is taken as the basis for the entry " ATOM, STRUCTURE OF " in this book.

Boltzmann's Constant. (Symbol k.) Ratio of the mean total energy of a molecule to its absolute temperature. The value of k is $1{\cdot}375 \times 10^{-22}$ J/ ° K.

Bond (Valency Bond). Force tending to retain two atoms within a molecule, often by means of two electrons, one from each atom, which are mutually shared.

Boost. To increase the total voltage acting in a circuit by the series connexion of an additional supply source.

Booster. An additional supply source included in a circuit in order to increase the total voltage available.

Booster Diode. A thermionic diode connected in the anode circuit of the output valve of the line timebase generator in a

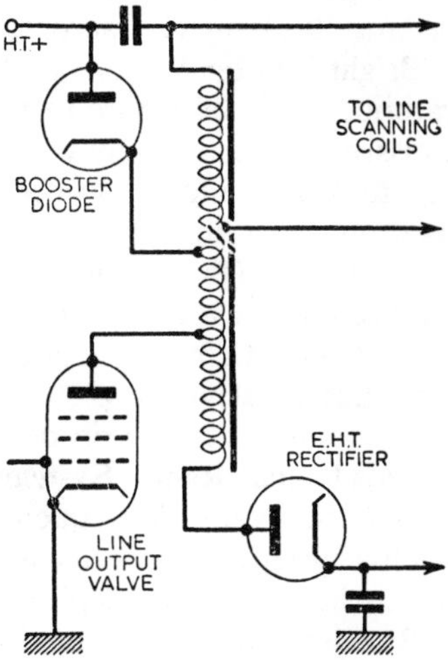

FIG. B-9.—BASIC CIRCUIT OF OUTPUT STAGE OF TELEVISION LINE TIMEBASE GENERATOR, WITH BOOSTER DIODE.

television receiver in such a way that it rectifies the oscillations set up in the circuit during the flyback time. Not only does the booster diode prevent these oscillations from degrading the linearity of the timebase but it also recovers much of the energy stored in the magnetic circuit of the line output transformer during the stroke and which would otherwise be dissipated as heat. The recovered energy is manifest as an increase in the voltage available for application to the anode of the line output valve. A typical basic circuit is given in Fig. B-9.

Bottom Bend. Non-linear region at the lower end of the anode current/grid volts characteristic of a thermionic valve. See ANODE BEND and ANODE BEND DETECTION.

Bottoming. A thermionic valve is said to " bottom " when, by reason of the potential applied to one or other of its grids, the anode current falls to zero. See also definition in addenda.

Box Baffle. An acoustic BAFFLE of box form, with the loudspeaker mounted at or near the centre of one face.

Break In. Method of telegraphic working in which incoming signals are received during the intervals between the characters of an outgoing message.

Bridge Circuit. A network consisting of four impedance arms, used in the measurement of electrical quantities such as resistance, inductance, capacitance, etc. See also WHEATSTONE'S BRIDGE.

Bridged-T Filter. A T- network in which there is a further impedance bridging (i.e. across) the two series arms.

Bright Emitter Valve. A thermionic valve with a directly-heated cathode made of a pure metal (usually tungsten) which attains full emissive properties only when heated to a temperature corresponding to bright incandescence. Bright emitting cathodes are now used only in a limited number of large transmitting valves.

Brightness (Brilliance). Average illumination over the whole picture area of a reproduced television picture.

Brilliance Control. Control of the average illumination of a reproduced television picture, usually by adjustment of the steady bias potential at the grid of the picture tube.

Broad-band Radio Systems. Systems of radiocommunication which occupy a wide frequency band, in the order, say, of 16 Mc/s. Such a system is necessary for television RADIO LINKS, and also for multi-channel radio telephony.

Broadcasting. Transmission of information, either sound or television, by radio for reception by the general public.

Brush Discharge. Discharge of electricity from sharp points on a conductor, at which the surface density of the charge is greatest.

Buffer Stage. Thermionic valve and associated circuits interposed between two parts of a system in order to prevent changes, such as variations of load, in the later stages, from affecting the characteristics of the earlier stages.

Bulb. The ENVELOPE of an electron tube.

Buncher. Arrangement of electrodes in a KLYSTRON which cause the electron stream through the tube to break up into discrete groups or " bunches ".

Burning Voltage (V_{burn}). The minimum voltage between the anode and cathode of a cold-cathode electron tube at which the discharge can be maintained. The burning voltage is less than the IGNITION VOLTAGE (V_{ign}) needed to start the discharge.

Busbar. A conductor maintained at a specific voltage, and to which a number of circuits or subcircuits are connected to deliver power or receive power.

Button Base. A standard seven-pin all-glass valve base, officially known as the B7G base. See VALVE BASE.

By-pass. A circuit or circuit element which offers an alternative path for the flow of current.

FIG. B-10.—PART OF THE CIRCUIT OF AN AMPLIFIER INCORPORATING A PENTODE.

C1, C2 and C3 are by-pass capacitors providing virtual short circuits for any alternating component of the current in the cathode, anode and screen-grid feeds, and thus avoiding feedback. The suppressor grid may be connected either internally or externally to cathode or to earth.

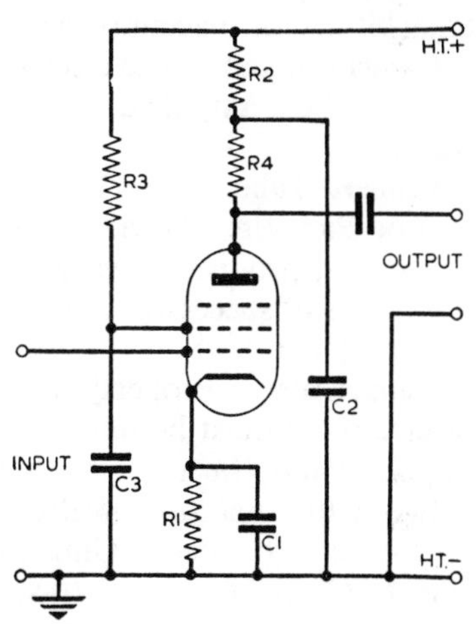

By-pass Capacitor. A capacitor connected in parallel with a circuit or part of a circuit in order to provide a low-impedance path for currents of certain frequencies (Fig. B-10).

C

C Battery. Battery used to maintain a steady direct potential at the control grid of a thermionic valve. A GRID BIAS battery.

Caesium. Element in the alkali metals group.

Caesium Cell. PHOTO-EMISSIVE CELL having a cathode consisting of a thin layer of caesium deposited on silver. Its maximum sensitivity is to incandescent and near infra-red radiation.

Cage. Workshop term for the electrode system of a thermionic valve before it is mounted on the valve base or sealed into the envelope.

Cage Aerial. Form of aerial consisting of a system of wires arranged in a cage-like formation and connected in parallel in order to reduce the copper losses and to increase the capacitance of the aerial.

Calcium. A metallic element the tungstate of which is used as a PHOSPHOR in cathode-ray tubes where a blue-violet luminescence of high actinic value and short persistence is required.

Calibration. Determination, by experimental observation, of the values (in appropriate units) of the readings of an instrument having an arbitrary or inaccurate scale.

Camera Signal. The electrical output of a television camera tube which, when amplified, is the basis of the picture information transmitted.

Camera Tube. Also known as a TELEVISION CAMERA, and as a VISION PICK-UP. Device which, as the result of the process of SCANNING, produces a varying electrical signal proportional to the brightness of successive elemental areas of the scene or picture to be transmitted.

Capacitance. Property of a body by virtue of which a quantity of electricity must be imparted to it in order to create a difference of potential between it and neighbouring bodies. Also the relation between the quantity of electricity so imparted and the potential difference produced. Unit the farad (coulomb/volt). See also INPUT CAPACITANCE, INTER-ELECTRODE CAPACITANCE, OUTPUT CAPACITANCE, SELF-CAPACITANCE.

Capacitance Bridge. BRIDGE network used for the measurement of capacitance. The basic circuit is shown in Fig. C-1, where C_x is the capacitance to be measured, C1 a variable, calibrated capacitor, and R1 and R2 are known resistances. C1 is adjusted until no signal is heard in the telephone instrument, when $C_x = C1 . R2/R1$. This relationship holds only when the resistance of the capacitor can be neglected. Otherwise a somewhat more complex arrangement must be used.

Capacitance Coupling. See CAPACITIVE COUPLING.

Capacitance Earth. See COUNTERPOISE EARTH.

Capacitive Coupling. Coupling between two circuits due to the capacitance of a circuit element, common to both circuits or connected between suitable points in the two circuits (Fig. C-2).

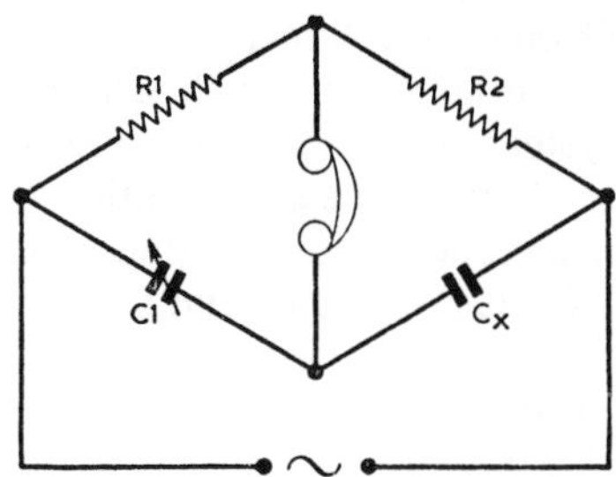

FIG. C-1.—SIMPLIFIED BASIC CIRCUIT OF A CAPACITANCE BRIDGE.

Capacitive Tuning. Method of tuning an oscillatory circuit by adjusting its capacitance.

Capacitor. Device consisting of two conductive bodies (the " plates ") separated by insulating material (the " dielectric "), and thus possessing the property of CAPACITANCE. The dielectric may be impregnated paper, mica, various plastics or air.

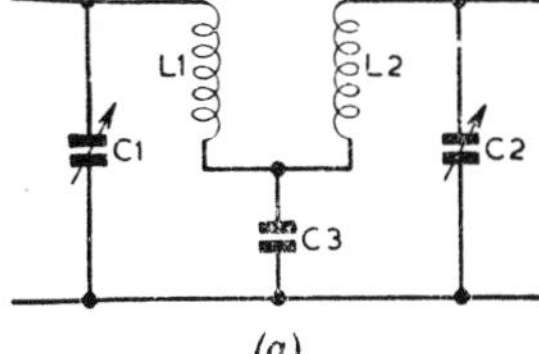

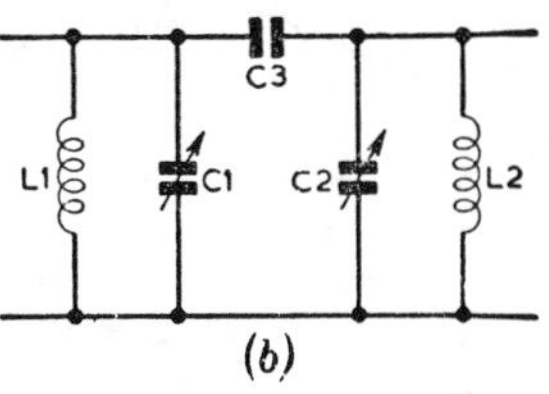

FIG. C-2.—CAPACITIVE COUPLING BETWEEN TWO TUNED CIRCUITS L_1C_1 AND L_2C_2.

In (a) capacitor C3 is common to both circuits. In (b) capacitor C3 joins two symmetrically selected points, one in each circuit.

Carbon Anode. Anode made of graphite and used in some thermionic valves which are intended for operation at high anode temperatures.

Carbon Microphone. MICROPHONE in which the sound (air pressure) waves impinge on a diaphragm, thus varying the pressure on a quantity of loosely-packed carbon granules, with corresponding variation of their resistance.

Carbon Track Potentiometer. POTENTIOMETER the resistive element of which is a circular path of carbon, usually deposited on a ceramic base. The variable tapping is obtained by a radial conducting arm, the outer end of which can be moved along the carbon track.

Carcinotron. Name sometimes given to the BACKWARD-WAVE OSCILLATOR TUBE.

Cardioid. Term descriptive of the POLAR DIAGRAM of an aerial system which is heart-shaped as illustrated in Fig. C-3. It can result from the combination of a frame aerial and an open aerial in a direction-finding equipment. A simple frame aerial situated at A1 has a figure-of-eight diagram and would indicate the bearing of

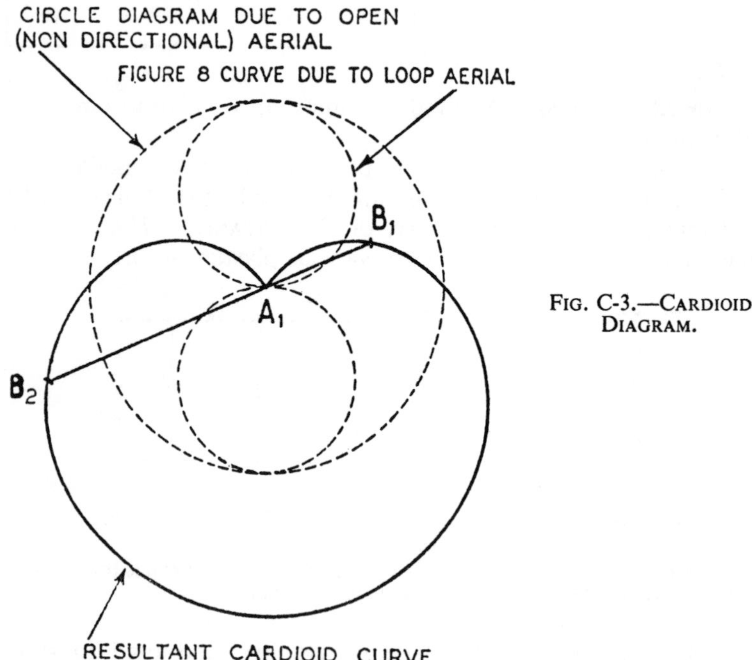

FIG. C-3.—CARDIOID DIAGRAM.

the transmitter to be either in the direction A1B1 or in the direction A1B2. If the open aerial is now put into operation in addition to the frame aerial, thus giving the cardioid diagram, and the observation is repeated, the stronger signal in the direction A1B2 fixes the actual bearing of the transmitter. The term is also applied to microphones which have a heart-shaped polar response.

Carrier. Electrical oscillation of a specified frequency upon which can be super-imposed variations termed MODULATION for the purpose of transmitting information.

Carrier Frequency. The frequency of a carrier wave before modulation.

Carrier Telegraphy. Transmission of telegraphic signals by the interruption or modulation of a CARRIER.

Carrier Telephony. Transmission of speech or other sound signals by modulation of a CARRIER.

Carrier Transmission. System of transmitting information by wire or by radio involving the modulation of a CARRIER.

Carrier Wave. Wave, generated at constant frequency, which is later interrupted, or modulated in amplitude, frequency or phase, in order to transmit information.

Cartridge (Rare Gas). Cold-cathode gas-filled tube designed for use as a SURGE ARRESTER.

Cascade. Two networks are said to be connected in cascade when the output of the first is employed as the input to the second network (Fig. C-4).

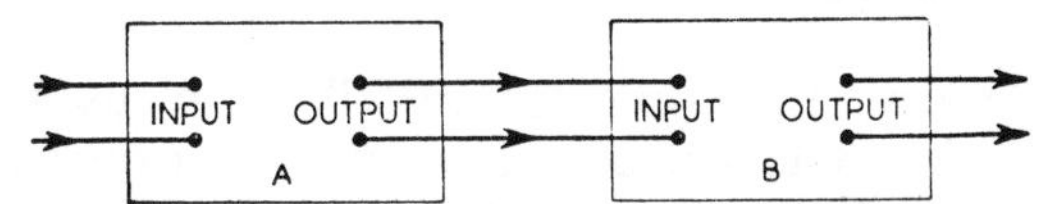

FIG. C-4.—BLOCK DIAGRAM OF TWO NETWORKS A AND B CONNECTED IN CASCADE.

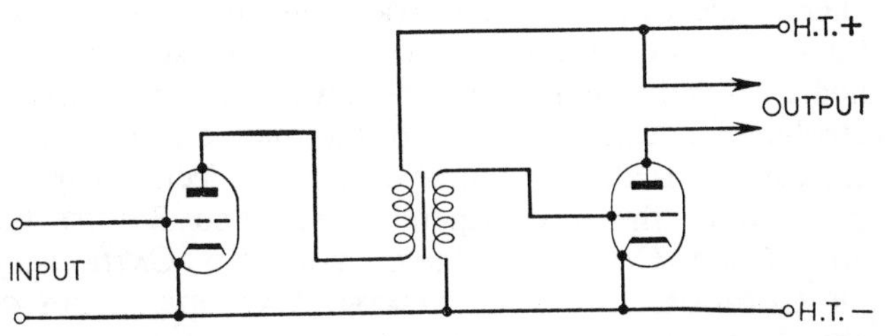

FIG. C-5.—TWO AMPLIFIER VALVES CONNECTED IN CASCADE.

Cascade Amplifier. Thermionic amplifier consisting of two or more stages connected in cascade (Fig. C-5).

Cascode Amplifier. Thermionic amplifier consisting of a GROUNDED CATHODE triode followed by a GROUNDED GRID triode, the two valves being connected in series as in the basic diagram, Fig. C-6. Such an amplifier is often used as a radio-frequency amplifier in television receivers, and has the important properties of a low noise figure and a substantially uniform gain over the necessary wide frequency. Also used in other applications where low noise is an important consideration.

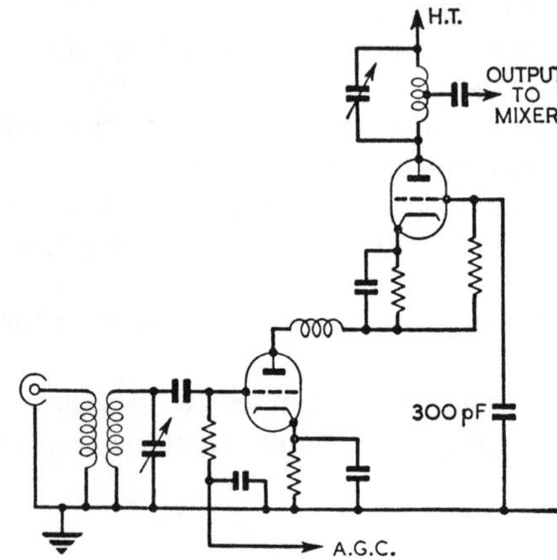

Fig. C-6.—Basic Circuit of a Cascode Radio-frequency Amplifier for a Television Receiver.

Cat's Whisker. Finely-pointed metallic wire used to form a point contact in crystal detectors and other semiconductor devices.

Cataphoresis. The migration of particles, held in suspension in a liquid, towards the cathode under the influence of an electric field.

Catchers. Electrodes in a Klystron which extract energy from the " bunches " of electrons produced by the Bunchers.

Cathode. Negative Electrode from which electric current enters an electrolyte, electron tube, etc. In thermionic and photo-electric tubes the cathode is also the source of the free electrons upon which the operation of the tube depends. See also Bright Emitter Cathode, Cold Cathode, Directly-heated Cathode, Dull Emitter Cathode, Indirectly-heated Cathode, Oxide-coated Cathode, Photo Cathode, Virtual Cathode.

Cathode Bias. A grid-bias potential derived for a thermionic valve by connecting a resistor between the cathode and the negative pole of the h.t. supply. Since a d.c. path is also provided between the control grid of the valve and the negative h.t. terminal, cathode bias is equivalent to applying a negative bias to the control grid (Fig. C-7). Unless Negative Feedback is required, it is necessary to decouple the cathode resistor by a capacitor as shown.

Cathode Current. Total electron current flowing between the cathode of a thermionic tube and all electrodes which are at positive potentials with respect to the cathode.

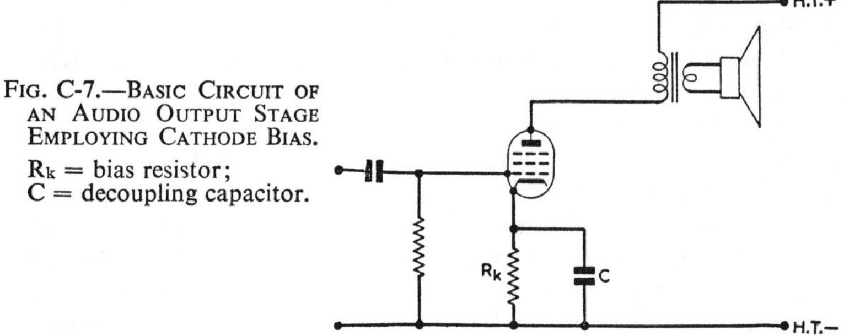

FIG. C-7.—BASIC CIRCUIT OF AN AUDIO OUTPUT STAGE EMPLOYING CATHODE BIAS.
R_k = bias resistor;
C = decoupling capacitor.

Cathode Follower. Arrangement of a thermionic valve such that the output is taken from a load connected between the cathode and the negative pole of the h.t. supply (Fig. C-8). Since this results in heavy NEGATIVE FEEDBACK, the gain is always less than unity.

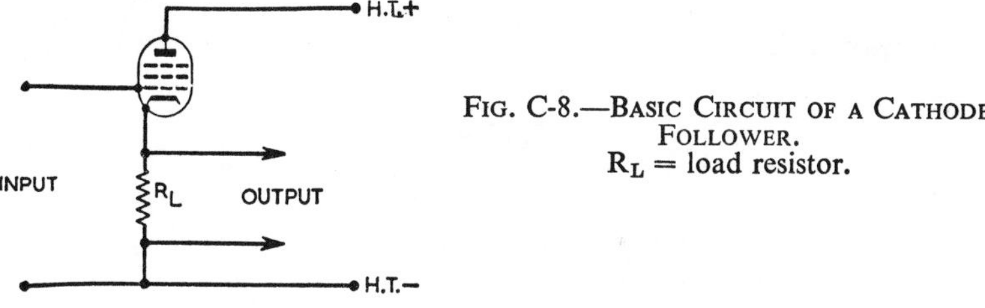

FIG. C-8.—BASIC CIRCUIT OF A CATHODE FOLLOWER.
R_L = load resistor.

However, the merit of the arrangement is that, by suitable choice of load resistance, the output impedance of the stage can be adjusted to match the input impedance of the following stage.

Cathode Modulation. Modulation of the radio-frequency current of a transmitting valve by a signal injected into the cathode circuit.

Cathode-ray Direction Finder. Direction-finding apparatus in which the desired bearing is indicated visually by a CATHODE-RAY TUBE without the use of a RADIOGONIOMETER.

Cathode-ray Oscilloscope. Instrument for examining electrical quantities, and particularly varying electrical quantities both periodic and transient, by means of a luminous trace on the screen of a CATHODE-RAY TUBE. The quantities to be investigated or measured are made to deflect the electron beam in the cathode-ray tube, and thus to produce corresponding movement of the light spot on the screen. In addition to examining electrical quantities as such, the oscilloscope is widely used to examine any physical quantity the changing values of which can be converted into corresponding changes of electrical potential.

Cathode-ray Tube. Electron tube of more or less conical shape, containing a thermionic cathode and an electron gun for the production of CATHODE RAYS which are directed axially along the tube in the direction of the flattened, wide end. The internal surface of the wider end of the tube is coated with a PHOSPHOR—a substance which emits light at the point and instant of impact of the high-speed electrons. Electric and/or magnetic fields of suitable form concentrate the electron stream into a convergent beam which comes to a focus at the surface of the screen, where it produces a small, clearly defined light spot.

The electron beam can be deflected by the application of electric or magnetic fields, and by this means the light spot can be directed to any point on the screen. The amount of deflexion is propor-

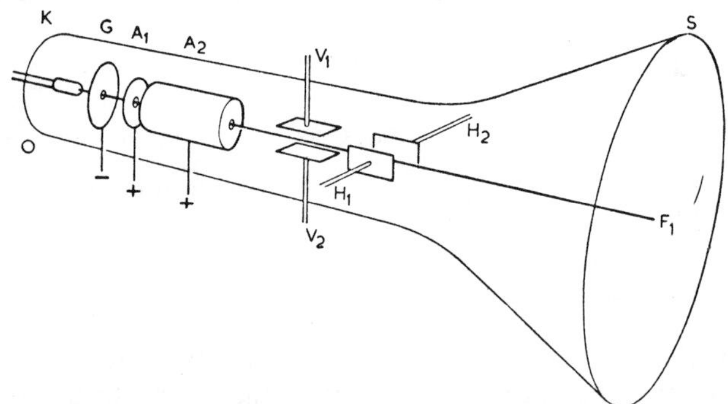

FIG. C-9.—BASIC CONSTRUCTION OF A CATHODE-RAY TUBE ARRANGED FOR ELECTROSTATIC DEFLEXION.

K —Thermionic cathode;
G— Control grid;
A_1—Focusing anode;
A_2—Accelerating or final anode;
V_1, V_2—Plates for vertical deflexion of the beam;
H_1, H_2—Plates for horizontal deflexion of the beam.
S— Luminescent Screen;

tional to the deflecting force and, by arranging that the beam can be deflected in two directions at right angles to each other, the relationship between two varying electrical quantities can be exhibited as a luminous trace, as in the cathode-ray oscilloscope.

The intensity of the light spot is determined by the velocity of the electrons reaching the screen and by the density of the electron beam (beam current). By modulating either of these quantities, therefore, the brightness of the trace or image in the screen can be varied. In television receivers the variations of light and shade in different parts of the picture are reproduced by modulating the beam current with the video signal.

Fig. C-9 shows the basic construction of a cathode-ray tube arranged for electrostatic deflexion. Magnetically deflected tubes are of very similar construction but have no deflexion plates, the deflecting system consisting of electromagnetic coils mounted externally on the tube neck.

Cathode Rays. Stream of electrons emitted from the cathode of an electron tube and accelerated to high velocity by an ELECTRON GUN. The rays can be deflected by magnetic or electric fields. The final velocity of the electrons is proportional to the square root of the potential difference which they traverse.

Cathode Sputtering. See SPUTTERING.

Cation. Positively charged ION which, in an electrolyte or in a gas-filled electron tube, travels towards the negative electrode or cathode.

Cavitation. Phenomenon occurring in a liquid through which pressure waves of high energy are transmitted, including pressure waves of ULTRASONIC frequency. It consists of the rapid expansion and collapse of small gas bubbles previously trapped in the liquid. The pressures thus produced may be sufficient to exercise an erosive effect on neighbouring solids. While in many cases cavitation has undesirable consequences, there are some applications in ultrasonics where its effects are beneficial as, for example, in ULTRASONIC SOLDERING AND TINNING.

Cavity Magnetron. MAGNETRON incorporating tuned circuits in the form of RESONANT CAVITIES contrived in the body of the anode.

Cell. (1) Vessel containing one or more electrolytes and two electrodes (e.g. a primary or secondary cell forming a unit of an electric battery).

(2) A light-sensitive electrical device (e.g. PHOTO-EMISSIVE CELL).

Centimetric Waves. Radio waves of wavelengths between 1 and 10 cm, corresponding to frequencies of between 30,000 and 3000 Mc/s (" super-frequency " waves).

Centre Tap. A connexion taken from the electrical centre of a network or circuit component as, for example, the mid-point of a resistor or of a transformer winding (Fig. C-10).

Centring. Adjustment of the beam of a cathode-ray tube so that, in the absence of deflecting forces, it impinges on the centre of the screen. Also, adjustment of the picture in a television receiver so that it is centrally disposed on the screen.

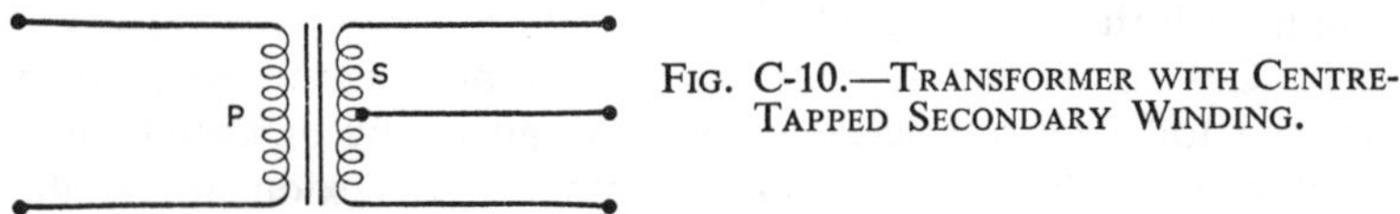

FIG. C-10.—TRANSFORMER WITH CENTRE-TAPPED SECONDARY WINDING.

Ceramic Capacitor. A capacitor in which the dielectric is a ceramic material, often of tubular form.

Ceramic Ferromagnetic Materials. Compounds of iron which, in addition to possessing desirable ferromagnetic characteristics, have a ceramic structure which confers other valuable properties: for example, they have a high resistivity, and their use is therefore accompanied by negligible eddy current losses. There are two general classes of these materials, the MAGNETIC FERRITES, such as Ferroxcube, which is used as core material in high-frequency transformers and inductors, and the MAGNETIC OXIDES, from which permanent magnets of special qualities are made.

Cermet. Name given to a class of materials consisting of finely divided ceramics bonded with a metal or alloy binder. Cermets show great resistance to wear and other mechanical stresses. Although the exact reason for these properties is not fully understood, it has been found that they depend critically on the electron states of the alloy system.

C.G.S. Units. System of physical units based upon the centimetre, the gramme and the second as the fundamental units of length, mass and time respectively. For scientific work this system is being replaced by the M.K.S. (metre–kilogramme–second) system.

Channel. Restricted band of frequencies used during one-way communication by means of CARRIER TRANSMISSION. In DOUBLE-SIDEBAND TRANSMISSION the channel width is equal to twice the maximum modulating frequency and is centrally disposed about the carrier frequency. See also MULTI-CHANNEL, SOUND CHANNEL, VISION CHANNEL.

Channel Selection. Device for adjusting a receiving equipment, e.g. a sound or television receiver, to respond to the particular channel on which the wanted programme is being transmitted. It may consist either of a switch by means of which any one of a number of pre-tuned circuits can be selected or means whereby the user can vary the tuning by hand.

Characteristic Curve. Graph showing the effect of varying the potential applied to one electrode of a thermionic valve upon the current to the same or to some other electrode, all other conditions remaining constant. The principal characteristics are the anode volts/anode current characteristic and, for valves with three or more electrodes, the anode current/grid volts characteristic. See also STATIC and DYNAMIC CHARACTERISTICS.

Charge of Electricity. (Symbol Q) A body having an excess or a deficiency of electrons, or a space containing free electrons or ions, is said to be electrically charged. The unit of electric charge or of quantity of electricity is the COULOMB.

Charge (Space). Electric charge existing in an electron tube due to the presence of free electrons or ions. The term SPACE CHARGE is mainly used for the cloud of free electrons in the region of the cathode of a thermionic valve.

Charge Carrier. A free electron is a negative charge carrier. Positive or negative ions are also charge carriers, and the imaginary " holes " in p-TYPE SEMICONDUCTOR MATERIAL are also considered to be positive charge carriers.

Charge Image (Charge Pattern). Pattern of electric charges on the surface of the TARGET of a television camera tube, from which, by means of SCANNING, the television signal is derived.

Charging Current. The current which flows into a capacitor when a steady direct voltage is applied between its plates.

Charging Resistor. Resistor connected in series with a capacitor to regulate the rate of rise of charging current, and hence the time taken to charge the capacitor (Fig. C-11).

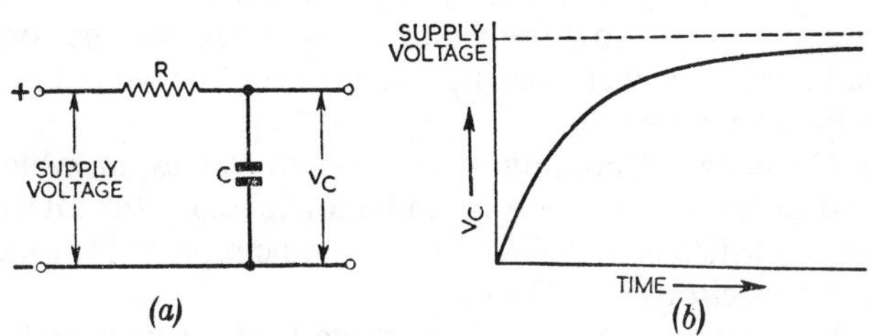

FIG. C-11.

(a) CAPACITOR C IS CHARGED FROM THE D.C. SUPPLY VIA CHARGE RESISTOR R.
(b) THE VOLTAGE TO WHICH C IS CHARGED INCREASES WITH TIME, BUT CAN NEVER EQUAL THE SUPPLY VOLTAGE.

Chassis. Metallic member, usually in the form of an inverted tray, on which are mounted the various components of an electronic equipment.

Cheese Aerial. Type of rotatable aerial employed in Radar on the centimetric waveband. It consists of a parabolic metallic reflector, and is usually fed by a waveguide (Fig. C-12).

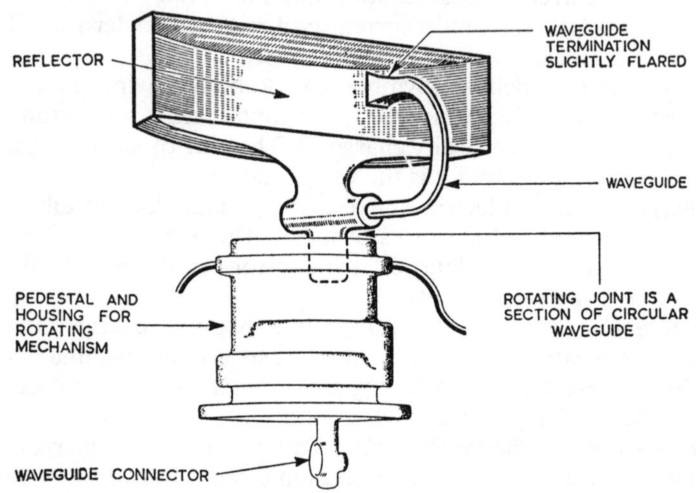

FIG. C-12.—" CHEESE " OR PARABOLIC REFLECTOR AERIAL.

Chemical Bond. Force retaining two atoms together in a molecule as, for example, the force exerted by a pair of shared electrons.

Choke. An inductor included in a circuit or network for the purpose of presenting a relatively high impedance to the flow of alternating current. Low-frequency chokes are wound on iron cores; radio-frequency chokes may be air-cored or wound on IRON DUST or FERRITE cores.

Choke Coupling. Coupling between two valves in which the anode load of the first valve is an inductor (choke), the alternating voltage across which is transferred to the grid circuit of the following valve via a capacitor (Fig. C-13).

Choke Modulation. Modulation of the (radio-frequency) anode current of a transmitting valve by means of a choke connected in the common h.t. feed to the modulator valve and the transmitting valve.

Chromatic Aberration. Presence of prismatic colours at the edges of an optical image, due to the refractive index of the lens material being different for light of different frequencies.

Circuit. Path for an electric current. Current can flow only when the circuit is " closed ", i.e. when it presents a continuous conductive path.

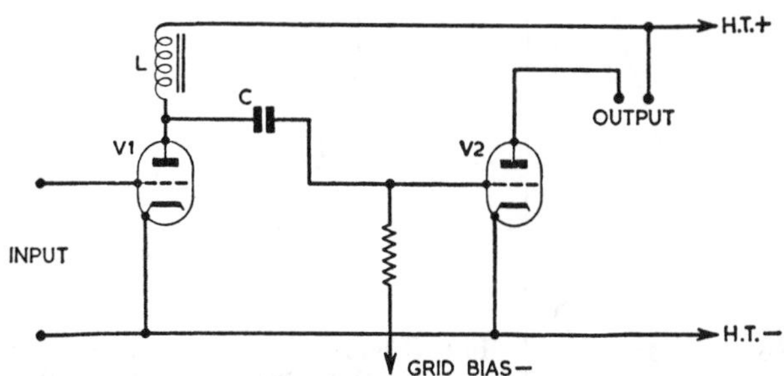

FIG. C-13.—BASIC CIRCUIT ILLUSTRATING CHOKE COUPLING BETWEEN VALVES V1 AND V2.

L—Coupling choke. C—Coupling capacitor.

Circuit Noise. Noise currents generated in an electric circuit as the result of the THERMAL AGITATION of the electrons. See also JOHNSON NOISE.

Circular Scanning. Method of scanning in a cathode-ray tube whereby the light spot describes a close spiral path. More correctly termed SPIRAL SCANNING.

Circular Timebase. TIMEBASE which causes the light spot in a cathode-ray tube to describe a circular path on the screen, moving at constant velocity. This is accomplished by applying sinusoidal voltages, of equal magnitude and frequency but with a phase difference of 90 degrees, to the two sets of deflexion plates.

Clamp Pulse Generator. Circuit in which are generated the pulses used in black level or in synchronizing pulse peak level CLAMPING in television transmitting equipment. The pulses may be derived either from the television signal itself or from an independent oscillator.

Clamping. Method of maintaining one or other of the reference levels (black level or synchronizing pulse peak level) in a television transmission by injecting pulses during appropriate parts of each line cycle.

Class A Amplifier

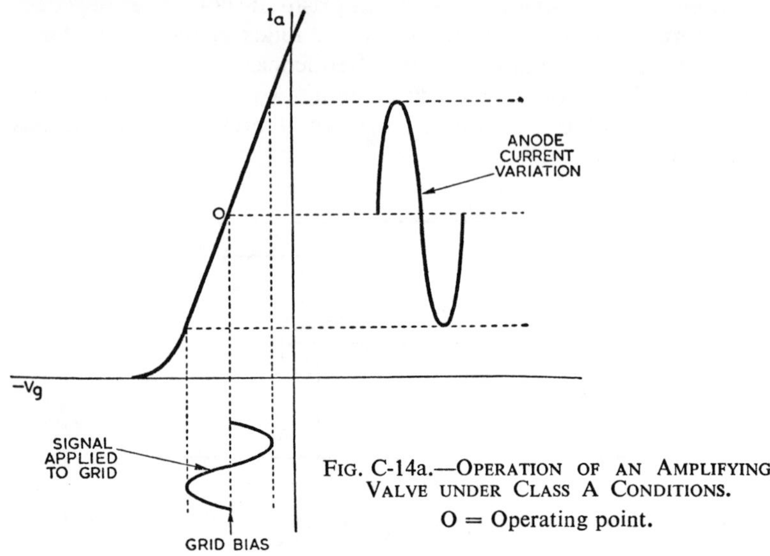

FIG. C-14a.—OPERATION OF AN AMPLIFYING VALVE UNDER CLASS A CONDITIONS.

O = Operating point.

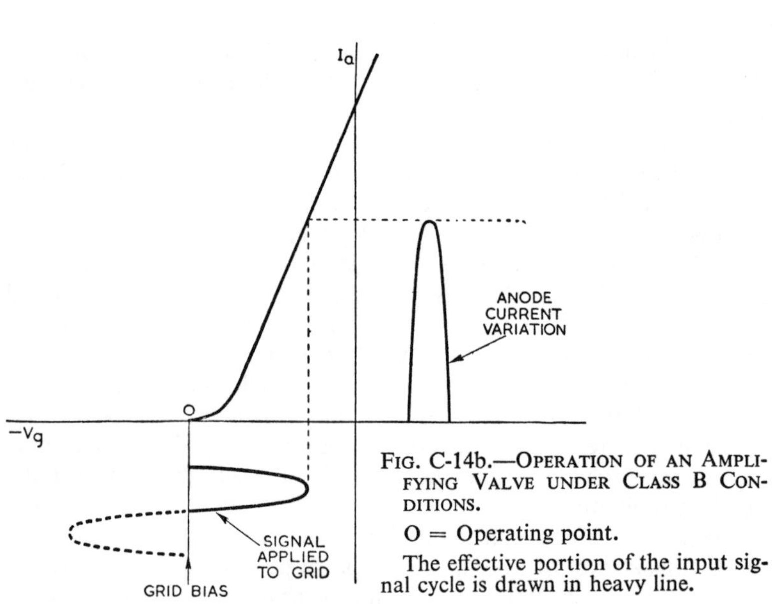

FIG. C-14b.—OPERATION OF AN AMPLIFYING VALVE UNDER CLASS B CONDITIONS.

O = Operating point.

The effective portion of the input signal cycle is drawn in heavy line.

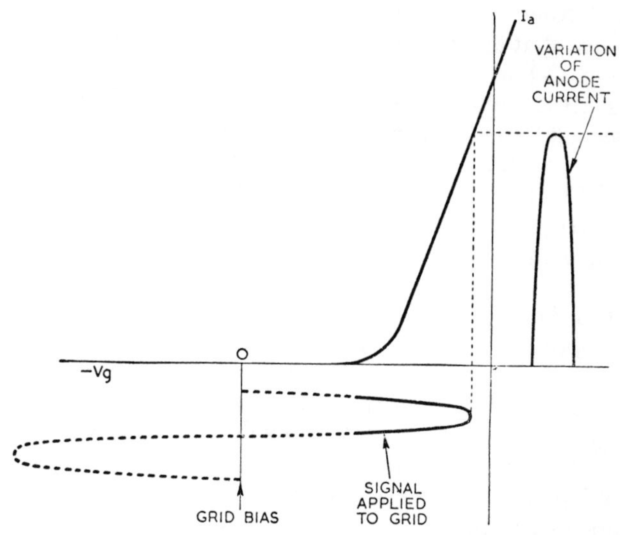

FIG. C-14c.—OPERATION OF AN AMPLIFYING VALVE UNDER CLASS C CONDITIONS.

O = Operating point. The effective portion of the input signal cycle is drawn in heavy line.

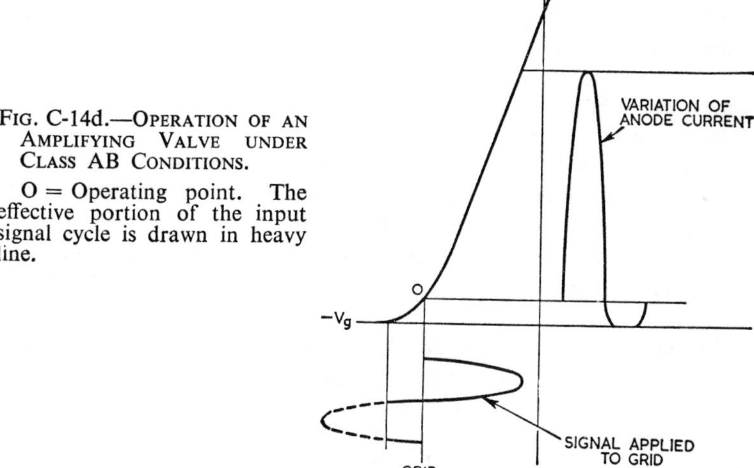

FIG. C-14d.—OPERATION OF AN AMPLIFYING VALVE UNDER CLASS AB CONDITIONS.

O = Operating point. The effective portion of the input signal cycle is drawn in heavy line.

Class A Amplifier. Thermionic amplifier in which conditions are so adjusted that anode current flows during the whole of the signal cycle (Fig. C-14a).

Class AB Amplifier. Thermionic amplifier in which the valve is so biased that anode current flows for more than half of the signal cycle. Class AB amplification conditions are intermediate between those of Class A and Class B (Fig. C-14d). Two conditions may arise in Class AB operation, namely Class AB_1, in which grid current is not allowed to flow, and Class AB_2, in which grid current does flow.

Class B Amplifier. Thermionic amplifier in which the valve is biased approximately to CUT-OFF so that anode current flows only during positive-going half-cycles of the signal (Fig. C-14b).

Class C Amplifier. Thermionic amplifier in which the valve is biased well below cut-off so that anode current flows during considerably less than one-half of the signal cycle (Fig. C-41c).

Clean Up (Gas Clean-up). Reduction of gas pressure in an electron tube due to the absorption of residual gas. Advantageous in high-vacuum tubes, gas clean-up is objectionable in gas-filled tubes, where it may be due to positive gas ions, accelerated towards the negative electrode, becoming embedded in the electrode material. The effect can, however, be minimized by maintaining suitable operating conditions, and mitigated by the inclusion of a member which releases gas during the life of the tube.

Clipping. (1) Suppression of initial or final sound elements in telephone or telegraph transmission.

(2) Suppression of that part of an amplitude-modulated signal which exceeds a given amplitude level, e.g. for the purpose of reducing noise. See NOISE LIMITER.

Closed Circuit. (1) Applied to a communication system in which current flows continuously and can be controlled for the purpose of signalling by any station connected to the system.

(2) Television system for local use, in which the television signal is transmitted from the transmitter to the receiver by wire and not by radio.

Closed Magnetic Circuits. Magnetic circuit, such as a transformer core, which contains no air-gap.

Cloud Chamber. Apparatus for investigating the tracks of a radiation which produces ionization, e.g. alpha particles, protons or gamma radiation. A vessel with a glass window is filled with air saturated with water vapour. The pressure is quickly reduced, rendering the air super-saturated. Since water tends to condense readily on ionized particles, any ions formed in the chamber will be rendered visible by the formation of water droplets. Thus the path of any radiation which causes ionization will be seen as a row of water droplets.

Cloud Warning. Radar application employing centimetric waves and a suitable scanning system, which gives warning of dangerous cloud formations and some protection against collision with other aircraft.

Coarse Control. Control device which provides only an approximate adjustment, e.g. of frequency, fine adjustment being obtained by a subsidiary control.

Co-axial Cable. Cable consisting of two conductors, one a central wire and the other a cylinder concentric with the wire, the space between them being filled with a dielectric. Air-dielectric cables of this type are used for carrying radio-frequency currents.

Code. System of impulses or combinations of impulses corresponding to letters, figures, etc., used in telegraphic signalling. Also letters or symbols used as abbreviations for various quantities, as for example the COLOUR CODES for resistors and capacitors.

Coefficient of Coupling. Ratio of the mutual impedance components (inductive, capacitive or resistive) of two circuits to the square root of the products of their total impedances *of the same kind*, i.e. inductive, capacitive or resistive.

Coherer. Early form of wireless DETECTOR in which the resistance of an imperfect contact, e.g. that of a quantity of metal filings, decreases when a radio-frequency signal is applied.

Coil. Conductor wound in spiral fashion and included in a circuit in order to introduce inductance. See also CHOKE COIL, LOADING COIL, SEARCH COIL, TUNING COIL.

Coil Aerial. Another name for a FRAME AERIAL.

Coils (Deflexion). Coils mounted on the neck of a cathode-ray tube and carrying currents which generate magnetic fields for deflecting the electron beam in the tube. See also DEFLEXION COILS.

Cold Cathode. Cathode from which electrons are emitted without the application of heat, at least initially. Strictly speaking, the term covers photo-emissive cathodes among others, but " cold cathode " is normally understood to mean any cathode in which emission is initiated by reason of a high voltage gradient at its surface.

Cold Cathode Tube. Electron tube having a COLD CATHODE. Such tubes are invariably gas-filled, and the electron emission initiated by the high voltage gradient applied is often enhanced by secondary emission due to the bombardment of the cathode by positive ions formed by the ionization of the gas filling.

Cold Emission. The emission of electrons from an electrode due to the high potential gradient at its surface. Also termed AUTO-EMISSION and FIELD EMISSION.

Collector. In a crystal diode or a transistor, the electrode the current in which is controlled by the input signal.

Collision (Ionization by). Impact between an atom and another particle, such as an electron or an alpha particle. It may result in EXCITATION of the atom or in IONIZATION.

Collision Warning. Development of radar employing the same principle as CLOUD WARNING, for detecting such obstacles as other aircraft or high ground, and giving the pilot of an aircraft information concerning the direction and height of the obstacle relative to the altitude of the aircraft.

Colloidal State. Matter is in the colloidal state when it is subdivided into particles having dimensions of the order of 10^{-7}–10^{-8} cm.

Colour Code. System of marking small circuit components with coloured dots or bands to denote their values and characteristics for ready identification. Details of recognized colour codes for resistors, fuses and ceramic capacitors are given in the Appendix.

Colour Television. System of television in which the information transmitted permits the scene or picture to be reproduced in colour. This necessitates a more complex signal than for monochrome television, since it must contain modulation corresponding to the three primary colours, red, green and blue. Similarly, it involves a reproduction system in which the three colour components are combined. This can be achieved in a number of ways. For example, three picture tubes may be employed, each having a phosphor which gives illumination of a different colour, the three images thus produced being superimposed on a viewing screen by means of a system of mirrors. Alternatively, a three-gun tube may be used in conjunction with a luminescent screen composed of closely spaced groups of three small patches (" dots ") of the three phosphors, the scanning system being such that each beam impinges only on " dots " of its own colour. Again, a single-beam tube may be used with a deflexion system which directs the beam so that it impinges in sequence on closely-packed lines of three different phosphors, the sequence conforming with that of the modulations corresponding to the colour scanning in the studio.

Colpitt's Circuit (Colpitt's Oscillator). Oscillator circuit comprising a triode with capacitive paths between grid and cathode and between anode and cathode, and an inductive path between anode and grid. A basic circuit is given in Fig. C-15.

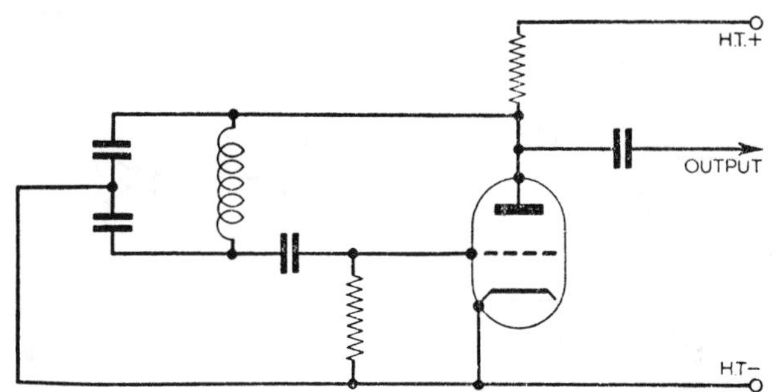

FIG. C-15.—BASIC CIRCUIT OF COLPITT'S OSCILLATOR.

Coma. Aberration of an optical system in which the images of points are distorted into pear-shaped figures at the edges of the field. A similar effect can also occur in an electron–optical system.

Common Base. Mode of operation of a TRANSISTOR in which the input is applied between emitter and base, and the output is taken between the collector and the base, the base being common to both input and output circuits. Also known as grounded-base operation (Fig. C-16 (*a*)).

Common Collector. Mode of operating a TRANSISTOR in which the input is applied between the base and the collector and the output is taken between the emitter and the collector, the collector being common to both input and output circuits. Also known as grounded collector operation (Fig. C-16 (*c*)).

Common Emitter. Mode of operating a TRANSISTOR in which the input is connected between the base and the emitter and the output is taken between the collector and the emitter, the emitter being common to both input and output circuits. Also known as grounded-emitter operation (Fig. C-16 (*b*)).

Compatible. A colour television system is said to be compatible when the signals transmitted can not only be reproduced in colour in a colour television receiver but can also be reproduced in monochrome in a black-and-white receiver. The term is also applied to

STEREOPHONIC signals which can be reproduced as monophonic without degradation.

Compensated Volume Control. Method of VOLUME CONTROL intended to improve the realism of sound reproduction by compensating for the fact that the response of the human ear to sounds

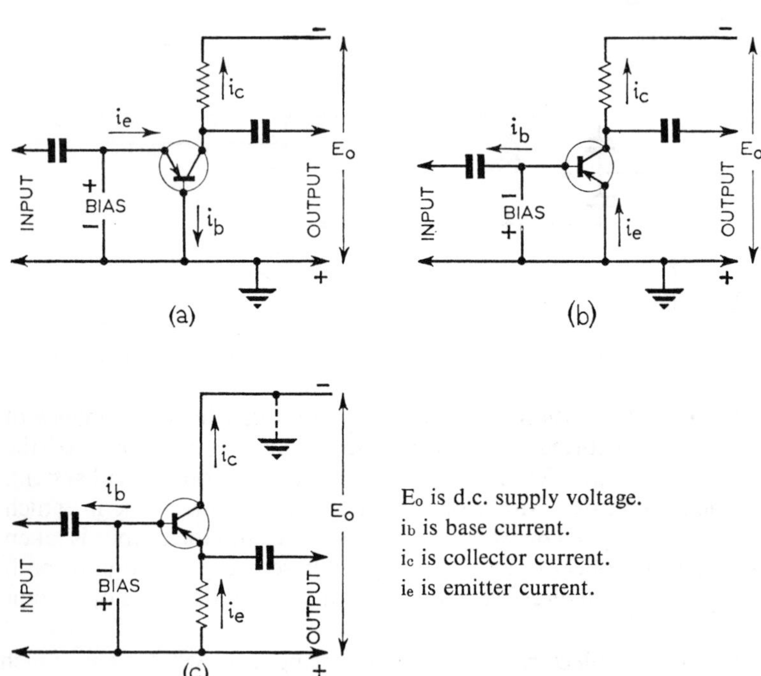

FIG. C-16.—THE THREE BASIC TRANSISTOR AMPLIFIER CIRCUITS.

(*a*) Common base or grounded base circuit. (*b*) Common emitter or grounded emitter circuit. (*c*) Common collector, grounded collector or emitter follower circuit. Note that these circuits show pnp transistors. With npn transistors the transistor symbol differs in that the direction in which the emitter arrow points is reversed; also with npn transistors the polarities of the bias voltages are reversed.

of different frequencies varies with the degree of loudness. Compensated volume control can be applied by employing negative feedback, the amount of which varies with the volume-control setting, or by using a tone control ganged with the volume control.

Component. (1) General name for any circuit element such as a resistor, capacitor, inductor or transformer, etc.

(2) That part of a complex magnitude which possesses a particular property or characteristic. For example, the total impedance of a piece of apparatus may consist of both reactive and resistive components.

Compton Effect. Slight increase in the wavelength of X-rays when subject to scattering by light elements.

Computer (Electronic). Electronic device for rapidly performing complex mathematical calculations. Popularly known as " electronic brains ", they can function only when relative data and detailed instructions regarding the calculation required are fed into them, usually in the form of electrical pulses. See ANALOGUE COMPUTER and DIGITAL COMPUTER.

Concentric Cable. Electric cable having two or more concentric conductors. The CO-AXIAL CABLE is a special form of concentric cable.

Condenser. Term formerly applied to the device now known as a CAPACITOR.

Condenser Microphone. Microphone consisting in essence of a capacitor, one plate of which is made to vibrate by the incident sound waves, thus varying the distance between the two plates and therefore the capacitance of the device. It responds to a very wide range of audio frequencies.

Condenser Pick-up. Gramophone pick-up in which the movement of the needle in the groove of the record varies the distance between the moving and fixed plates of a capacitor.

Conductance. (Symbol G) Reciprocal of the resistance of a conductor. Unit the MHO. See also CONVERSION and MUTUAL CONDUCTANCE.

Conductivity. Reciprocal of the RESISTIVITY or specific resistance of a material.

Conductor. A substance in which free electrons and/or ions are available to move under the influence of an electric field, and thus to produce the phenomenon known as an electric current. A conductor must therefore exist in a state of at least partial IONIZATION. In a solid conductor the current consists in the drift of free electrons through the inter-atomic space, in the general direction of the positive pole of the electric field. In an electrolyte positive and negative ions, consisting of atoms or groups of atoms, move in opposite directions through the liquid. In a gas the current consists of the flow of electrons towards the positive pole and of positive ions towards the negative pole, ionization of the gas atoms having been produced by such agencies as collision or irradiation. A perfect vacuum is a perfect insulator, and conduction can occur through it only if free electrons are made available by emission from a thermionic or photo-emissive cathode.

Cone Loudspeaker. Loudspeaker in which the reproduced sound is propagated by the vibration of a conical diaphragm, the audio-frequency power being applied at the apex.

Constant-k Filter. A filter in which the product of the series and shunt impedances is a constant which is independent of frequency.

Contact Potential Difference. Potential difference generated when two different conductors are in contact, and due to the passage of electrons from the conductor with the lower WORK FUNCTION to the conductor with the higher work function. The contact potential difference between the cathode and grid of a thermionic valve is a factor in determining the CUT-OFF value of the grid voltage.

Continuous Oscillations. Oscillations which are produced continuously and not as short trains of DAMPED oscillations.

Continuous Waves. Electromagnetic waves generated as a continuous train of identical oscillations. They can be interrupted according to a code, or modulated in amplitude, frequency or phase in order to convey information.

Continuous-wave Telegraphy. System of telegraphy in which the information or message is transmitted as a continuous wave which is modulated or is broken up into short and long periods according to a code.

Contrast. Ratio between the brilliancy of the brightest and the darkest portions of an image such as a reproduced television picture.

Contrast Control. Regulation of the CONTRAST in a television picture by adjusting the GAIN in the vision amplifier.

Control Characteristic (of a Thyratron). Graph showing the relation between the CRITICAL GRID VOLTAGE of a thyratron and the anode voltage. Typical curves are included in the entry THYRATRON.

Control Electrode. Electrode in a thermionic tube to which a potential is applied in order to govern the value of the electron current flowing from the region of the cathode to other electrodes.

Control Grid. A control electrode in the form of a GRID and situated between the cathode and all other electrodes of a thermionic tube.

Control Ratio (of a Thyratron). Ratio between the firing voltage of a thyratron and the CRITICAL GRID VOLTAGE as shown by the slope of the linear part of the CONTROL CHARACTERISTIC.

Conversion Conductance. (Symbol g_c) The ratio of the intermediate frequency component of the output current of a FREQUENCY CHANGER to the r.f. input voltage.

Conversion Gain. Ratio of the intermediate frequency output voltage of a frequency changer to the r.f. input voltage.

Cooled-anode Valve. Thermionic valve in which provision is made for removing the heat produced at the anode. The anode may be fitted with radiating fins, or a coolant such as air, water or oil may be made to circulate round the anode.

Copper Oxide Rectifier. Rectifying device which makes use of the unilateral conductivity of the junction between a layer of cuprous oxide and a copper base.

Core. The material, which may be air or a ferromagnetic material, encircled by the windings of an inductor or transformer. For radio-frequency applications the core is usually air, or an iron DUST CORE or one of the magnetic FERRITES. For low-frequency applications iron laminations are employed.

Core Losses. Power losses in the ferromagnetic core of an inductor (e.g. choke or transformer) due to eddy currents, hysteresis effects, etc.

Cosmic Rays. High-energy radiation reaching the earth from outer space, and mainly consisting of protons, although a small proportion of electrons and possibly heavy atomic nuclei may also be present. On reaching the earth's atmosphere secondary processes result in the production of MESONS of different kinds.

Coulomb. Unit of quantity of electricity, equal to the amount of electricity delivered when a current of one ampere flows for one second (one ampere-second).

Counter. Measuring device which records the number of impulses received. These may be current pulses applied to an electromagnetic system, or voltage pulses applied to the control electrode of an electron tube, or the pulses may arise from the impact of charged particles, etc.

Counterpoise (Counterpoise Earth). A conductor or system of conductors mounted slightly above ground level and employed in association with an aerial instead of or in addition to a buried earth.

Coupling. Two circuits or networks are said to be coupled when electrical energy can be transferred from one circuit to the other.

Coupling may be obtained by means of a circuit element the impedance of which is common to both circuits, or by two inductors, one in each circuit, having a mutual flux linkage.

Coupling Capacitor. A capacitor included in the path between two circuits or networks so that alternating voltages generated in one circuit are transferred to the second circuit.

Coupling Coefficient. See COEFFICIENT OF COUPLING.

Coupling Coil. An inductor in one circuit and so positioned that it has a common magnetic field with an inductor in a second circuit.

Coupling Resistor. Resistor which is common to two circuits, thus permitting energy to be transferred from one circuit to the other.

Coupling Transformer. Static transformer the primary of which is included in one circuit and the secondary in another circuit, allowing energy to be transferred from the first circuit to the second (Fig. C-17).

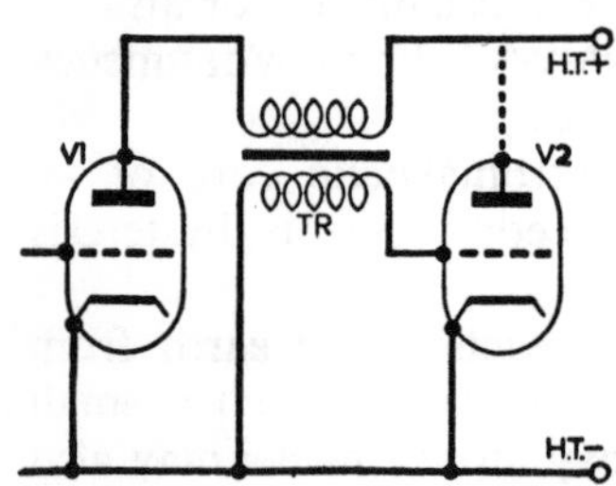

FIG. C-17.—THE TRANSFORMER TR COUPLES THE ANODE CIRCUIT OF V1 TO THE GRID CIRCUIT OF V2.

Covalency. The bonding of two atoms in a molecule by the mutual sharing of a pair of electrons, one from each atom.

Crest Value. Another name for the PEAK VALUE of an alternating current, voltage, etc.

Crest-to-crest Value. Another name for the PEAK-TO-PEAK VALUE of an alternating current, voltage etc.

Critical Damping. The amount of DAMPING which, when applied to the moving system of a measuring instrument, causes the system to take up its final, steady deflexion in the shortest time.

Critical Frequency. (1) The highest frequency of a radiation which, if propagated vertically, is reflected from the E or F layer of the IONOSPHERE.

(2) The frequency below which a travelling wave in a given MODE cannot be maintained in a waveguide.

Critical Grid Current (of a Thyratron). The instantaneous value of grid current flowing in a thyratron immediately prior to the commencement of anode current flow.

Critical Grid Voltage (of a Thyratron). The instantaneous value of grid potential at which anode current commences to flow in a thyratron operated at a given anode voltage.

Critical Reaction. The maximum amount of REACTION which can be applied to a thermionic valve before the system reaches a condition of self-oscillation.

Crookes Dark Space. In a gas discharge tube a dark region situated between the cathode and the luminous NEGATIVE COLUMN. The length of the Crookes dark space varies inversely as the gas pressure.

Cross Modulation. Transfer of the modulation of a strong unwanted signal to the carrier of the wanted signal, due to non-linear characteristics of a circuit element, and more particularly non-linearity of the characteristics of a radio-frequency amplifying valve.

Cross Talk. Penetration of telephone transmission from one channel to another, and the resulting confusion of messages. May be due to electrical leakage or to unwanted coupling between circuits.

Cryotron. Device exploiting the phenomenon of SUPER-CONDUCTION, and having an important potential field of application in computer practice. In essence it comprises a fine super-conducting wire surrounded by a coil of fine wire having normal resistance characteristics. Super-conductance in the first wire can be destroyed by the magnetic field generated by passing a current through the coil. The circuit also contains means for detecting whether, at a given instant, the wire is super-conducting or not. The complete device can be employed as a binary memory element.

Crystal Control. Use of a PIEZO-ELECTRIC crystal, usually quartz, as a resonant element in a radio transmitter in order to maintain constant frequency.

Crystal Detector. CRYSTAL RECTIFIER employed as a detector in a radio receiver.

Crystal Diode. In general, the combination of a crystal and a point contact (cat's whisker) to produce unilateral conductivity. Early forms used such crystals as galena, but the more recent crystal diodes consist of germanium or silicon with a tungsten wire as point contact.

Crystal Filter. A BAND-PASS filter in which PIEZO-ELECTRIC crystals are employed as frequency-discriminating elements. In carrier telegraphy the use of a number of such filters permits many signals to be sent simultaneously along a single conductor.

Crystal Loudspeaker. Loudspeaker in which the audio-frequency output of a radio receiver or an amplifier is applied across a PIEZO-ELECTRIC crystal, the resulting deformation of the crystal driving a vibrating diaphragm.

Crystal Microphone. Microphone in which the electrical signal is generated by the variation of pressure across a PIEZO-ELECTRIC crystal by sound waves which are allowed to fall upon the crystal directly or upon a vibrating diaphragm which bends the crystal. Crystal microphones are simple in construction, light in weight and are not affected by stray magnetic fields.

Crystal Oscillator. Oscillator, the frequency of which is determined by a PIEZO-ELECTRIC crystal.

Crystal Pick-up. Gramophone pick-up in which the movement of the stylus in the groove of the record varies the pressure between faces of a PIEZO-ELECTRIC crystal such as Rochelle salt, resulting in the generation of a corresponding audio-frequency voltage.

Crystal Receiver. Radio receiver in which the detector is a CRYSTAL RECTIFIER.

Crystal Rectifier. Combination of a crystal and a point contact, or of two crystals, the junction possessing unilateral, or at least asymmetrical conductivity.

Crystal Transducer. TRANSDUCER in which the conversion of electrical energy into mechanical energy (or vice versa) is the result of the PIEZO-ELECTRIC effect.

Cumulative Grid Rectification. Method of using a high-vacuum

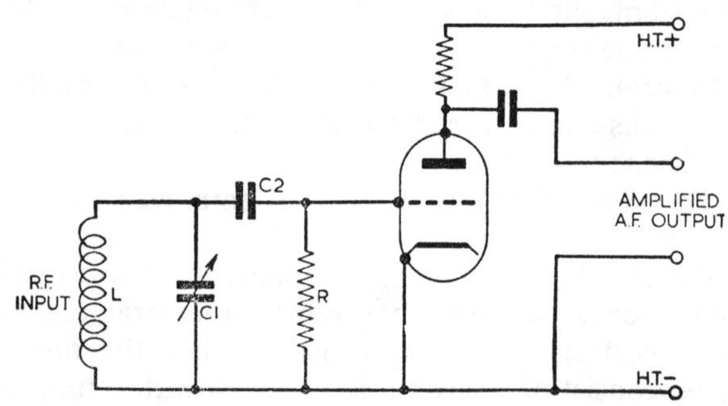

FIG. C-18.—BASIC CIRCUIT OF A CUMULATIVE GRID RECTIFIER.

triode or pentode as a radio detector. In the circuit of Fig. C-18 the radio-frequency signal voltage developed across the tuned circuit LC1 is applied between the grid and cathode of a triode via the grid capacitor C2. The GRID LEAK resistor R is connected between grid and cathode of the valve. The grid and cathode act as a rectifying diode so that a negative voltage with audio-frequency modulation appears at the grid, and forms the input signal, which is amplified by the valve in the normal way. Also called LEAKY GRID detection.

Curie. Measure of the radioactivity of a substance. It is defined as the quantity of a given RADIOACTIVE ISOTOPE which decays at the rate of $3{\cdot}7 \times 10^{10}$ disintegrations per second.

Curie Point. Temperature above which the permeability of a given ferromagnetic material falls to less than unity.

Current. See ELECTRIC CURRENT and ELECTRON CURRENT.

Current Feedback. FEEDBACK, usually negative, the amount of which is proportional to the current in the output circuit or load.

Current Gain. The ratio of output current to input current of an amplifier or amplifying device such as a transistor.

Cut-off. A thermionic tube is said to be cut-off when the operating conditions are such that the tube becomes non-conductive. Cut-off can be achieved, for example, by applying a sufficiently high negative voltage to the control grid of a high-vacuum tube.

Cut-off Voltage. The negative potential which must be applied to the control grid of thermionic valve (Fig. C-19), or to the modu-

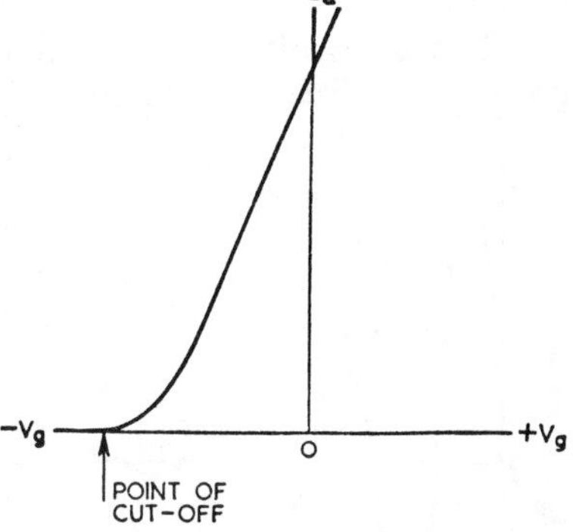

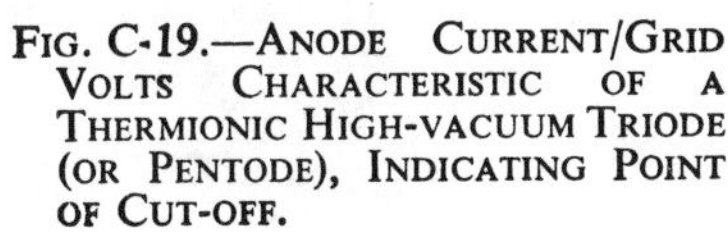
FIG. C-19.—ANODE CURRENT/GRID VOLTS CHARACTERISTIC OF A THERMIONIC HIGH-VACUUM TRIODE (OR PENTODE), INDICATING POINT OF CUT-OFF.

lator electrode (grid) of a cathode-ray tube, to reduce the electron current to zero. The value of the cut-off voltage depends upon the potentials at the other electrodes.

Cybernetics. The study of systems in which the action of a mechanism is controlled by information received from an external source.

Cycle. Complete series of changes occurring in or performed periodically by a system, such that the condition at the end of the series is the same as that at the commencement. See also DUTY CYCLE.

Cyclic. Said of a phenomenon, or a series of changes, which occurs in regular succession at a definite frequency. Also termed a PERIODIC phenomenon.

Cyclotron. Apparatus for imparting energies in the order of millions of ELECTRON-VOLTS to charged particles by causing them to follow a spiral path inside a pair of hollow semicircular electrodes between which an oscillating voltage is applied.

Cylinder (Wehnelt). Modulator electrode of a cathode-ray tube. See WEHNELT CYLINDER.

D

D Layer. Lowest region of ionized gas in the IONOSPHERE. It exists only during the hours of daylight, at an altitude of about 70 km.

Dag. Deflocculated Acheson Graphite, a suspension of finely divided graphite, in water more commonly known as Aquadag (trade name).

Damped Oscillations. Oscillations the amplitude of which progressively decreases (Fig. D-1).

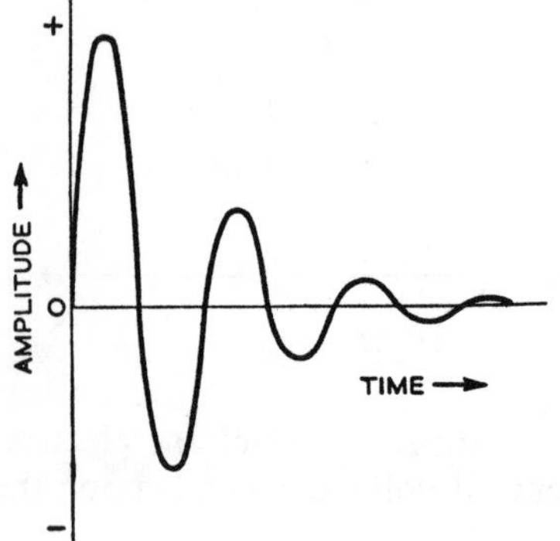

FIG. D-1.—TYPICAL WAVEFORM OF A DAMPED OSCILLATION.

Damped Waves. Waves produced as a series of trains of oscillations, the amplitudes of successive oscillations in each train progressively decreasing.

Damping. (1) Electrical damping: (*a*) the progressive reduction of the amplitudes of oscillations due to conditions in the circuit, or (*b*) the properties of a circuit, e.g. stray capacitances or shunt resistance, which cause such reductions.

(2) Mechanical damping—reduction of the amplitude of oscillations in a mechanical system due to such agencies as friction or viscosity.

Damping Constant. See DECAY FACTOR.

Dark Current. The small electron current which flows in a PHOTOCELL in the absence of illumination.

Dark Resistance. The resistance of a selenium or other photoconductive cell when not illuminated.

Dark Trace Cathode-ray Tube. Cathode-ray tube having a screen phosphor which gives a magenta trace under electronic bombardment. If the screen is illuminated by the greenish light from a mercury discharge lamp the trace appears black against a green background. This tube, also called the SKIATRON, is used in the PLAN POSITION INDICATOR when it is desired to project an enlarged image of the display.

D.C. Amplifier. Thermionic amplifier which can amplify not only alternating signals but also signals of zero frequency, that is to say, d.c. signals. See also DIRECT-COUPLED AMPLIFIERS.

D.C. Coupling. DIRECT COUPLING, that is to say, a coupling between stages of an amplifier via a path which permits d.c. signals to be transferred from the output of one stage to the input of the following stage.

D.C./A.C. Receiver. A radio receiver designed to obtain its h.t. and l.t. supplies from either d.c. or a.c. mains.

D.C. Resistance. The resistance of a conductor measured under d.c. conditions, the resistive component of its impedance. The term is, however, deprecated.

D.C. Restoration. The process of restoring the d.c. component of a television waveform after it has been removed by, for example, the action of a resistance–capacitance coupling in the video amplifier. In one method a diode is so connected that it conducts at peak instants of the synchronizing pulses and thus restores the datum level from a direct reference voltage source.

Dead Beat. Said of a measuring instrument or other mechanical vibrating system which is CRITICALLY DAMPED so that when a deflecting force is applied the system takes up its final position in minimum time without oscillation.

Dead End. That part of a tapped inductor which is not included in a resonant circuit (Fig. D-2).

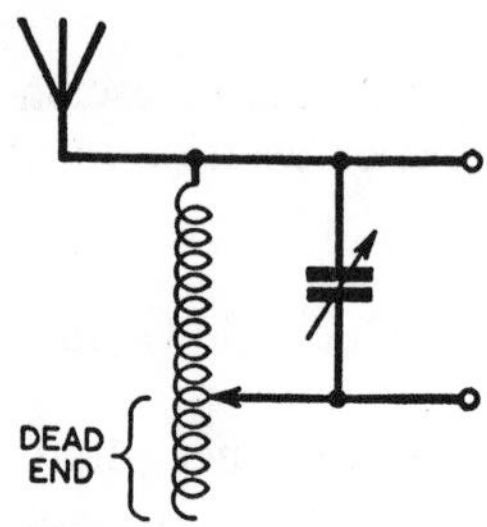

FIG. D-2.—AERIAL TUNING CIRCUIT WITH TAPPED INDUCTOR, ILLUSTRATING " DEAD END ".

Dead-end Effect. Increase of the effective resistance of an inductor due to the current circulating in the circuit comprised by the DEAD END shunted by its self-capacitance.

Deaf Aid. Combination of a microphone, an amplifier and a telephone receiver, specially designed for use by deaf persons. Preferred term " hearing aid ".

Decade. A consecutive series of ten equal magnitudes. Originally used only to indicate a series of ten consecutive years, it is now used in a wider sense as, for example, ten equal steps in a variable resistance box.

Decade Counter. A counter which registers in the scale of ten.

Decametric Waves. Electromagnetic waves having wavelengths between 10 and 100 m, corresponding to frequencies between 30 and 3 Mc/s. The HIGH FREQUENCY waves.

Decay Constant. Measure of the rate at which a radioactive substance disintegrates. If N_0 is the original amount of the substance and N_t is the quantity remaining after a time t, then

$$N_t = N_0 e^{-\lambda t},$$

where λ is the decay constant.

Decay Factor. Measure of the rate of decay of a damped oscillation. It is equal to the natural logarithm of the ratio of the amplitudes of two successive oscillations, divided by the time interval between them. Also termed the damping coefficient. See also LOGARITHMIC DECREMENT.

Decay Period. See HALF-LIFE.

Decay Time. Period of time required for oscillations to die away to zero once the stimulus has been removed.

Decibel. (Symbol dB) Unit used when comparing two amounts of power, current, voltage, etc., e.g. when indicating the gain in an amplifier. Equal to one-tenth of a BEL. A table for converting such ratios to decibels is given on page 370 of the Appendix.

Decimetric Waves. Electromagnetic waves having wavelengths between 0·1 and 1·0 m, corresponding to frequencies between 3000 and 300 Mc/s. The ULTRA HIGH FREQUENCY waves.

Deck. One of a series of CHASSIS mounted above each other and forming one unit of an electronic apparatus, e.g. the " tape deck " of a tape recorder, which accommodates the tape spools and the recording, playing and erasing heads.

Decoherer. Mechanical device which rendered a COHERER once more non-conductive after having detected a radio signal, thus making it ready to respond to the next signal.

Decoupling. The elimination or reduction of unwanted COUPLING between two circuits, such as that which exists by reason of the fact

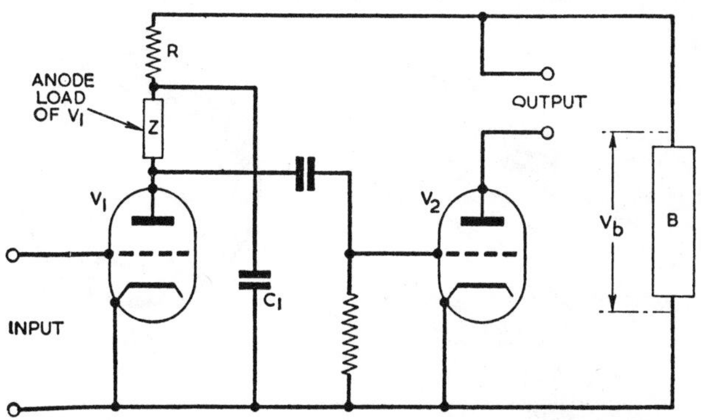

FIG. D-3.—BASIC CIRCUIT OF A TWO-VALVE AMPLIFIER IN WHICH THE ANODE CIRCUIT OF V1 IS DECOUPLED BY R.C1.

that the resistance of the h.t. supply source is common to the anode circuits of all the valves connected to that supply. In Fig. D-3 the resistor R is included in the anode circuit of valve V1. The alternating voltage drop across R, due to the variations of V_b as the result of the modulated anode current of V2 flowing in the supply unit B, are by-passed to earth via C1, thus leaving a substantially constant voltage for application to the anode circuit of V1.

Dee. Hollow semi-cylindrical electrode used for continuously accelerating the electrons in the spiral beam in a CYCLOTRON.

De-emphasis. Reduction of the relative strength of the higher audio frequencies in a radio signal to compensate the PRE-EMPHASIS introduced at the transmitter for the purpose of improving the SIGNAL-TO-NOISE RATIO.

Definition. The clearness with which a picture or a sound is reproduced. In sound reproduction good definition calls for linear amplification over the full audio-frequency range, good transient response, and linear response by the loudspeaker. In television important factors are spot size and sharp focus, correct setting of the contrast control, and the bandwidth of the video signal.

Deflexion. Change of direction of the electron beam in a CATHODE-RAY TUBE, resulting from the application of electric or magnetic fields. See ASYMMETRIC DEFLEXION, ELECTROSTATIC DEFLEXION, MAGNETIC DEFLEXION and SYMMETRICAL DEFLEXION.

Deflexion Coils. Sets of coils carrying currents which generate magnetic fields for deflecting the beam in a cathode-ray tube. Two sets of coils, one for vertical deflexion and one for horizontal deflexion, are required for a television picture tube. They are

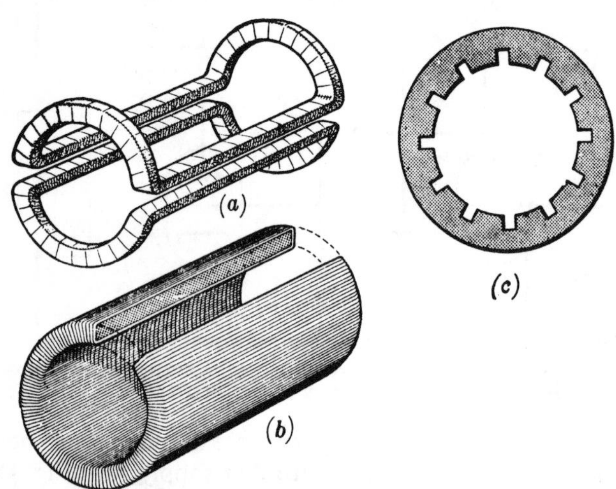

FIG. D-4.—TYPICAL CONSTRUCTIONS OF DEFLEXION COILS FOR CATHODE-RAY TUBES.

(a) One pair of a set of air-core coils. A further set mounted at right angles completes the deflexion system.
(b) Toroidal deflexion coil wound on a laminated steel core (cut-away view).
(c) Section of deflexion coil with slotted ferromagnetic core.

shaped to form a compact unit which fits snugly on the neck of the tube. They may have a ferromagnetic core. Fig. D-4 shows typical constructions.

Deflexion Defocusing. Progressive reduction of sharpness of focus towards the edges of a cathode-ray tube screen, due to the beam impinging on the screen at an angle other than a right angle.

Deflexion Plates. Pairs of flat metal electrodes mounted in the neck of a cathode-ray tube so that the electron beam passes between the two plates of a pair. A difference of potential applied between

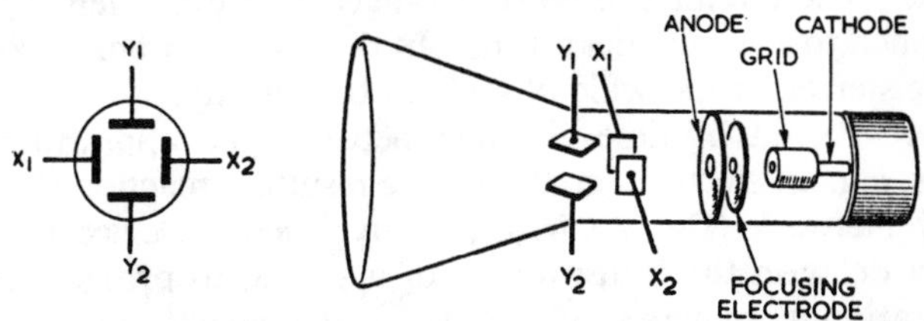

FIG. D-5.—SIMPLIFIED CROSS AND LONGITUDINAL SECTIONS OF AN ELECTROSTATICALLY DEFLECTED CATHODE-RAY TUBE, INDICATING THE POSITION OF THE DEFLEXION PLATES.

the two plates deflects the beam towards the higher (positive) potential. Two pairs of plates, mounted mutually at right angles, permit the beam to be deflected both vertically and horizontally. The plates for horizontal deflexion are termed the X plates, and those for vertical deflexion the Y plates (Fig. D-5).

Deflexion Sensitivity. Amount of linear displacement of the light spot on a cathode-ray tube screen, for a difference of potential of 1 V applied between a pair of deflexion plates, the final anode voltage being specified.

Degassing. Final processes in the evacuation of the envelope of an electron tube. In the early stages the envelope itself is heated and as much gas as possible is removed by pumping. The electrodes are then subjected to HIGH-FREQUENCY HEATING to a temperature higher than the normal working temperature of the tube, in order to drive off occluded gases, which are also removed by pumping. Finally, a GETTER, incorporated in the electrode structure, is fired and combines with the residual gases.

Degeneration. See NEGATIVE FEEDBACK.

De-ionization. Recombination of positive ions and electrons in an ionized gas, thus restoring the gas atoms to their electrically neutral condition.

De-ionization Time. Period of time which elapses after the removal of the ionizing influence (e.g. the positive anode potential in a thyratron) before de-ionization is substantially complete. See also RECOVERY TIME.

Dekatron. A gas-filled cold-cathode electron tube, having a central anode and ten effective cathodes, used in electronic counting circuits. The application of successive pulses to subsidiary electrodes, called transfer electrodes and situated between adjacent cathodes, causes the glow discharge to move from one cathode to the next. The circuit can be so arranged that every tenth pulse is also applied to a second dekatron. In this way a complete counting train registering in the scale of ten can be built up.

Delay. Period of time elapsing between the application of a stimulus, e.g. an electric signal, and the resulting reaction thereto.

Delay Network (Delay Circuit, Delay Line). Device for introducing a delay in the transmission of a signal, to provide time for the operation of switches, relays, etc., by the signal.

Delayed A.G.C. (Delayed A.V.C.). System of AUTOMATIC GAIN CONTROL which ensures that weak signals are fully amplified and that the control feature which gives substantially constant output is applied only to signals which exceed a pre-determined strength. This is achieved by applying a standing bias to the diode which supplies the a.g.c. voltage.

Delta Rays. Term sometimes applied to a stream of electrons moving at relatively low velocity.

Demodulation. Process whereby the modulation of a carrier is separated from the carrier itself. The term is mainly applied to DETECTION in a radio receiver, in which the wanted output is the modulating signal waveform. However, strictly speaking, demodulation also covers such processes as the operation of a smoothing filter in which the required output is the constant-voltage d.c. supply and not the superimposed ripple frequency.

Depth of Focus. The distance between the nearest and farthest points which a given optical system at a given setting (including a television camera) can focus with reasonable sharpness.

Depth of Modulation. Factor, usually expressed as a percentage, indicating the extent to which a carrier is modulated. In the case of amplitude modulation it is equal to half the difference between the maximum and minimum amplitudes divided by the mean amplitude of the waves.

Depth Sounding. See ECHO SOUNDING.

Derived Units. Units other than those of length, mass and time, derived from two or more of them. Thus, the unit of velocity in the c.g.s. system is the centimetre-per-second.

Detection. The process of extracting the signal information from a modulated carrier wave (see DEMODULATION). In the case of an AMPLITUDE MODULATED transmission, detection involves only the rectification of the radio-frequency signal. In the frequency-modulated system of transmission the frequency-modulated oscillation must first be converted into an amplitude-modulated oscillation.

Detector. A device to which a modulated carrier is applied and which provides an output which is a reasonably accurate reproduction of the original modulation. It is essentially a device having unilateral, or at least non-linear, conductivity. Typical detectors are crystal and thermionic diodes.

Detuning. Adjustment of the capacitance and/or inductance of an oscillating circuit so that the natural frequency of the system differs from the frequency of the applied signal.

Deviation. In general, the amount by which the measured value of any quantity differs from either the mean or the nominal value. The term has, however, a special connotation in relation to frequency modulation. See FREQUENCY DEVIATION.

Diagnostic X-ray Tube. Tube for producing X-rays of suitable character and intensity for X-ray examination of the body, as distinct from tubes giving X-rays for therapeutic purposes.

Diagonal. Since the ASPECT RATIO of television pictures is standardized at 4 : 3, the length of the diagonal of the reproduced picture is a convenient way of indicating picture size.

Diamagnetic. Said of a substance which can be slightly magnetized in the opposite direction of the magnetizing field.

Diamond Lattice. Crystal structure typified by that of the diamond. Germanium crystals have the same general structure (Fig. D-6).

Diaphragm. A resilient or resiliently mounted plate or membrane, and particularly one used for propagating or receiving sound waves.

Diathermy. Therapeutic treatment in which heat is produced in body tissues by passing high-frequency electric currents through them. The valve oscillators used in diathermy apparatus are apt to produce interference in television and other v.h.f. radio applications.

Dichroic Mirror. Mirror consisting of a glass plate on which is deposited a very thin film of metal. It will transmit light of a particular colour, but reflects light of other colours. Dichroic mirrors are used in some colour television systems for combining the images from three cathode-ray tubes, each giving a picture of a different primary colour.

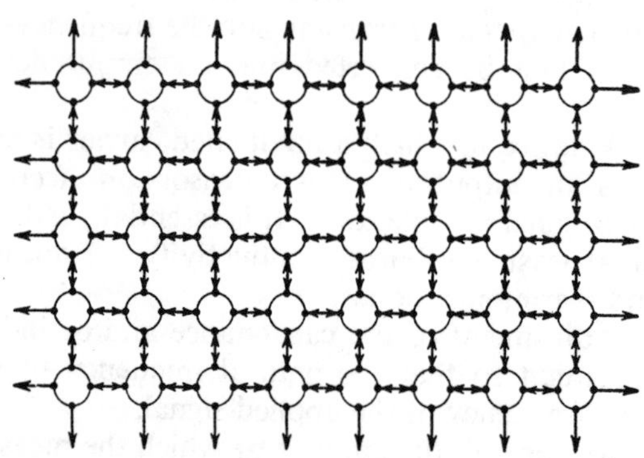

FIG. D-6.—DEVELOPMENT, SHOWN DIAGRAMMATICALLY IN ONE PLANE, OF THE "DIAMOND" TYPE CRYSTAL LATTICE.

The circles represent atoms (e.g. carbon), each with four valency electrons (black dots). Inter-atomic bonds are shown as short lines and two arrows represent a satisfied bond.

Dielectric. A non-conductor of electricity. Application of an electric field to a dielectric results only in a displacement of electric charge within the material, due to the molecules becoming polarized and orienting themselves in the direction of the electric field.

Dielectric Constant. A constant, characteristic of a particular dielectric, and numerically equal to the ratio of the capacitance of a capacitor in which that substance forms the dielectric, to that of the same capacitor but having air (strictly speaking a vacuum) in the space between the plates. Also termed specific inductive capacity and permittivity.

Dielectric Loss. The energy dissipated in a dielectric when subjected to an alternating electric field.

Dielectric-loss Heating. Method of heating non-conducting material by placing it in a high-frequency electric field. It is employed in a number of industrial processes, including the manufacture of plywood, gluing operations in furniture making and the pre-heating of plastic charges prior to moulding.

Difference Frequency. The frequency of one of the oscillations produced by the BEATING of two oscillations of different frequency, and equal to the difference between the frequencies of the two oscillations.

Differential Anode Resistance. Resistance of the anode-to-cathode path within a multi-electrode thermionic valve, all other electrodes remaining at constant potentials with respect to the cathode.

Differential Capacitor. A variable capacitor having one set of moving plates and two sets of fixed plates, so mounted that when the moving plates are adjusted to increase their capacitance to one set of fixed plates the capacitance to the other set of fixed plates is decreased.

Differentiation. In general, the determination of the rate of change of a varying quantity. Specifically, the production of a waveform the amplitude of which is at all times proportional to the rate of change of amplitude in an original waveform.

Differentiating Circuit or Network. A network, the output waveform of which corresponds to the rate of change of amplitude in the

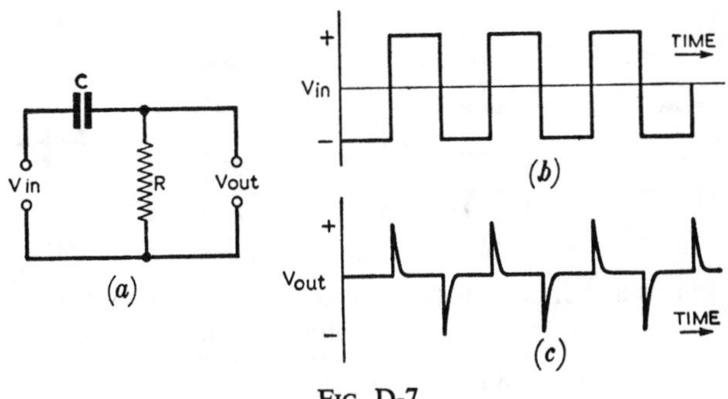

FIG. D-7.

(a) Basic differentiating circuit.
(b) The square-wave input.
(c) The output waveform if time-constant C.R. is small compared with the pulse time.

input waveform. A basic arrangement consisting of a series capacitor and a shunt resistor as shown at A in Fig. D-7. A square-wave input pulse as indicated at B appears in the output as at C, if the time-constant R.C is small compared with the pulse time.

Diffraction. Slight spreading of rays which occurs when a beam moves past the edge of an opaque obstacle. Although in radio transmission it involves some losses, in the case of very short waves it permits reception at distances somewhat greater than the visual distance.

Diffused-junction Transistor. Transistor in which the impurity element is allowed to diffuse into the semiconductor, controlled by time and temperature, to produce the requisite pnp or npn construction. Another layer may be added to this type, forming a pnip transistor.

Digital Computer. Computer which operates on, and records in terms of, numbers represented by simple pulses.

Diode. (1) Electron tube having only two electrodes—anode and cathode. Thermionic diodes, whether of the high-vacuum type or gas-filled, are mainly employed as RECTIFIERS, i.e. for delivering a uni-directional output from an alternating input. A special case of rectification for which high-vacuum diodes are employed is the DETECTION (demodulation) or radio signals. Cold cathode diodes, possessing special properties, are used as VOLTAGE STABILIZERS and SURGE ARRESTERS.

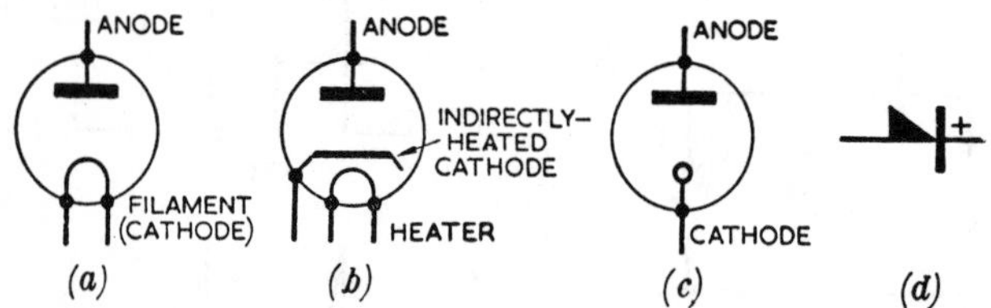

FIG. D-8.—STANDARD GRAPHICAL SYMBOLS FOR DIODES.
(a) Directly heated thermionic diode;
(b) Indirectly heated thermionic diode;
(c) Cold cathode diode;
(d) Crystal diode.

(2) The term diode is also applied to two-electrode semiconductor devices. See CRYSTAL DIODE. Fig. D-8 shows several types of diode.

Diode Detector. Detector circuit in which the rectifying element is a thermionic diode. A typical circuit is shown in Fig. D-9, where R is the diode load and C1 is a capacitor which smooths out the radio-frequency component of the rectified output, leaving only the direct component with audio-frequency modulation.

Capacitor C2 blocks the steady direct component and transfers the audio-frequency signal to the low-frequency amplifier.

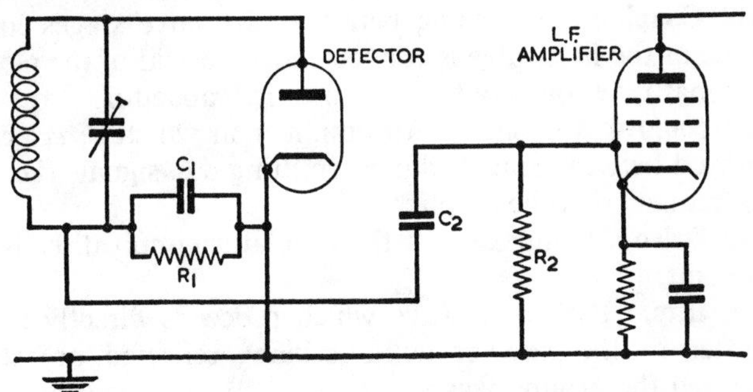

FIG. D-9.—BASIC CIRCUIT OF DIODE DETECTOR AND FOLLOWING AMPLIFIER.

R1 is the diode load and R2 the grid resistor of the amplifier valve. Either R1 or R2 could be tapped to serve as a volume control.

Diode-pentode. Multiple valve consisting of a diode system and a pentode system in a common envelope (Fig. D-10).

Dipole. (1) Two equal electric charges of opposite sign, situated very close together. When an electric field is applied to a DIELECTRIC the atoms behave as if their electron shells were distorted so that the centre of gravity of the electrons no longer coincides with that of the nucleus. The atoms are then said to be polarized, and are, in effect, electric dipoles.

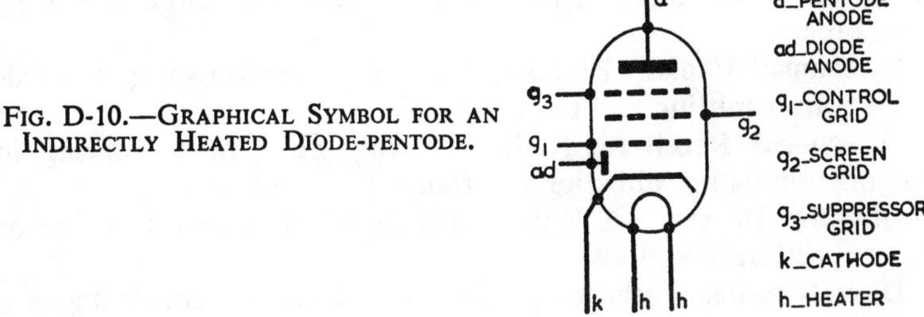

FIG. D-10.—GRAPHICAL SYMBOL FOR AN INDIRECTLY HEATED DIODE-PENTODE.

(2) Two equal but opposite magnetic poles situated very close to each other.

(3) AERIAL consisting of two straight conductors mounted in line, end-to-end, the connexions being made to the two inner ends.

If the electrical length of the arrangement is one-half (resonant dipole) of the signal wavelength, STANDING WAVES will be set up in it, and maximum current will be available at the feeding points.

Direct Coupling. Coupling between two valve stages in which the anode of the first valve is connected to the grid of the next valve by a d.c. path, i.e. one containing no series capacitor.

Direct-coupled Amplifier. An amplifier in which *direct coupling* is employed between stages, thus permitting d.c. signals (i.e. signals of zero frequency) to be amplified.

Direct Drive. Connexion of the oscillator circuit directly to the aerial circuit.

Direct Ray. Path of a wave which proceeds directly from the transmitter to the receiver without being reflected or refracted. Also termed the ground wave.

Direct Viewing. Viewing the reproduced television picture on the actual face of the cathode-ray tube, as opposed to PROJECTION VIEWING, in which an enlarged image of the picture is optically projected on to a separate viewing screen.

Direct Wave. A wave which follows the direct path between transmitter and receiver. See DIRECT RAY.

Direction Finder. The complete equipment, comprising essentially a directional aerial and a radio receiver, required for direction finding.

Direction Finding. Determination of bearings by ascertaining from what direction incoming radio waves have been transmitted or reflected.

Directional Aerial. An aerial system which has the property of radiating in, or receiving from, certain directions more effectively than others.

Directional Radio. Radio system employing directional aerials at both transmitting and receiving ends.

Directional Receiver. Radio receiving equipment working in conjunction with a directional aerial.

Directive Beacon. A RADIO BEACON which radiates in one or more specified directions.

Directly-heated Cathode. THERMIONIC CATHODE consisting of a metallic wire or FILAMENT which is heated by passing an electric current through it.

Director. A straight conductor located in front of a dipole aerial, i.e. between the aerial and the transmitter. It is usually slightly shorter than the aerial itself, and is mounted one-quarter or one-eighth of a wavelength from the aerial. Sometimes more than one director is fitted (Fig. D-11). Directors increase the directional properties of the dipole.

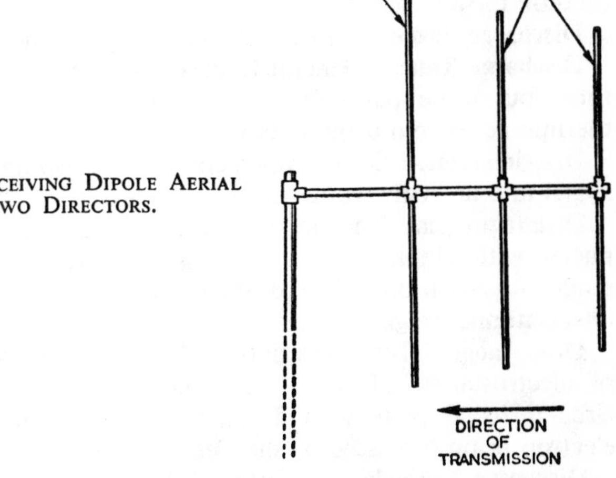

FIG. D-11.—RECEIVING DIPOLE AERIAL WITH TWO DIRECTORS.

Disk Seal Valve. Thermionic valve for operating at very high frequencies, of 500 Mc/s and over. The connexions between the electrodes and the external circuit are formed by flat disks or metal rings sealed into the envelope (Fig. D-12).

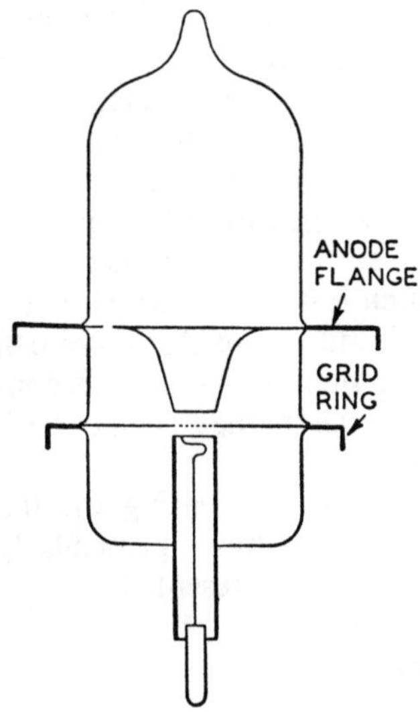

FIG. D-12.—GENERAL CONSTRUCTION OF A DISK SEAL VALVE.

Discharge (Electric). Passage of electricity through an ionized gas.

Discharge Lamp. Electric lamp which emits light during the discharge of electricity between two electrodes. See GAS DISCHARGE LAMP.

Discharge through Gases. See GAS DISCHARGE.

Discharge Tube. General term applied to all forms of electron tube, but more particularly to gas-filled tubes, whether of the thermionic or cold-cathode type.

Discriminator. Device which converts a FREQUENCY MODULATED signal into an AMPLITUDE MODULATED signal.

Disintegration. The break-up (natural or otherwise) of atomic nuclei with simultaneous emission of particles and/or electromagnetic radiation. The disintegration results in a nucleus of lower atomic weight.

Disk Anode. Term descriptive of the final anode in some types of electrostatically-focused cathode-ray tubes. The anode is a circular metal plate with a central aperture through which the electron beam produced by the electron gun emerges.

Dispenser Cathode. A form of indirectly-heated THERMIONIC CATHODE particularly suitable for valves and tubes employed for generating ultra-short waves (e.g. magnetrons, klystrons, etc.) and for tubes such as X-ray tubes in which large emission combined with great mechanical strength and reliability are required. It consists of a quantity of barium–strontium oxide enclosed in a metallic chamber composed mainly of molybdenum, but with one wall of porous tungsten which forms the emitting surface. The whole is heated by an independent heating wire or filament. At the working temperature, which is in the region 900–1350° C, barium, strontium and also barium oxide escape through the porous wall and form a monatomic layer on the surface, thus reducing the WORK FUNCTION, which for pure tungsten is 4·5 V, to between 1·6 and 2·0 V so that an emission of some hundreds of A/sq. cm can be obtained under pulse conditions. The monatomic layer is continuously renewed automatically, hence the name "dispenser" cathode. Also known as the "L" cathode.

Display. In general, the pattern or image appearing on the luminescent screen of a cathode-ray tube, but more particularly applied to the form in which information is presented by the cathode-ray tube in radar equipment.

Dissector. American term for SCANNER.

Dissipation (Electrode). Energy dissipated in an electron tube as heat at an electrode, and particularly the anode, either due to bombardment by electrons or ions, or radiation from other electrodes.

Distance Measuring Equipment. Development of RADAR by which the pilot of an aircraft can ascertain his distance from a fixed station or beacon. The aircraft transmits an " interrogating " signal pulse, upon receipt of which the beacon automatically sends out a reply signal. Apparatus in the aircraft measures the time which elapses between the transmission of the interrogating pulse and the receipt of the answer, and indicates it on an instrument calibrated in miles.

Distortion. The departure of the output waveform of an amplifier, etc., from the waveform of the original signal. See AMPLITUDE DISTORTION, HARMONIC DISTORTION, PHASE DISTORTION and TOTAL DISTORTION.

Divalent. Said of an element the atom of which is capable of combining with two atoms of hydrogen or their equivalent.

Dolly. A mobile mounting for a cinematograph camera or television camera.

Domain. Small region, having a volume in the order of 10^{-8} cu. cm, in a magnetic material. It is considered that each domain is magnetized, but that the directions of their magnetization are distributed at random so that the resultant magnetization is zero except when a magnetic field (magnetizing force) is applied, when the magnetic axes of the domains arrange themselves parallel to the direction of the field.

Donor Impurity. An adulterant which, added in controlled quantity to a pure semiconductor, liberates electrons which become available as negative charge carriers. For example, when a pentavalent adulterant, such as antimony or arsenic, is added to germanium (which is tetravalent), each atom of the adulterant provides one free electron. Germanium treated in this way is termed n-TYPE germanium (cf. ACCEPTOR).

Doorknob Transformer. Device for converting co-axial line transmission to waveguide transmission.

Dot. Unit impulse in telegraphic transmission.

Dot Frequency. In television, half the number of picture elements transmitted per second.

Double Amplitude. PEAK-TO-PEAK value of an alternating electric current, voltage, etc.

Double-beam Cathode-ray Tube. CATHODE-RAY TUBE in which two separate electron streams are produced—permitting two phenomena to be displayed simultaneously on the luminescent screen.

Double Diode. Multiple valve consisting of two diode systems in a common envelope (Fig. D-13).

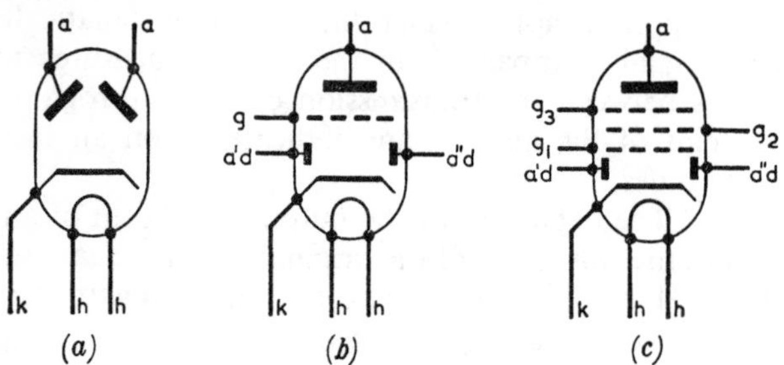

FIG. D-13.—GRAPHICAL SYMBOLS FOR:
(a) Indirectly heated double diode;
(b) Indirectly heated double-diode-triode;
(c) Indirectly heated double-diode-pentode.

Double Diode Triode. Multiple valve consisting of two diode systems and one triode system in a common envelope (Fig. D-13).

Double Diode Pentode. Multiple valve consisting of two diode systems and one pentode system in a common envelope (Fig D-13).

Double-hump Tuning. Effect of using two coupled resonant circuits tuned to slightly different frequencies, one just above and

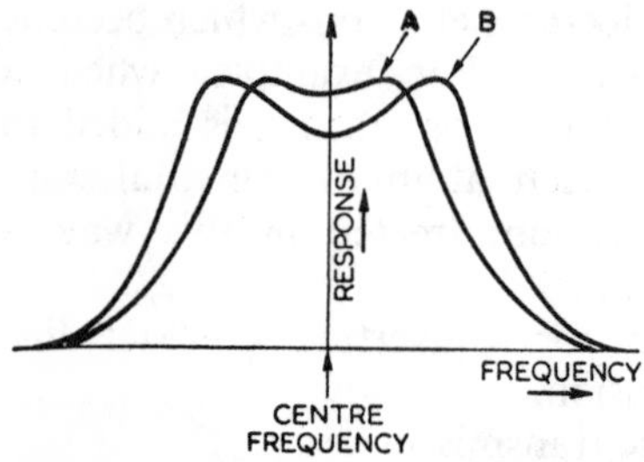

FIG. D-14.—RESPONSE CURVES SHOWING THE EFFECT OF DOUBLE-HUMP TUNING.

Optimum adjustment results in a response curve similar to A.

the other just below the signal frequency. Response is maximum at the two resonant frequencies, but if the system is properly adjusted the trough in the frequency response curve (see Fig. D-14) is shallow. The arrangement gives good selectivity without undue sacrifice of sidebands. See also BANDPASS TUNING.

Double Image. Production of two images on the screen of a television receiver, the second being slightly displaced. One picture is due to the signal received directly from the transmitter, and the second, sometimes called the GHOST IMAGE, resulting from waves which have been reflected from some object, such as a large building or a hill, and arriving at the receiver a short time after the direct wave.

Double-layer Screen. Cathode-ray tube screen coated with two phosphors having different characteristics as regard colour and persistence. For example, one phosphor may give a bluish luminescence of relatively short persistence, suitable for photographic recording, and the second a greenish trace of long persistence, more useful for visual inspection of the trace.

Double Pentode. Multiple valve consisting of two pentode systems in a common envelope (Fig. D-15).

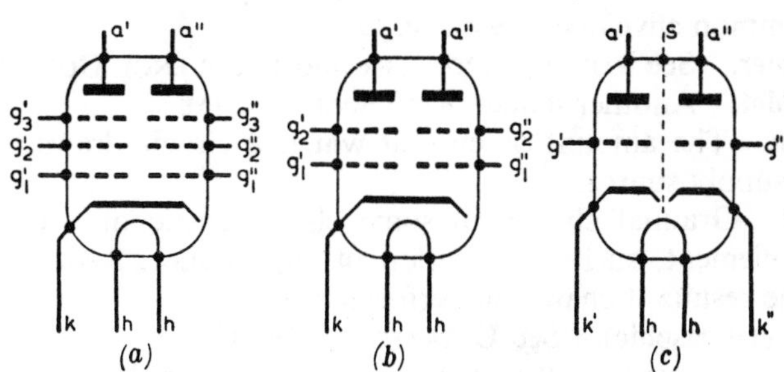

FIG. D-15.—GRAPHICAL SYMBOLS FOR:
(a) Indirectly heated double pentode;
(b) Indirectly heated double tetrode;
(c) Indirectly heated double triode.

Such valves may have common cathodes as in (a) and (b), or the two systems may have separate cathodes and an electrostatic screen between the two sections as in (c).

Double-sideband Transmission. When information is transmitted by radio in the form of a modulated carrier wave, the transmission occupies two frequency bands, one on either side of the carrier frequency, and extending from f_c to $f_c + f_m$ (the upper sideband) and from f_c to $f_c - f_m$ (the lower sideband), where f_c is the frequency of the carrier wave and f_m the highest frequency in the modulation (Fig. D-16). Since in the process of DETECTION the radio-frequency signal is rectified by suppressing one of the received sidebands, both transmitting power and space in the frequency spectrum can be saved by suppressing one of the sidebands at the source. This system is then known as single-sideband transmission.

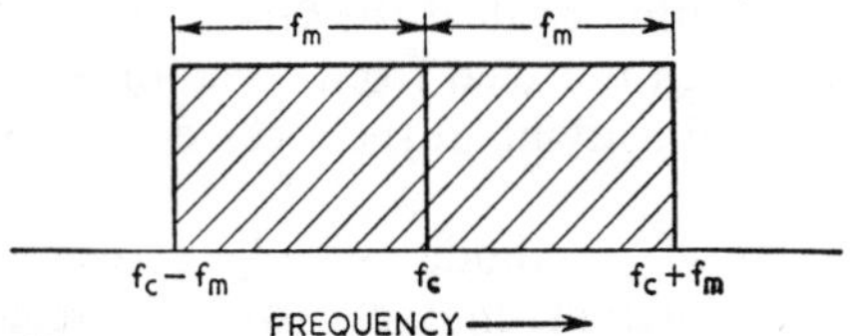

FIG. D-16.—FREQUENCY BAND OCCUPIED BY A DOUBLE-SIDEBAND TRANSMISSION.

f_c is the carrier frequency and f_m is the highest modulation frequency.

Double Tetrode. Multiple valve consisting of two tetrode systems in a common envelope. See Fig. D-15.

Double Triode. Multiple valve consisting of two triode systems in a common envelope. See Fig. D-15.

Doubler. See VOLTAGE DOUBLER and FREQUENCY DOUBLER.

Doublet. Another name for a DIPOLE AERIAL.

Drain. The amount of current which a circuit draws from its power supply source.

Drift. Gradual change in some characteristic of a circuit or circuit element, such as variation of capacitance, frequency, etc. Also the resultant change in performance.

Drill (Ultrasonic). See ULTRASONIC DRILL.

Drive. In general, the alternating-voltage signal applied to the control grid of a thermionic amplifier. Also used for the complete MASTER OSCILLATOR unit of a transmitter.

Drive Potential (Drive Voltage). Term sometimes used to indicate the positive potential applied to the anode of a photo-emissive cell.

Drop. See POTENTIAL DROP or VOLTAGE DROP.

Dropper Resistor. A resistor included in a circuit in order to reduce the voltage available at some point in the system. A dropper resistor is used, for example, to permit a piece of apparatus rated for a particular voltage to be operated on a supply of higher voltage. In electronic equipment it frequently happens that it is necessary to operate various valves at different anode voltages from a common supply source. A dropper resistor is then included in the anode circuit of each valve.

Dry Battery. Primary battery in which the electrolyte is provided in the form of a paste to prevent spilling. Dry batteries are used for the h.t. and l.t. supplies of battery-operated radio receivers, and also for the operation of equipment incorporating transistors.

Dry Joint. Soldered joint in which, due to insufficient heating or lack of sufficient flux during the soldering operation, the solder has not adhered to the metals to be joined, thus producing a joint which is weak mechanically and of high electrical resistance.

Dual Amplifier. See REFLEX AMPLIFICATION.

Dub. To transfer separately recorded programme material to another record, e.g. the insertion of speech, music, etc., on the sound track of a cinematograph film.

Ducting. In certain atmospheric conditions, usually where the dielectric constant decreases with height at a greater than normal rate, v.h.f. signals may be bent back to the earth, and thus propagated over considerable distances. Alternatively, when the dielectric constant at first increases and subsequently decreases, the signals may be trapped between these two layers. Such processes are generally referred to as ducting.

Dull Emitter Filament. A DIRECTLY-HEATED thermionic cathode made of a material which gives adequate electron emission at a temperature corresponding to dull red heat.

Dumb Aerial. A resistive network which can be coupled to a transmitter in place of the normal aerial, and is not capable of radiating energy.

Dummy Aerial. See ARTIFICIAL AERIAL.

Dust Core. Slug composed of iron dust mixed with a non-conductive binding medium, and used as the core of an inductor or transformer for operation at high frequencies. This construction minimizes eddy-current losses. Adjustment of the position of the core within the coil varies the inductance of the combination.

Duty Cycle. For equipment employing PULSE TECHNIQUE, the duty cycle is equal to the pulse width in seconds, multiplied by the repetition frequency in pulses per second.

Dyad. A divalent atom.

Dynamic Characteristics. Characteristics (particularly the anode current/grid volts characteristic) of a thermionic valve measured under working conditions, i.e. with a signal applied to the control grid and a load included in the anode circuit. In Fig. D-17 the full line represents the STATIC characteristics showing the variation of anode current with change of grid voltage, the anode voltage remaining constant. The dotted curve is the dynamic characteristic, which is flatter than the static curve because the increase of anode current due to a reduction of negative grid potential causes a voltage drop in the anode load so that at point B the anode voltage is lower than at point A.

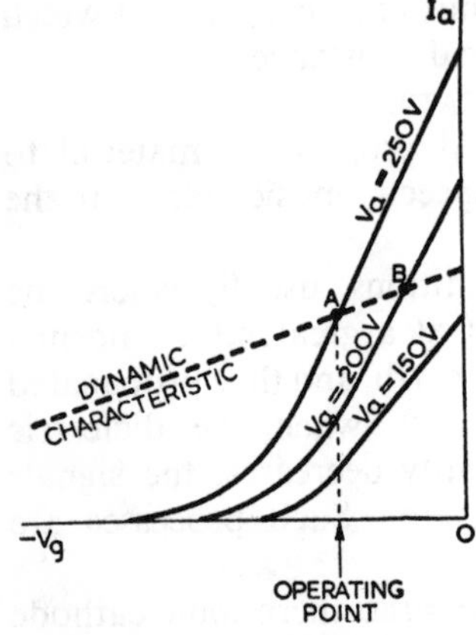

FIG. D-17.—I_a/V_g CHARACTERISTICS OF A THERMIONIC VALVE.

The static characteristics are in full line. The dynamic characteristic (for a particular anode load) is in broken line.

Dynatron. Multi-grid thermionic valve, usually a TETRODE, so operated that it exhibits the effect of NEGATIVE RESISTANCE.

Dynatron Oscillator. Circuit for generating electrical oscillations by making use of the negative resistance kink in the anode current/anode volts characteristic of a tetrode.

Dyne. Unit of force; that force which, acting on a mass of one gramme, imparts to it an acceleration of one centimetre per second per second.

Dynode. An electrode which is fitted in an electron tube mainly for the purpose of emitting secondary electrons. See ELECTRON MULTIPLIER.

E

E-core. Shaped member composed of ferromagnetic material, either in the form of steel laminations or of solid ferrite, employed as part of the core of an inductor or of a transformer. Used in conjunction with an **I**-core as illustrated in Fig. E-1, it forms a closed magnetic circuit. The winding or windings are usually located on the centre limb of the E but may also be distributed on the two outer limbs or, in the case of three-phase windings, all three limbs may be used.

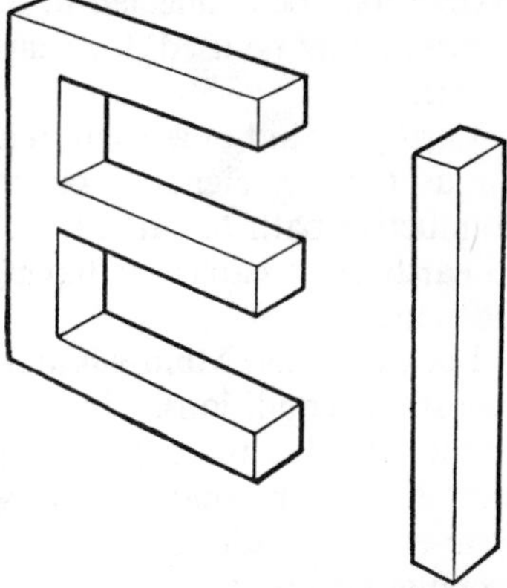

FIG. E-1.—E AND I MEMBERS OF AN INDUCTOR OR TRANSFORMER CORE.

E Layer. Region of ionized gas in the IONOSPHERE, which reflects practically all incident medium frequency radiation, absorbing very little. Also known as the KENNELLY–HEAVISIDE LAYER.

E-mode. A particular field configuration in WAVEGUIDE technique. See MODE.

E-type Waves. Waves propagated in the E-mode, i.e. in which there is an electrical component of the field in the direction of propagation, but no magnetic component in that direction.

Earth. The main body of the earth is considered to be at zero electrical potential. The earth itself, therefore, and any conductor connected thereto is termed " earth ".

Earth Plate. A metal plate buried in the earth in order to provide a good earth connexion.

Earth Potential. The electrical potential of the main body of the earth, and taken as the zero or reference level of potential. A body may be at a positive or at a negative potential with respect to earth, or, if connected to earth by a path of negligible resistance, it may be at earth potential.

Earthed-cathode Operation. Method of connecting and operating an amplifying valve such that the cathode is effectively at earth potential so far as the signal is concerned. Also known as GROUNDED CATHODE operation.

Earthed-grid Operation. Method of connecting and operating an amplifying valve such that the grid is effectively at earth potential, the signal being applied across an impedance in the cathode circuit. Also known as GROUNDED GRID operation.

Earthing Switch. A switch whereby some point in an electrical system may be connected to earth by a low-resistance path. Such a switch may be used, for example, to " earth " an aerial when not in use.

Earthy. Said of a point in a circuit which is at earth potential so far as the a.c. signal is concerned. This point may not have a conductive path to earth for direct current, but may be connected to earth via a capacitor having relatively low impedance at signal frequency.

Eccles–Jordan Multi-vibrator. A MULTI-VIBRATOR circuit having two stable conditions. In one, valve A is conductive while valve B is cut off. On the application of a triggering pulse to the control circuit, valve B conducts and valve A is cut-off. Also known as a FLIP-FLOP circuit. Used, among other things, for generating rectangular pulses.

Echo. Signal received a short time after receipt of the main signal, the delay being due to reflexion of part of the original wave so that it takes a longer route.

Echo Methods of Measurement. Detection of the presence and determination of the distance of obstructions or discontinuities by measuring the time between the transmission of a signal and the reception of its echo.

Echo Sounding. Measurement of the depth of the ocean by directing a sonic or ultrasonic pressure wave vertically downward and determining the time taken before the echo is received. Similar methods are used for detecting shoals of fish and in geological prospecting. Ultrasonic echo equipment is also used for the detection of flaws in engineering materials and structures.

Eddy-current Heating. The heating of a conductor due to the circulation of EDDY CURRENTS. Although this represents a power loss in most instances, eddy-current heating is usefully employed for many industrial metal-heating processes, using magnetic fields generated by high-frequency alternating currents. See INDUCTION HEATING.

Eddy-current Losses. Power loss represented by the heat generated by the circulation of eddy currents. In the case of magnetic cores these losses are minimized by the use of laminations with insulation between them or, for high-frequency components, by using DUST CORES or cores composed of high-resistivity magnetic FERRITES.

Eddy Currents. Electric currents induced in a conductor by a varying magnetic field, for instance, in the core of an inductor or transformer. Also termed Foucault currents.

Edison Effect. An early and basic observation by Thomas A. Edison that an electric current will pass across a vacuous space between a heated filament and a cold electrode which is at a positive potential with respect to the filament. This discovery marked a major step in the development of the thermionic valve.

Efficiency. (Symbol η) Ratio of useful output power to total input power.

Efficiency Diode. Thermionic diode connected in the anode circuit of the output valve in the line timebase generator of a television receiver, and operated in such a way that it recovers much of the energy stored in the magnetic circuit of the anode load, and which would otherwise have to be dissipated in damping resistors. In the most recent form, the BOOSTER DIODE circuit, the recovered energy is manifest as an increase of some 40–60 V in the effective h.t. supply to the timebase generator which, in the case of d.c./a.c. receivers, would otherwise not greatly exceed 180 V.

Electric Charge. See CHARGE.

Electric Current. (Symbol I) Movement of electric charge. In a conductor the current consists of a drift of electrons towards the positive pole of the applied electric field. In an ELECTROLYTE or in a gas it consists of the migration of positive ions towards the negative electrode and of negative ions and/or electrons towards the positive electrode. Unit, the AMPERE.

Electric Discharge. Passage of electricity through a gas as the result of ionization of gas atoms. It is accompanied by luminous and sometimes thermal phenomena.

Electric Field. Region within which a potential gradient exists so that a force is exerted upon electric charges (and thus upon electrons and ions) present in the field.

Electric Field Strength. Indicated in magnitude and direction by the force in dynes experienced by a unit electric charge at a specified point in an electric field. Usually expressed in terms of potential gradient (V/cm).

Electric Welding. Method of welding metals in which the necessary heat is produced electrically, either by an arc or as the result of high contact resistance. See WELDING, ELECTRONIC CONTROL OF.

Electrical Oscillation. Alternating electric current the frequency of which is determined by the constants (inductance and capacitance) of a resonant circuit.

Electrical Polarization. Displacement of the electrons in an electrically neutral atom when an electric field is applied. This results in the production of an electric DIPOLE.

Electrical Resonance. The impedance of a circuit possessing inductance and capacitance varies with the frequency and, at a particular frequency termed the NATURAL FREQUENCY, the impedance of the circuit is a minimum. If an oscillation having this same frequency is applied to the circuit, the circuit is said to be in resonance with the applied oscillation.

Electrode. Conductor by which an electric current enters or leaves an electrolyte or an electron tube. The positive electrode is the ANODE and the negative electrode the CATHODE.

Electro-dynamic Loudspeaker. See MOVING-COIL LOUDSPEAKER.

Electroluminescence. Emission of light from a phosphor powder which is embedded in an insulating material and excited by an alternating electric field. As a practical source of illumination its efficiency at the present time is in the range of 9 lumens/watt. Electroluminescent units can be made in almost any size and shape, and produce glare-free light. A wide range of colours is obtainable by suitable choice of phosphor.

Electrolyte. Conductor, normally a liquid, in which the flow of current consists of the migration of ions, negative ions moving towards the positive electrode and positive ions towards the negative electrode.

Electrolytic Capacitor. Capacitor in which the dielectric is a thin film of oxide deposited upon aluminium foil which forms the positive plate, the effective negative plate being a non-corrosive electrolyte. The great advantage of this type of capacitor is that a large capacitance can be obtained in a component of small dimensions.

Electromagnet. Device in which a core of ferromagnetic material is encircled by a coil of wire carrying an electric current. The core exhibits magnetization only while the current is flowing in the coil.

Electromagnetic Deflexion. Deflexion of the beam in a cathode-ray tube due to the field or fields produced by one or more electromagnets mounted on the neck of the tube.

Electromagnetic Induction. Generation of an electromotive force in a conductor or system of conductors due to the relative movement between the conductor and a magnetic field. The movement may consist of physical motion of the conductor, or the field or of both, or it may consist of increase or decrease of the magnetic field strength.

Electromagnetic Loudspeaker. See MOVING-IRON LOUDSPEAKER.

Electromagnetic Microphone. Microphone in which the sound waves cause relative movement between a magnetic field and a coil, thus causing an electro-motive force to be generated in the coil.

Electromagnetic Pick-up. Gramophone PICK-UP in which the movement of the stylus in the groove of the record produces relative movement between a magnetic field and a coil so that an electro-motive force is generated in the coil.

Electromagnetic Radiation. Radiation of energy in the form of variations of electric and magnetic fields. See ELECTROMAGNETIC WAVES.

Electromagnetic Screen. Screen composed of conducting and magnetically permeable materials which minimize penetration of electric and magnetic fields into the region enclosed by the screen.

Electromagnetic Spectrum. The complete range of frequencies over which energy in the form of ELECTROMAGNETIC WAVES is radiated. A general analysis of the electromagnetic spectrum is given in the Appendix.

Electromagnetic Waves. Rhythmic variations of an electric field and of a magnetic field at right angles to it, propagated in space at a uniform velocity of $2{\cdot}9978 \times 10^8$ metres per second (about 186,000 miles per second). Their properties and effects are determined by their frequency (see ELECTROMAGNETIC SPECTRUM) so that they may be classified as radio, heat, light, X-rays, gamma rays, etc.

Electrometer. Strictly speaking, an instrument for measuring difference of potential while drawing no current from the source. The electrostatic voltmeter is thus a true electrometer. However, special forms of thermionic valves, termed ELECTROMETER VALVES, draw almost negligible negative grid current, and thus can be used for amplifying very small electrical effects, the amplified output then being applied to normal measuring instruments.

Electrometer Valves. Thermionic valves of special design, which impose negligible load on the signal source, and are thus suitable for amplifying very small electrical effects before application to conventional measuring instruments. High gain and very stable performance are important qualities in an electrometer valve, but the prime requirement is that the negative grid current of the valve shall be small compared with the current in the circuit under measurement. To this end, special measures are taken to minimize the risk of current leakage between grid and cathode, and to avoid photo-electric effects and the risk of bombardment of the grid by positive ions, either emitted by the cathode or formed by collision between electrons and the atoms of residual gases. The working value of negative grid current may be as low as 10^{-15} A under working conditions.

Electro-motive Force (e.m.f.). Force which causes the movement of electric charges. Unit the VOLT.

Electron. One of the fundamental constituents of the ATOM, having a mass $\frac{1}{1840}$ that of a hydrogen atom. It carries a negative electric charge equivalent to $1{\cdot}6 \times 10^{-19}$ coulomb. See ATOM, STRUCTURE OF.

Electron Beam. Stream of electrons moving at high velocity, such as that projected by an ELECTRON GUN, and particularly after having been focused so that the stream becomes convergent.

Electron Camera. See TELEVISION CAMERA.

Electron Cloud. Congregation of relatively stationary electrons in a region between two electrodes in an electron tube. See also SPACE CHARGE.

Electron-coupled Frequency Changer. One form of FREQUENCY CHANGER valve for use in superheterodyne receivers. It usually has five or six grids, the cathode and first two grids forming a triode oscillator for generating the LOCAL OSCILLATOR frequency. The electron stream, now modulated at local oscillator frequency, is accelerated towards the anode, but on its way is further modulated by the signal, which is introduced at one of the other grids. The BEATING of the local and signal frequencies produces the intermediate-frequency signal.

Electron Current. Flow of electrons in an electric field from a point of lower to a point of higher potential, as in an electron tube.

Electron Diffraction. DIFFRACTION which occurs in an electron stream when it passes through a very thin metal foil.

Electron Gun. System of electrodes in an electron tube which projects a stream of electrons moving at uniform velocity in a straight line. It consists in essence of an emitting cathode (see Fig. E-2) and an accelerating electrode (anode), the latter having a small aperture through which some of the electrons can pass into the region beyond the anode. Here they will continue to move in a straight line, at the velocity corresponding to the potential difference they have traversed between the cathode and anode, unless acted upon by some other electric field or a magnetic field. Practical forms of electron gun usually include one or more additional electrodes for modulating and focusing the electron beam. An electron gun is an essential part of the structure of a cathode-ray tube, and of most forms of television camera tube.

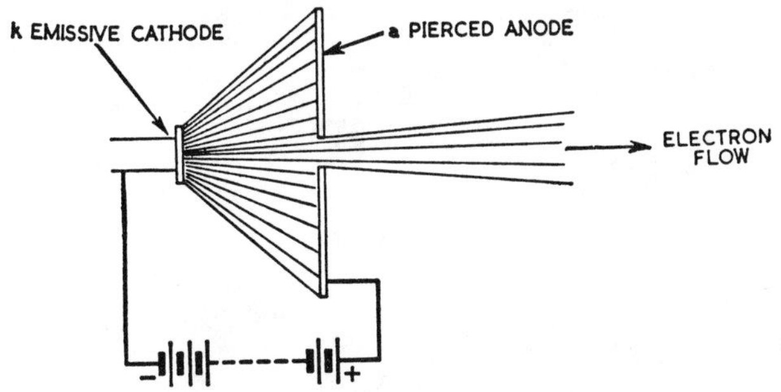

FIG. E-2.—PRINCIPLE OF THE ELECTRON GUN.

Electrons emitted from cathode k and accelerated by the positive potential at anode a, pass through the central orifice of the anode and continue to travel in the direction of the arrow without change of velocity.

Electron Lens. Electrical or magnetic field distribution, or a combination of the two, which has the same effect upon an electron beam as an optical lens has upon a beam of light. An electron lens system is used in cathode-ray tubes for focusing the beam on to the luminescent screen. See ELECTROSTATIC FOCUSING and MAGNETIC FOCUSING.

Electron Microscope. Device serving much the same purpose as an optical microscope, but using a stream of electrons for producing the image. Because of its very great RESOLVING POWER, the electron microscope can produce useful images of extremely small objects. The action of the electron microscope is based upon the fact that a high-velocity electron beam possesses many properties similar to those of a beam of light. The basic construction of the electron microscope is shown diagrammatically in Fig. E-3. High-velocity electrons are projected from the ELECTRON GUN A as a parallel beam B directed on to the object to be examined. The specimen must be so thin that it is more or less transparent to the electron beam. Electrons passing through the specimen are converted into a divergent beam by the ELECTRON LENS L1 (magnetic type) and produce an enlarged image at the plane P1. A small part of this image is further magnified by electron lens L2, and the final image is produced at plane P2, at which is situated either a photographic plate or a luminescent screen, as in a cathode-ray tube.

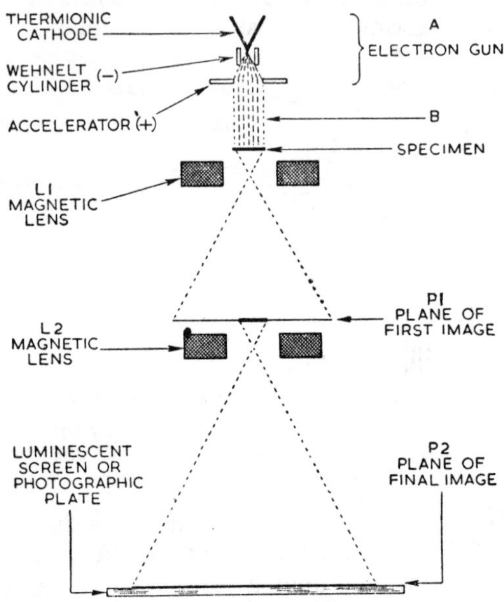

FIG. E-3.—DIAGRAM ILLUSTRATING THE PRINCIPLE OF THE ELECTRON MICROSCOPE.

Electron Multiplier. Form of electron tube in which an electron stream is magnified by directing it on to an electrode from which it expels a larger number of secondary electrons, these in turn being directed on to a further secondary emission electrode, the process being continued for a number of stages. Electron multipliers are incorporated in some forms of photo-emissive cell, which are then termed PHOTO-MULTIPLIERS, and also in some forms of television camera. The secondary-emission electrodes are called DYNODES (Fig. E-4).

Electron Optics. The study of the behaviour of electrons in electric and magnetic fields, and particularly the deflexion and focusing of electron beams by such fields. Fields of suitable configuration have similar effects upon an electron beam as optical systems have on a beam of light.

Electron Storage Tube. A form of electron tube used in some radar applications for producing an enlarged DISPLAY. It is of somewhat similar construction to a cathode-ray tube, but instead of a luminescent screen it has a metallic target plate, one side of which is coated with a layer of insulating material. The radar signal is caused to modulate an electron beam called the " writing beam " which scans the insulated side of the target, thus building up a CHARGE IMAGE. A second electron beam, the " reading beam ", scans the charge image, discharging it element by element, and thus to produce corresponding changes in the potential of the metal backing plate. These changes of potential, after amplification, are made to modulate the electron beam in a cathode-ray tube of conventional design, so producing a display on the luminescent screen either for direct viewing or for optical projection.

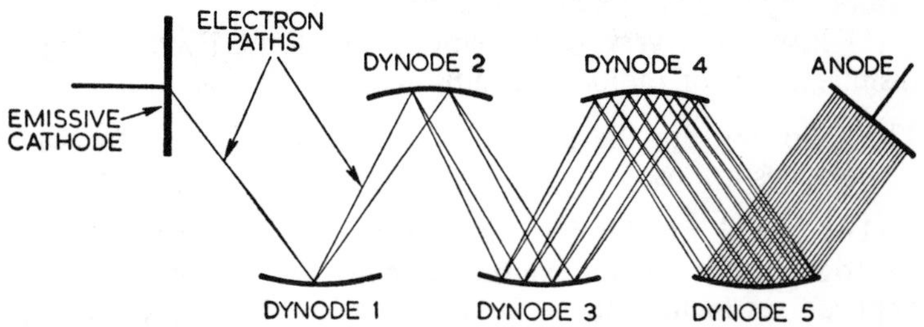

FIG. E-4.—THE PRINCIPLE OF THE ELECTRON MULTIPLIER.

Dynodes 1, 2, 3, 4, 5 . . . and the anode are maintained at successively higher positive potentials with respect to the cathode.

Electron Tube. An evacuated or gas-filled enclosure or ENVELOPE, usually of glass but sometimes of metal or glass-and-metal construction, in which free electrons or other charged particles are caused to move in a controlled manner. Sealed into the envelope, with connexions to the outside, are two or more ELECTRODES. One, the ANODE, is maintained at a positive potential with respect to a second electrode called the CATHODE. Electrons or other negatively charged particles are accelerated in the direction of the anode; positively charged ions, if present, are accelerated in the direction of the cathode. The intensity, velocity and direction of the flow of electrons is controlled by the potentials applied to the anode and, usually, to other electrodes. In some tubes further control is exercised by external magnetic fields. Electron tubes are of very many types, but may be roughly classified according to: (*a*) the method by which the free electrons or other charge carriers are produced, and (*b*) the task which the flow of charge carriers is made to perform.

The principal sources of charge carriers are:

(1) THERMIONIC EMISSION, or the release of electrons from a heated cathode.

(2) PHOTO-EMISSION, or the release of electrons from a cathode irradiated by light or similar short-wave radiation.

(3) IONIZATION, or the ejection of electrons and the simultaneous formation of positive ions due, for example, to collisions between free electrons and gas atoms.

(4) IONIC BOMBARDMENT, or the ejection of electrons from a solid when bombarded by ions.

(5) FIELD EMISSION, or the withdrawal of electrons from a cold cathode by means of a strong electric field.

(6) RADIO-ACTIVITY, or the emission of BETA RAYS during the disintegration of radioactive substances.

The following are the general classes of application for which electron tubes are used:

(1) Control of the intensity, frequency or duration of an electric current in an external circuit. Tubes used for such applications include those familiarly referred to as VALVES and employing thermionic cathodes, those termed PHOTOCELLS and employing photo-emissive cathodes, and certain types of COLD-CATHODE TUBES.

(2) The electron stream in the tube may be used to produce some form of radiant energy such as illumination (in the CATHODE-RAY TUBE) or RÖNTGEN RAYS (in the X-ray tube).

Electron tubes are also classified in accordance with the conditions within the envelope (HIGH-VACUUM or GAS-FILLED) and according to the number of electrodes they contain.

Electron Valve. See THERMIONIC VALVE.

Electron-volt. (Symbol eV) The amount of energy expended in moving an electron through a potential difference of one volt, and equal to approximately $1{\cdot}6 \times 10^{-12}$ erg. It is a convenient unit for expressing very small amounts of energy.

Electronic Methods of Film Making. Method of making cinematograph films by using a bank of electronic cameras (television cameras) in place of the conventional photographic film camera.

The scene as " televised " by these electronic cameras is simultaneously displayed on a corresponding number of monitor cathode-ray tubes. The film director can thus select and mix shots while the scene is in progress, and the shots thus selected are simultaneously recorded on film, thus greatly reducing the time taken for the completion of a given film.

Electronic Scanning. The SCANNING of the CHARGE PATTERN in a television camera or equivalent device by an electron beam produced by an electron gun.

Electronic Switch. In general, an arrangement of one or more electron tubes so operated that the flow of current in the output circuit can be started or interrupted by the application of a small pulse or signal to the control circuit. The term is used specifically for a device for permitting two traces to be observed simultaneously on the screen of a cathode-ray tube employing only one electron beam. It consists essentially of two similar amplifiers for amplifying the

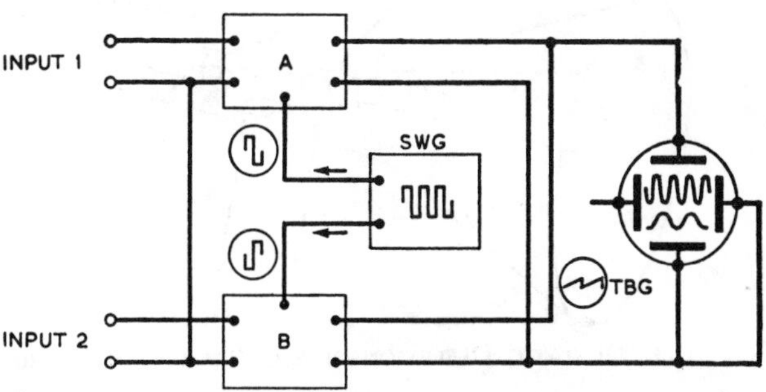

FIG. E-5.—BLOCK DIAGRAM OF AN ELECTRONIC SWITCH FOR OBSERVING TWO TRACES SIMULTANEOUSLY WITH A SINGLE-BEAM CATHODE-RAY OSCILLOSCOPE.

A, B—Identical amplifiers;
S.W.G.—Square wave generator;
T.B.G.—Time base generator.

two vertical deflexion voltages to be applied to the tube, and a circuit for generating an alternating current of square waveform. The square wave is applied to each of the amplifiers but in antiphase, in such a way that when one amplifier is functioning the other is cut off, and vice versa. The traces corresponding to the signals applied to the two amplifiers thus appear on the screen alternately at a repetition frequency equal to that of the square wave, but owing to the persistence of the screen phosphor they are both visible at the same time. See Fig. E-5.

Electronics. The study of the conduction of electricity *in vacua*, in gases and in semiconductors, and the design and application of devices whose actions are consequent upon this feature.

Electrophoresis. Migration of charged particles in a colloidal solution towards the electrode of opposite sign. The speed of their movement depends only upon their surface charge, and is the same for all molecules of the same material, but differs for different materials. Also termed cataphoresis.

Electrostatic. Refers to phenomena produced solely by electric charges or fields, and not combined with magnetic effects.

Electrostatic Coupling. See CAPACITIVE COUPLING.

Electrostatic Deflexion. Deflexion of the electron beam in a cathode-ray tube as it passes through an electric field produced between two metal electrodes, the beam being bent towards the more positive plate. See Fig. E-6.

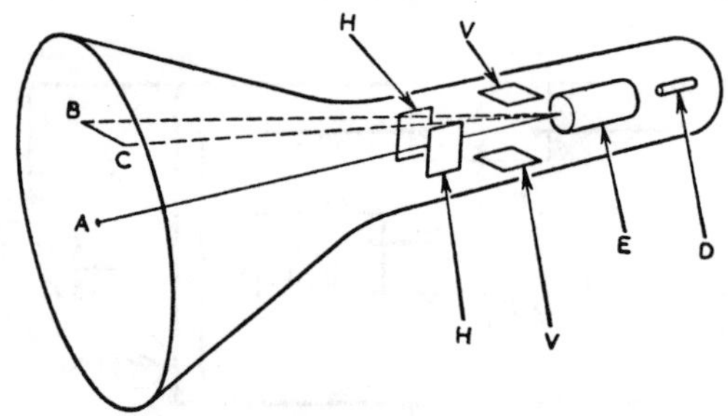

FIG. E-6.—ELECTROSTATIC DEFLEXION OF THE BEAM IN A CATHODE-RAY TUBE.

VV—Vertical deflexion plates;
HH—Horizontal deflexion plates;
A —Central position of the light spot;
B —Position of the light spot when vertical deflexion field is applied;
C —Position of light spot when both vertical and horizontal fields are applied.
D, E—Electron gun.

Electrostatic Focusing. Focusing of the electron beam in a cathode-ray tube by an ELECTRON LENS consisting of an electric field produced by two or more electrodes of suitable shape and dimensions and maintained at suitable potentials.

Electrostatic Loudspeaker. Loudspeaker in which the audio-frequency signal is applied between the plates of what is, in effect, an air–dielectric capacitor. One plate is fixed and the other is free to move and to serve as a sound radiator. See Fig. E-7. It effectively reproduces only the higher audio frequencies (above 500 c/s) and is used in conjunction with a conventional loudspeaker in high-fidelity sound-reproducing equipment. In recent years a push–pull form of electrostatic loudspeaker, capable of reproducing the full range of audio frequencies at low distortion, has been developed.

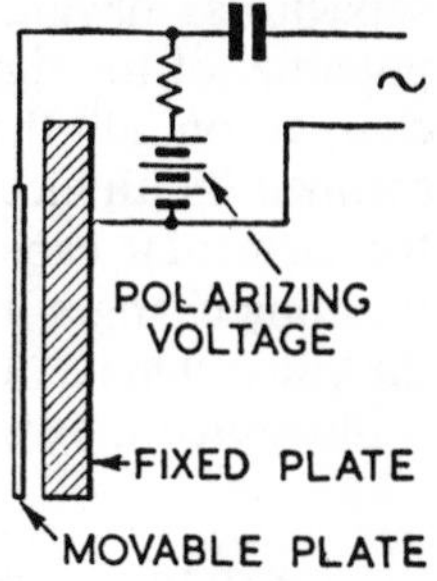

FIG. E-7.—PRINCIPLE OF THE ELECROSTATIC LOUDSPEAKER.

Electrostatic Microphone. See CONDENSER MICROPHONE.

Electrostatic Screen (Electrostatic Shield). Metallic screen surrounding electrical apparatus, or separating two electrical circuits, to prevent the penetration of the space enclosed by external electric fields or to prevent mutual interference by capacitive coupling.

Electrostriction. Small changes in the dimensions of a dielectric when placed in an electric field.

Element. (1) A chemical element is a substance composed of atoms, all of which are of the same atomic number.

(2) A circuit element is a distinct component of an electrical circuit, e.g. a resistor, a capacitor, a thermionic valve, etc., and which can be represented in a circuit diagram by a single symbol.

(3) In television a picture element is a small area of picture corresponding to a square having a side equal in length to the distance between successive scanning lines.

Eliminator. See BATTERY ELIMINATOR.

Emanations. Radioactive inert gases which are by-products of the disintegration of radium and other radioactive elements.

Emission. The release or ejection of electrons from the surface of a conductor as the result of such agencies as heat, irradiation by light or X-rays, etc,, or by electronic or ionic bombardment. See also COLD EMISSION, FIELD EMISSION, PHOTO EMISSION, SECONDARY EMISSION and THERMIONIC EMISSION.

Emitron. Proprietary name for a class of television camera tubes in which the scene to be televised is projected on to a MOSAIC of photo-emissive material formed on a dielectric plate backed by a conductive signal plate. Each small area of the mosaic emits electrons proportional to the intensity of the light falling upon it, and so a charge image of the picture is built up on the mosaic. The mosaic is electrically equivalent to a large number of very small capacitors, having one common plate (the signal plate). The potential of the signal plate is thus dependent upon the sum of the charges on all the elemental capacitors. The charge image is scanned by an electron beam projected from an electron gun, and the elemental capacitors are thus discharged in succession. The resulting changes in the potential at the signal plate are the basis of the video signal. One form of Emitron, termed the Super-emitron, is illustrated diagrammatically in Fig. E-8.

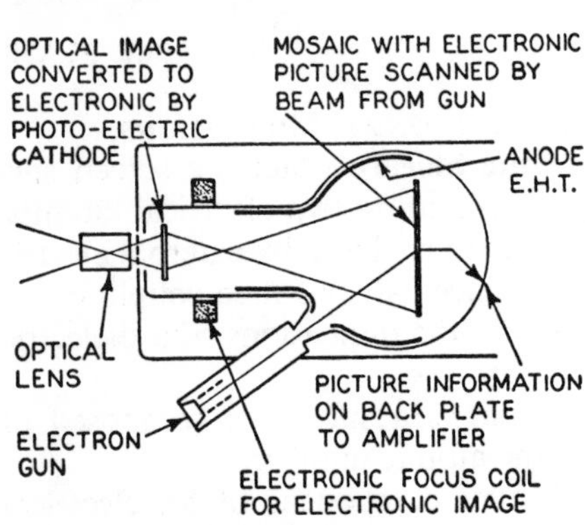

Fig. E-8.—Diagrammatic Representation of a Super-emitron Television Camera.

Emitter. That element in a Transistor which, in conjunction with an external source, supplies the current which is modulated by the input signal applied between the emitter and the base.

Emitter Follower. A transistor operated in Common Collector connexion, with the output taken from a load in the emitter circuit. An emitter follower has properties similar to those of a Cathode Follower.

Emulsification (Ultrasonic). The intimate intermixture of two normally non-miscible liquids by the application of ultrasonic vibrations.

Envelope. (1) Enclosed vessel, usually of glass but sometimes of silica, metal or combined glass and metal, containing the electrode system of an electron tube.

(2) Figure enclosing the peak values of an unmodulated or modulated high-frequency oscillation. See Fig. E-9.

Erasing. The process of demagnetizing the tape used in a tape recorder, and thus expunging a previous record so that the tape can be used over again for making a fresh recording.

Erg. The c.g.s. unit of work or energy, and equal to the work done when a force of one DYNE acts through a distance of one centimetre.

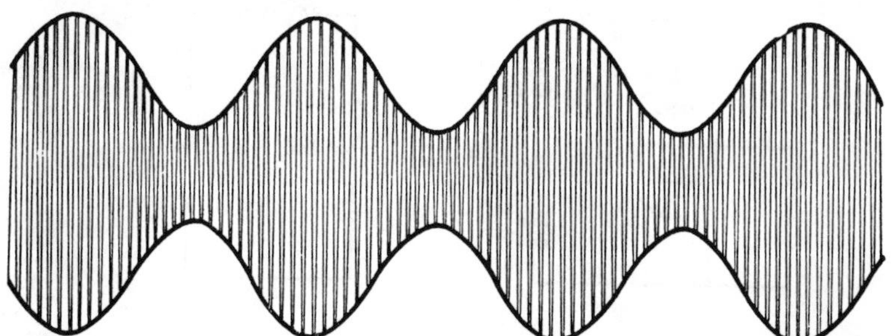

FIG. E-9.—THE FINE LINES INDICATE THE VARIATIONS IN AMPLITUDE OF A HIGH FREQUENCY WAVE AMPLITUDE-MODULATED WITH A LOW FREQUENCY WAVE.

The heavy line indicates the " envelope " of the modulated wave.

Ether. (Alternative spelling aether.) All-pervading, hypothetical non-material medium advanced to explain the transmission of electromagnetic waves. In the light of more recent concepts, however, its assumption is now unnecessary.

Equipotential Cathode. An emissive cathode, the whole of the surface of which is at the same electrical potential, as in the case of the INDIRECTLY-HEATED thermionic cathode, the heating element of which is electrically insulated from the emissive material.

Equipotential Line. A line lying in an electric field, every point on the line being at the same electrical potential.

Equipotential Surface. A surface every point on which is at the same electrical potential.

Equi-signal Beacon. Navigational radio beacon which radiates waves on the two sides of a prescribed course, the waves being so modulated that the two signals, as received by an aircraft flying on the set course, interlock so that a neutral signal is received.

Equivalent Circuit. A comparatively simple imaginary circuit composed of resistors, inductors, capacitors and current or voltage sources, which would have the same electrical characteristics as a more complex practical circuit or electrical device. In Fig. E-10 the practical circuit (*a*) can be represented by the equivalent circuit (*b*).

Equivalent Noise Resistance. The value of a resistor which, if introduced into the control grid circuit of a hypothetical noiseless valve, would produce the same amount of NOISE as the SHOT and PARTITION NOISE in the actual valve for which the equivalent noise resistance is quoted.

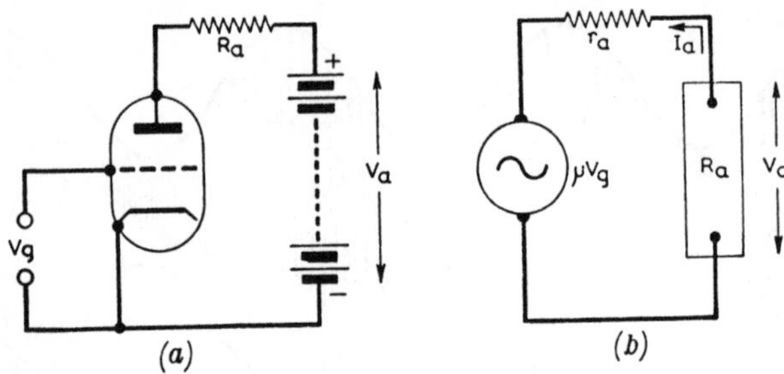

FIG. E-10.

(a) Practical circuit of an amplifying valve having an amplification factor μ, internal resistance r_a and external load R_a.
(b) Equivalent circuit in which the valve is represented as a voltage source giving an e.m.f. of μV_g.

Evacuation. Process of withdrawing the air and other gases from a closed vessel, such as the envelope of an electron tube, and thus producing a vacuum.

Excitation. Stimulation of the onset of a phenomenon, e.g. the production of electrical oscillations by applying a suitable electrical pulse to a resonant circuit.

Excited. An atom is said to be excited when one of its electrons is displaced from its normal shell. Return of the atom to its original shell is accompanied by the emission of QUANTA of electromagnetic radiation.

Exciter. Low-level stages of a radio transmitter usually comprising the oscillator and immediately subsequent stages used to drive the main amplifying stages.

Exciter Lamp. Electric lamp which provides the beam of light which is subsequently modulated at audio frequency for producing the sound track on a cinematograph film.

Excitron. Gas-discharge, grid-controlled rectifier tube with MERCURY-POOL CATHODE and capable of giving a large current output. The cathode hot-spot is initiated by an igniter electrode but maintained by an auxiliary anode fed from an external d.c. source. See Fig. E-11.

Extinction Voltage. The anode–cathode voltage of a gas-filled electron tube below which the discharge cannot be maintained.

Extra High Tension. (e.h.t.) Direct voltages, usually in excess of 1000 V, and greater than those required for the anode supply to normal thermionic valves. Refers especially to the voltages applied to the accelerating electrodes of cathode-ray tubes, X-ray tubes and the like, which may amount to many kilovolts.

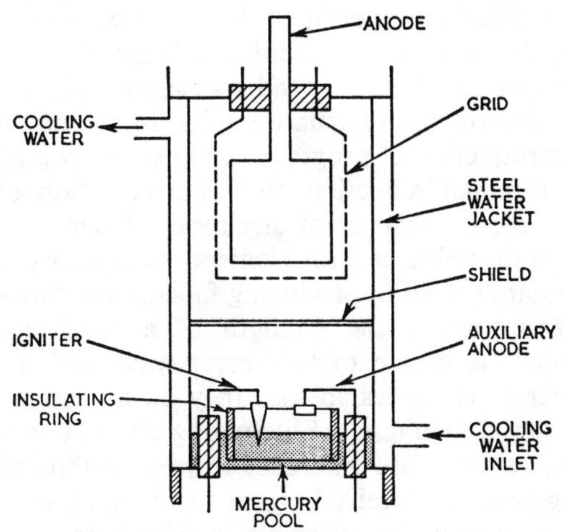

Fig. E-11.—Diagrammatic Section of an Excitron.

Extra-high-tension Supply. The extra-high-tension supply to electronic apparatus is usually obtained from a source other than that which provides the High Tension supply. It may be derived, for example, from the a.c. electricity mains via a separate step-up transformer and a rectifier, either with or without a voltage doubler or tripler arrangement. An alternative, which is more usual in television receivers, is the rectification of the pulses which occur in the output circuit of the line timebase during the flyback period.

F

F Layer. Region of ionized gas in the Ionosphere, and known also as the Appleton layer. It is the most important layer from the point of view of long-distance radio communication.

Faceplate. Workshop term for the flattened end of the envelope of a television picture tube. It is made separately from the cone portion, to which it is attached by a welding or fusion process.

Facsimile Radio. Transmission of a still picture via a radio link.

Facsimile Telegraphy. Transmission of a still picture by means of an electrical signal. The original picture is scanned by a light spot, the light reflected from each picture element being directed on to the cathode of a photocell. The variations of current in the photocell circuit are used to modulate a carrier, the signal being transmitted either by wire or by radio or a sequence of both.

Fade-in. Term used in cinematography, radio and television for the gradual introduction of programme material—sound or picture.

Fade-out. Gradual reduction and final cessation of sound or vision programme material or of any received signal.

Fader. An adjustable control element, such as a potentiometer or other attenuator, used in producing fade-in and fade-out effects.

Fading. Variation of the strength of a radio signal at the receiving aerial. It is due to the direct wave and the sky wave travelling different distances so that they do not necessarily reach the receiving aerial in phase. Fluctuating conditions in the ionosphere may cause the phase difference to vary rhythmically, causing the net strength of the received signal to fluctuate between values equal to the sum and the difference of the strengths of the two waves. Fading is minimized by the use of AUTOMATIC GAIN CONTROL.

Fall of Potential. See VOLTAGE DROP.

Farad. (Symbol F) Unit of capacitance. A capacitor has a capacitance of one farad if a quantity of one COULOMB has to be imparted to it in order to raise the potential difference between the plates by one volt. More convenient units for small capacitances are the microfarad (μF) and the picofarad (pF) equal respectively to 10^{-6} and 10^{-12} farad.

Faraday Cage. An earthed metallic wire or gauze screen enclosing electrical equipment to shield it from the influence of external electric fields.

Faraday Screen. An earthed wire screen placed in an equipment so as to prevent electrostatic but not electromagnetic coupling between components.

Feed. The introduction of electrical energy to a circuit; also the electrical energy introduced. Thus, the anode circuit of a thermionic valve is " fed " from the h.t. supply, and a radiating aerial is " fed " from the transmitting equipment.

Feedback. Return of energy from the output of a piece of equipment to the input. In the case where an alternating input signal produces an alternating output, the feedback may be in phase with the input (POSITIVE OR REGENERATIVE FEEDBACK) or in anti-phase (NEGATIVE OR DEGENERATIVE FEEDBACK). The former may be used for increasing the gain of an amplifier, or for generating oscillations. The latter, while reducing gain, can be used for reducing or even eliminating certain forms of distortion.

Feed Current. The d.c. component of the anode current of a thermionic valve.

Feeder. A non-radiating system of conductors connecting two parts of a radio or other high-frequency equipment, and particularly that connecting an aerial to a transmitter or to a receiver.

Ferrite Beads. Small perforated beads of one of the MAGNETIC FERRITES, intended to be threaded on the control-grid, screen-grid or anode lead of a thermionic valve, and located as close as possible to the valve itself, for the purpose of damping out parasitic oscillations.

Ferrite-rod Aerial. Receiving aerial consisting of a small coil mounted on a short rod of MAGNETIC FERRITE. The coil is, in effect, a small FRAME AERIAL, and the function of the ferrite rod is to concentrate the magnetic flux from a large area surrounding the aerial. Like all frame aerials, the ferrite-rod aerial has pronounced directional properties. Its main advantage, however, lies in its compact dimensions.

Ferrites. A class of chemical compounds having the general formula MFe_2O_4, where M is a divalent metal. Certain of these compounds are ferromagnetic, and possess in addition other properties which render them valuable for use in circuit components operating at high frequencies. See MAGNETIC FERRITES.

Ferromagnetic. Said of materials, such as iron, cobalt, nickel and certain alloys, which have a magnetic permeability very much greater than unity and which varies with the strength of the applied field.

Ferroxcube. Proprietary name for a range of MAGNETIC FERRITES, notably mixed crystals of magnesium and zinc ferrite or nickel and zinc ferrite or manganese and magnesium ferrite, produced by first grinding the various ferrites to a fine powder, mixing them in the correct proportions, and then pressing them or extruding them to the desired shape, after which they are sintered in a high-temperature furnace, producing a material of ceramic structure and having very desirable magnetic and electrical characteristics.

Fidelity. The degree to which the output waveform of an apparatus is an accurate replica of the waveform applied at the input. See HIGH FIDELITY.

Field. (1) In television, the American term for FRAME.
(2) See ELECTRIC FIELD and MAGNETIC FIELD.

Field Emission. Emission of electrons from a cold cathode as the result of a high field strength (potential gradient) at its surface. Also termed COLD EMISSION.

Field Frequency. See FRAME FREQUENCY.

Field Strength. See ELECTRIC FIELD STRENGTH and MAGNETIC FIELD STRENGTH.

Fieldistor. A form of TRANSISTOR in which a signal voltage is applied between a reverse-biased pn junction and a metallic electrode spaced away from the semiconductor system. Variations of signal voltage cause variations of the charge density in the region of the junction, and thus variations of the reverse current through the junction.

Filament. In general, a metallic wire heated by the passage of an electric current through it. Particular reference to a THERMIONIC CATHODE of the DIRECTLY-HEATED type.

Filament Battery. A primary or secondary battery which supplies the filament current for directly-heated thermionic valves. A LOW TENSION battery.

Filament Current. (Symbol I_f) The current flowing in the filament of a directly-heated thermionic valve.

Filament Voltage. (Symbol V_f) The electromotive force applied across the filament of a directly-heated thermionic valve in order to drive the heating current through it.

Filter, Filter Circuit or **Filter Network.** Network which will permit the passage of electrical signals of a particular frequency or band of frequencies, while offering a much greater impedance to signals of higher or lower frequencies. It may therefore be employed either to accept or to reject signals of given frequencies. It consists of an arrangement of resistive and/or inductive elements and capacitive elements, and its action relies on the facts that the impedance of an inductor increases and of a capacitor decreases with increasing frequency, i.e. a frequency-discriminating network. See ACCEPTOR CIRCUIT, BAND-PASS FILTER, HIGH-PASS FILTER,

LOW-PASS FILTER, REJECTOR CIRCUIT, RIPPLE FILTER and SCRATCH FILTER.

Final Anode. The main accelerating electrode in a cathode-ray tube, to which the e.h.t. potential is applied.

Fire. A gas-filled electron tube is said to " fire " or IGNITE when it becomes fully conductive due to the ionization of the gas filling. The term arises from the fact that the discharge through the tube is normally accompanied by luminous effects.

Firing Voltage. The potential which must be applied to a gas discharge tube before ignition occurs. See IGNITION VOLTAGE.

First Detector. Name sometimes used for the MIXER portion of the FREQUENCY CHANGER in a superheterodyne receiver. The latter term is, however, preferred.

Fixed Plate(s). The plate or plates in a variable capacitor which remain stationary. In order to adjust the capacitance one or more moving plates are made to approach or to interleave with the fixed plates.

Flank (of a Response Curve). That part of the response curve of an oscillatory circuit over which the response drops rapidly with change of frequency. See Fig. F-1.

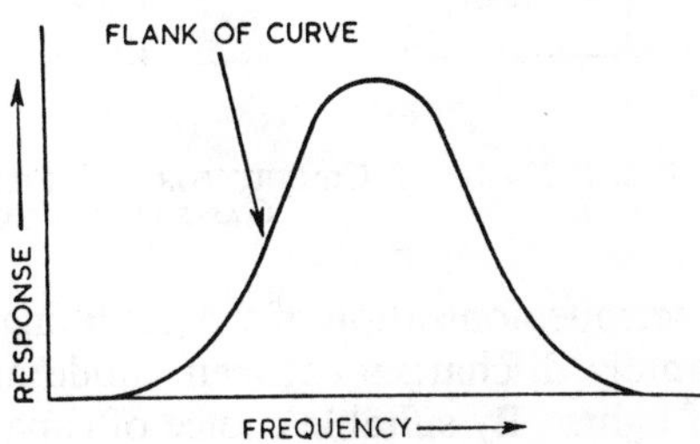

FIG. F-1. — TYPICAL RESPONSE CURVE OF AN OSCILLATORY CIRCUIT.

Note the steep flank.

Flare. Appearance of streaks or smudges which follow black-and-white images horizontally across the screen in a television picture tube. Usually due to excessive low-frequency response in the video amplifier. Also termed STREAKING.

Flash Over. Arc discharge between two parts of an electrical apparatus, and particularly between electrodes of an electron tube, due either to the application of an excessive potential difference or to the breakdown of the insulation.

Flash Test. Application of a voltage considerably higher than the working voltage to a component or to a piece of equipment in order to test its insulation resistance.

Flash Tube. A source of intense illumination of short duration, used in high-speed photography. It consists of a gas-filled glass envelope containing a cold cathode, an anode and a " grid " or trigger electrode. Anode and cathode are connected to the two plates of a capacitor which is charged to a voltage somewhat lower than that required to initiate a discharge through the tube. When, however, a suitable positive voltage is applied to the trigger

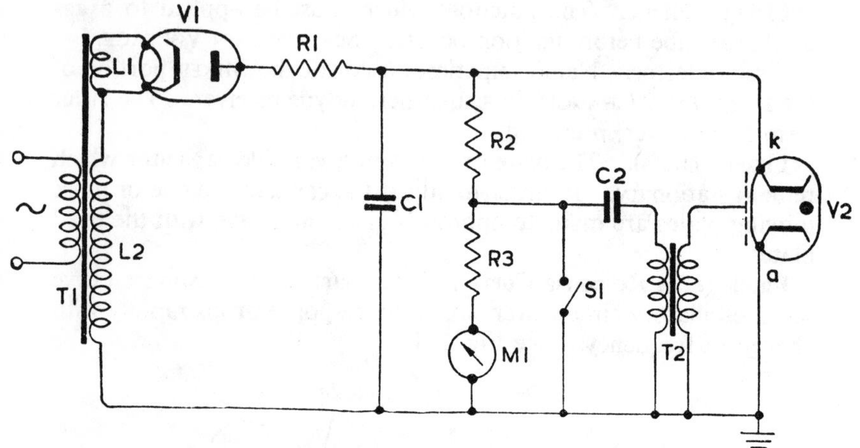

FIG. F-2.—BASIC CIRCUIT FOR A PHOTOGRAPHIC FLASH-LIGHT USING A GAS-FILLED FLASH TUBE.

electrode, ionization of the gas filling commences, and the capacitor rapidly discharges between anode and cathode, with the emission of light. By suitable choice of capacitance and of voltages, flashes of very high intensity and of durations down to micro-seconds can be obtained. A typical circuit is shown in Fig. F-2.

Flashing. Process sometimes employed in the manufacture of thermionic tubes, whereby the cathode is considerably over-heated for a short period.

Flat Response. The form of the FREQUENCY RESPONSE CURVE of an amplifier or other network when the output is substantially constant over a specified band of frequencies. See Fig. F-3.

Flat Tuning. A circuit is said to be flatly tuned when the normal tuning adjustment produces only small variations in its overall impedance so that it does not discriminate sharply between signals of slightly different frequencies.

Fleming Valve. Term sometimes applied to the thermionic diode, in honour of its inventor, Sir John Ambrose Fleming.

Flip-and-flop Generator. Oscillator of the MULTI-VIBRATOR type having two stable states. An input pulse of short duration causes a change-over from one stable state to the other, and this second state persists until the next input pulse causes the circuit to revert to the first stable state.

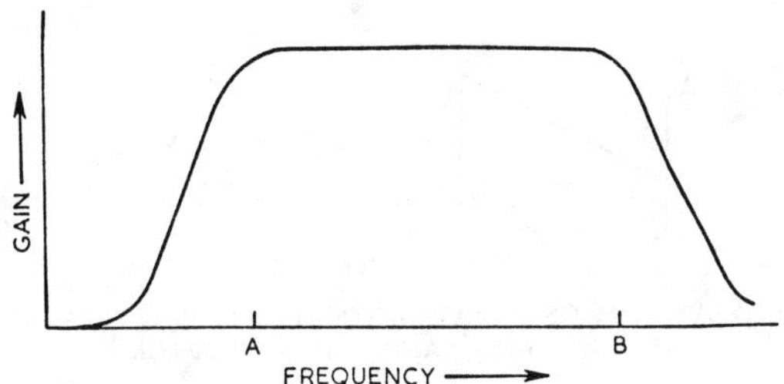

FIG. F-3.—GENERAL FORM OF RESPONSE CURVE OF AN R–C COUPLED AMPLIFIER GIVING FLAT RESPONSE OVER THE FREQUENCY RANGE A–B.

Flip-flop Generator. Pulse generator of the MULTI-VIBRATOR type having one stable and one quasi-stable state. A pulse of short duration applied to the input causes a change-over from the stable state to the quasi-stable state, but the circuit automatically reverts to the original, stable state after a period, the duration of which is determined by a TIME-CONSTANT (resistance–capacitance element) included in the circuit.

Fluorescence. The emission of light by a substance following irradiation by radiation of a different (usually lower) wavelength. The term is also used, not entirely correctly, for the production of visible light at the luminescent screen of a cathode-ray tube when excited by electronic bombardment.

Fluorescent Screen. Term sometimes employed for the luminescent screen of a cathode-ray tube.

Flutter. (1) Fluctuations, at frequencies in excess of 20 cycles per second, in the sound reproduced in a gramophone or tape recorder and caused by eccentric or unbalanced driving. Similar fluctuations but having frequencies below 20 cycles per second are known as WOW.

(2) Variations of quality in the reproduced television picture due to movement of the dipole aerial, e.g. by swaying in the wind.

(3) Similar variations of picture quality but due to the receipt of signals reflected from passing aircraft. See AIRCRAFT FLUTTER.

Flyback. The rapid decay of the voltage or current at the end of each cycle of a sawtooth timebase waveform, and the resulting return of the scanning spot from the end of one line or frame to the beginning of the next.

Flyback Period or Time. The time required for the flyback, and corresponding to the region bc in Fig. F-4.

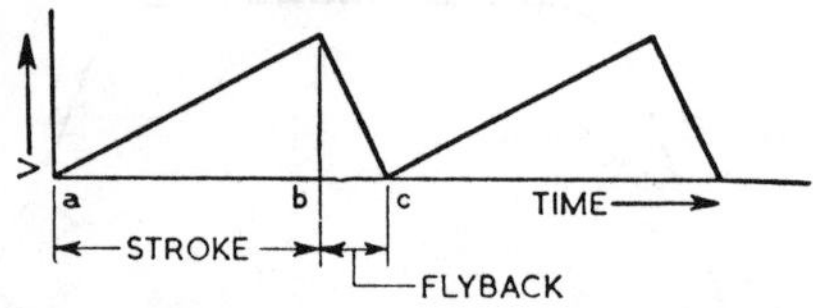

FIG. F-4.—WAVEFORM OF A SAWTOOTH TIMEBASE VOLTAGE, SHOWING THE "STROKE" AND THE "FLYBACK".

Flying-spot Microscope. Development of the FLYING-SPOT SCANNER for obtaining a large-scale image of a very small object, such as a microscope slide. For this purpose, the optical system B in Fig. F-5 consists of a compound microscope, operating in reverse.

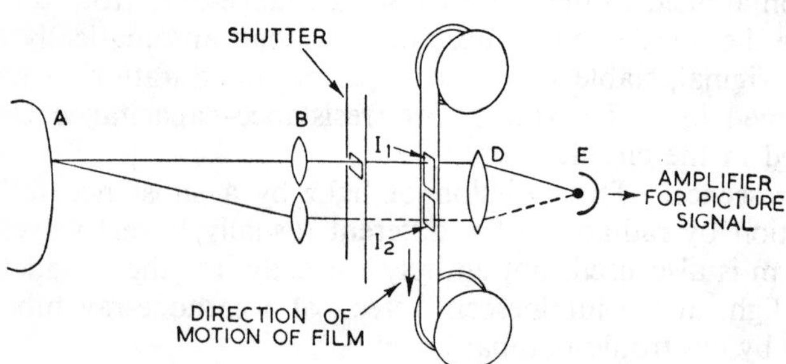

FIG. F-5.—PRINCIPLE OF THE FLYING-SPOT FILM SCANNER.

Flying-spot Scanner. Device for translating the light variations over the surface of a picture into a train of electric signals, as required for television, by scanning the original picture with a small but intensely bright light spot. The light reflected from successive PICTURE ELEMENTS (or transmitted by successive picture elements in the case of a transparent picture) are directed on the cathode of a photo-emissive cell, thus generating the required signal. Fig. F-5 is a diagrammatic representation of a flying-spot scanner used for televising cinematograph films. The screen of the high-intensity cathode-ray tube A is scanned by an unmodulated electron beam, and an image of the moving light spot on the screen is focused on the film by the optical system represented by B. The film is thus scanned by the light spot (the flying spot) in synchronism with the electronic scanning of the screen in the cathode-ray tube A. The light transmitted through each successive picture element of the film is directed by the optical system D on the photocell E, the output of which is the basis of the video signal.

Flywheel Synchronization. System of maintaining the frequency of the line timebase of a television receiver in step with that of the transmitted synchronizing pulses while avoiding the triggering of the timebase generator by random noise pulses as can easily happen in FRINGE AREAS. The synchronizing pulses are applied to a network to produce fresh pulses which are compared with similar pulses derived from a FREE-RUNNING timebase generator. Only when the frequency of the timebase departs from that of the synchronizing pulses will the latter react to correct the timebase frequency.

Focus. A stream of electrons or rays of light may be made to converge to a point (by electromagnetic or electrostatic methods in the first case and by optical methods in the second case), this point being termed the focus.

Focusing. The process of causing rays to converge and to meet at a focus, and more particularly to form a focus at a desired distance. In a cathode-ray tube the electron stream is focused by means of an electron lens. See also ELECTROSTATIC FOCUSING and MAGNETIC FOCUSING.

Focusing Coil. Coil mounted on the neck of a cathode-ray tube and carrying an adjustable electric current for generating a variable magnetic field employed for focusing the electron beam.

Focusing Field. An electric or magnetic field used for focusing the electron beam in a cathode-ray tube.

Focusing Magnet. A magnetic system the field of which can be adjusted in order to focus the beam in a cathode-ray tube.

Folded Dipole. Dipole aerial consisting of two conductors in parallel, only one of which is broken at the centre for connexion to the FEEDER. If similar conductors are used, this construction quadruples the centre impedance of the aerial and increases its effective bandwidth.

Follower, Cathode. See CATHODE FOLLOWER.

Foot of a Valve. That part of the envelope of a thermionic valve on which the electrodes are mounted, and through which pass the wires for connecting the electrodes to the external circuit.

Force. That which produces, or tends to produce, acceleration of a body. Unit, the DYNE (c.g.s.) or newton (m.k.s.).

Forced-air Cooling. Process of abstracting heat from a body, e.g. from the anode of a large thermionic valve, by directing a stream of cold air over its surface.

Forced Oscillation. Oscillation in a system, maintained by an external source, and of a frequency determined by that source and not by the constants of the system.

Forward Scatter Radiation. Medium-distance propagation of v.h.f. signals by the random scattering produced in the ionosphere or troposphere due to refraction.

Foucault Currents. See EDDY CURRENTS.

Frame. In television, the picture area scanned during one complete cycle of the vertical timebase. In the British television system the frame consists of 202½ horizontal lines, each separated from the preceding line by a distance equal to the width of the line. Each frame scans the lines left blank in the previous frame.

Frame Aerial. Aerial consisting of one or more turns of wire wound on a rectangular or circular frame, the receiver being connected to the two ends of the coil. It functions by reason of the fact that the horizontal magnetic component of the radiation field induces radio-frequency currents in the loop. It has pronounced directional characteristics. Also termed a LOOP AERIAL (Fig. A-4).

Frame Frequency. In television, the number of FRAMES scanned per second. With the interlaced scanning system adopted in Great Britain, the frame frequency is twice the picture frequency, and thus equal to 50 frames per second.

Frame Grid. A form of control GRID of exceptionally rigid construction for thermionic valves. The skeleton of the grid is a rectangular structure consisting, for example, of two longitudinal molybdenum wires held rigidly in position by stiff molybdenum cross-straps. The grid wires, which are of tungsten and are wound over the longitudinal supports under tension, and to a very close pitch, may be less than $\frac{1}{2000}$ in. in diameter. The result is a grid with two parallel and very fine sets of meshes, accurately spaced apart and free from risk of sagging. Very close cathode-to-grid clearances can thus be obtained, and this, combined with the fine mesh, makes possible the production of high-frequency pentodes with mutual conductances as high as 15 mA/V.

Frame Hold. See VERTICAL HOLD.

Frame Synchronizing Pulses. A series of pulses included in a television transmission at the end of every frame period, and used in the receiver to keep the frame timebase in step with the frame scanning in the television camera.

Frame Timebase. Circuit which generates a current of sawtooth waveform for application to the frame or vertical deflecting coils of a television picture tube.

Framing. Adjustment of the television picture to the correct rectangular shape, and positioning it correctly on the screen.

Franklin Aerial. A directional or beam aerial consisting of a number of radiating elements, uniformly spaced on a line at right angles to the desired direction of maximum radiation.

Free Oscillation. Oscillation the frequency of which is equal to the natural frequency of the system in which it occurs.

Free Path. See MEAN FREE PATH.

Free Running (of Timebase). Operation of a TIMEBASE generator in such a way that the scanning power is supplied by the device itself, and is not initiated by synchronizing pulses.

Frequency. The number of times a periodic phenomenon repeats itself in unit time. For audio- and electromagnetic waves, the frequency is expressed in cycles per second or, for the higher frequencies, in kilocycles per second or megacycles per second.

Frequency Band. The frequencies lying between specified upper and lower limits, and thus constituting a continuous interval in the FREQUENCY SPECTRUM.

Frequency Changer. A device consisting of one or two transistors or valves and their associated circuits, used for transferring the modulation of a carrier to a carrier of lower frequency. It forms an essential feature of the SUPERSONIC-HETERODYNE radio receiver.

The circuit comprises: (*a*) means for generating an oscillation (the local oscillation) the frequency of which differs from that of the incoming signal by a specified amount; (*b*) means for combining the local oscillation with the incoming signal, thus producing a number of BEAT FREQUENCIES, including one equal to the sum and one equal to the difference between the two frequencies, and each carrying the signal modulation; (*c*) a filter circuit which selects the difference frequency (the intermediate frequency) and transfers it to further stages for amplification and detection. The local oscillator is usually a thermionic triode and the MIXER a pentode or hexode, and these may be separate valves, or the two electrode systems may be enclosed in a common envelope. In the ELECTRON-COUPLED FREQUENCY CHANGER a single electrode system, either a heptode or an octode, is employed.

Frequency Deviation. The difference between the maximum instantaneous frequency and the constant carrier frequency of a FREQUENCY-MODULATED radio transmission.

Frequency Discriminator. See DISCRIMINATOR.

Frequency Distortion. Distortion of a signal due to components having different frequencies being amplified to different degrees.

Frequency Doubler. A FREQUENCY MULTIPLIER in which the output oscillations have twice the frequency of the input pulses.

Frequency Drift. Variation in the natural frequency of an oscillatory circuit or of an oscillator due, for example, to changes of capacitance with change of temperature.

Frequency Modulation. (Abbreviation f.m.) System of radio transmission in which the amplitude of the carrier remains constant but the frequency is varied in accordance with the amplitude of the modulating waveform, as opposed to AMPLITUDE MODULATION (Fig. F-6). In frequency modulation the loudness of the applied audio-frequency modulation is represented by the amount of change (deviation) of carrier frequency, and the frequency of the signal is

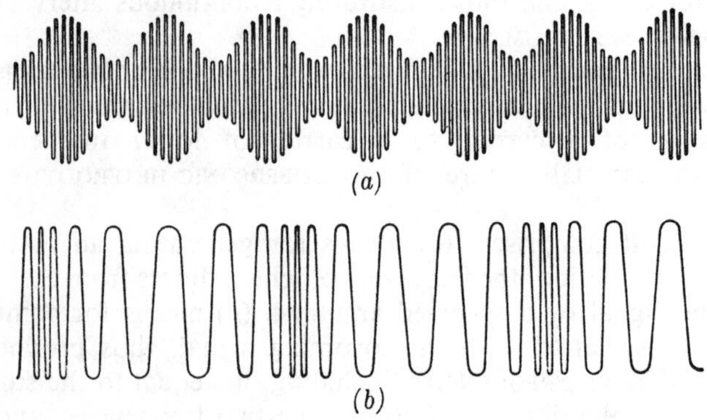

FIG. F-6.—COMPARISON BETWEEN AMPLITUDE MODULATION (a) AND FREQUENCY MODULATION (b).

represented by the number of times the carrier frequency is changed every second. The main advantage of the system is that, the modulation being independent of the amplitude of the carrier, transmissions are not seriously affected by the more usual forms of interference.

Frequency Multiplier. A valve-operated device for producing oscillations having a frequency which is a whole multiple of the frequency of the input. Typically it consists of an amplifying valve operated under CLASS C conditions, that is to say only the positive-going peaks of oscillations of a given frequency affect the anode current. Owing to the non-linearity of the anode current/grid volts characteristic of the valve, the output current is rich in harmonics of the signal frequency. The desired harmonic is selected by a sharply-tuned system included in the anode circuit. See Fig. F-7.

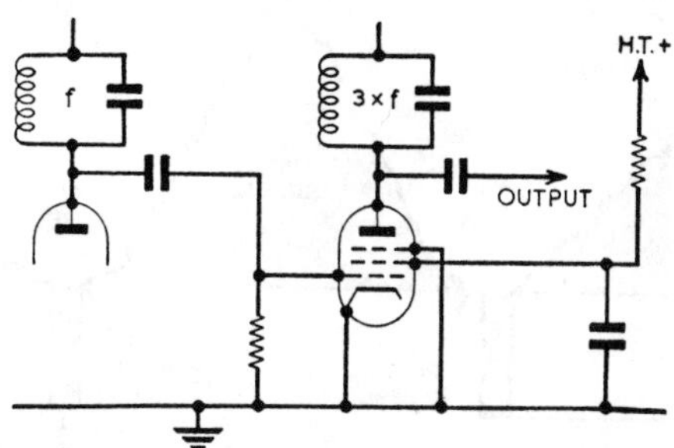

FIG. F-7.—A SIGNAL OF FREQUENCY f IS APPLIED TO THE GRID OF THE MULTIPLIER VALVE, THE ANODE CIRCUIT OF WHICH CONTAINS AN OSCILLATORY CIRCUIT TUNED TO THE REQUIRED HARMONIC OF f (IN THIS INSTANCE THE THIRD HARMONIC).

Frequency Response. The relative impedance of, and hence the relative voltage developed across, an oscillatory circuit when signals of various frequencies are applied to it. See RESPONSE CURVE.

Frequency Spectrum. The display, either physically or descriptively (e.g. in tabular or graphic form), of a complete range of frequencies (e.g. of electromagnetic waves) in ascending or descending order of frequency. The electromagnetic spectrum is tabulated in Appendix 4.

Frequency–Wavelength Conversion. See Appendix.

Fringe Area. Region at a greater or less distance from a television transmitter over which, for topographical reasons, reliable reception is not consistently obtainable because the field strength is liable to fall to a value at which the signal-to-noise ratio is too low. In such an area it is usually necessary to use a more elaborate aerial array and/or to incorporate in the receiver an additional pre-amplifier stage or a noise-limiter circuit.

Front End. General term, originated in America, for the early stages of a radio or television receiver or similar equipment, that is to say, that part of the apparatus which includes the tuning system, the radio-frequency amplifiers, if any, and the frequency changer.

Front Porch. Short time interval in the television waveform (see TELEVISION) between the end of each line scan and the commencement of the line synchronizing pulse, during which the signal is maintained at BLACK LEVEL (Fig. F-8). See also BACK PORCH.

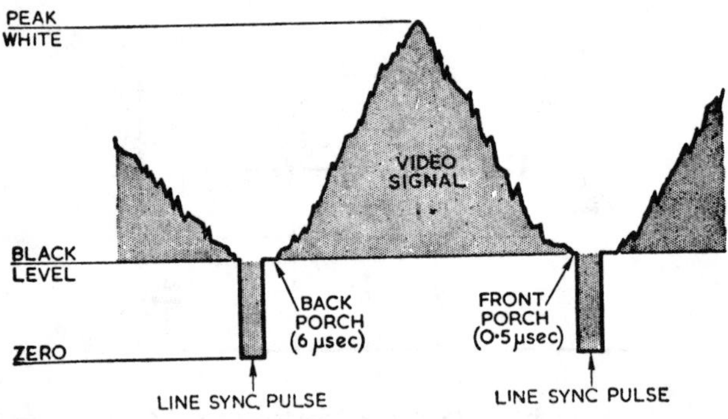

FIG. F-8.—TELEVISION WAVEFORM INDICATING THE BACK AND FRONT PORCH INTERVALS.

Full-wave Rectification. RECTIFICATION of an alternating current such that a unidirectional supply is obtained from the alternating supply source during both halves of the cycle. This is achieved by using two rectifying elements which operate alternately. If the rectifiers are thermionic diodes they may be separate valves, as in Fig. F-9 (upper), or a double diode consisting of two anodes and a common cathode enclosed in a single envelope may be employed, as in Fig. F-9 (lower).

Fundamental Frequency. In a complex waveform consisting of two or more harmonically-related frequencies the lowest of the component frequencies is the fundamental frequency.

Fundamental Mode. See MODE.

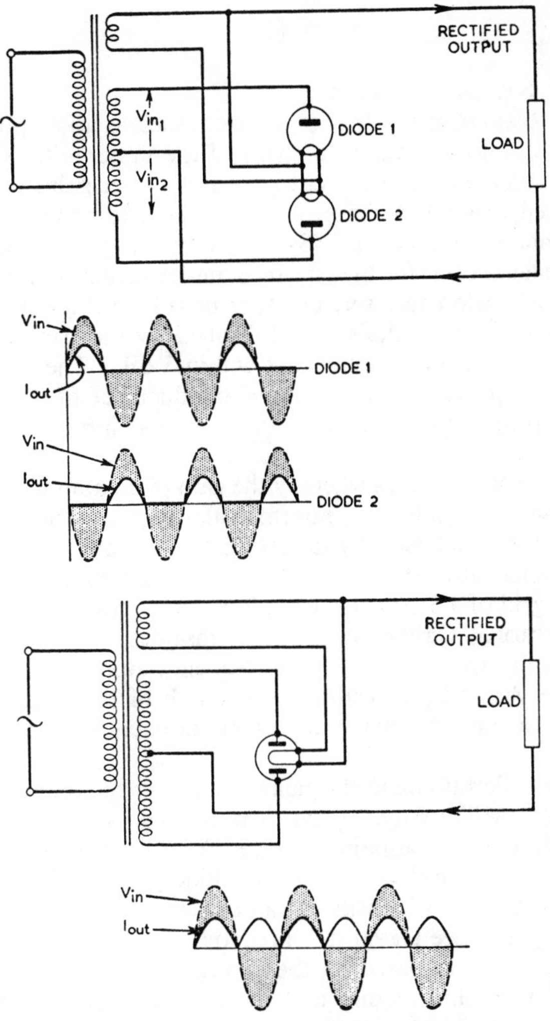

FIG. F-9.—FULL-WAVE RECTIFICATION.
(*Upper*) Using two separate diodes.
(*Lower*) Using a double diode.

Fundamental Units. The units of length, mass and time, from which all other units are derived. In the c.g.s. system these units are, respectively, the centimetre, gramme and second. In the m.k.s. system they are the metre, kilogramme and second.

G

γ-rays. See GAMMA RAYS.

Gain. Ratio of the output of a system such as an amplifier to its input, both being expressed in terms of the same unit. Gain may thus be a voltage gain, a current gain or a power gain. Gain may be expressed either as a simple arithmetical ratio or in DECIBELS.

Gain–Bandwidth Product. (Symbol g.b.) Figure of merit used in design calculations for the intermediate-frequency amplifier stages of, say, a television receiver, or other broad-band amplifier. It is equal to the GAIN of the stage multiplied by the bandwidth over which the amplification is constant within 3 dB. The g.b. product is directly proportional to the mutual conductance of the valve and inversely proportional to the sum of its input and output capacitances.

Gain Control. Process whereby the gain of an amplifier is varied. In the case of a radio- or intermediate-frequency amplifier gain control can be exercised by adjusting the cathode bias resistance of a VARIABLE-MU VALVE or by adjusting the potential applied to the screen grid of a SLIDING-SCREEN PENTODE. See also AUTOMATIC GAIN CONTROL. Gain control in the sense described above cannot be successfully applied to an audio-frequency amplifier, but the output can be varied by adjusting the strength of the input signal by means of a potentiometer or other attenuator. See VOLUME CONTROL.

Galactic. Pertaining to the galaxy or star system more familiarly known as the Milky Way. Galactic noise in a radio receiver is thus noise resulting from radiation received from outer space.

Galena. A natural crystalline sulphide of lead, used in conjunction with a CAT'S WHISKER as a detector in early radio receivers of simple type. See CRYSTAL DETECTOR.

Gamma. A ratio based on the contrast between two points on a received television picture and the contrast between the corresponding points on the scene transmitted. If R_x and R_y are the brightnesses of the two spots on the received picture and S_x and S_y are the brightnesses of the corresponding spots in the actual scene, then the gamma equals $(\log R_x - \log R_y)/(\log S_x - \log S_y)$.

Gamma Rays (γ-rays). Electromagnetic waves of higher frequency than X-rays and with greater powers of penetration. They are emitted by radioactive substances during their disintegration.

Gang. Two or more adjustable or other control components, e.g. variable capacitors, potentiometers, switches, etc., mechanically coupled together and operated by a single control knob or other mechanism.

Gang Capacitor. Two or more variable capacitances coupled mechanically for operation by one knob, and thus permitting the simultaneous tuning of the circuits in which they are included.

Gap (Air). Discontinuity in a system composed of ferromagnetic material. See AIR GAP.

Gap (Spark). Space between two electrodes and across which are produced disruptive electrical discharges. See SPARK GAP.

Gas Amplification. The increase of electron current in an electron tube due to the production of secondary electrons as the result of ionization of the gas filling. See also AMPLIFICATION FACTOR (GAS).

Gas Current. Current composed of positive gas ions produced as the result of ionization of the gas filling of a gas discharge tube, and flowing towards the cathode.

Gas Diode. Two-electrode electron tube, the envelope of which is filled with gas at low pressure (Fig. G-1).

Gas Discharge. Passage of electricity through a gas. All gases are good insulators, but a gas-filled space becomes conductive when charge carriers, i.e. electrons and/or negative and positive ions, are present. Primary electrons can be derived from the cathode of a gas discharge tube by thermionic, photo- or cold emission; secondary electrons and positive ions by ionization of the gas filling. See IONIZATION.

Gas Discharge Lamp. Electric lamp in which the light is produced during an electric discharge between electrodes in a gas-filled tube. Typical examples are the mercury-vapour and sodium discharge lamps; fluorescent lamps, in which the ultra-violet radiation produced during the discharge through mercury vapour at very low pressure is converted into visible light by coating the inner surface of the envelope with a fluorescent powder; and the neon and other luminous tubes used in advertising signs, etc.

Gas Discharge Tube. General name for any gas-filled tube provided with electrodes between which an electric discharge takes place.

Gas Focusing. In cathode-ray tubes containing a small quantity of residual gas, the electron stream ionizes gas atoms by collision. The positive ions thus formed constitute a kind of positive " core " in the centre of the electron beam and produce a focusing field.

Gas Tetrode. A four-electrode, gas-filled thermionic tube, having a cathode, an anode and two intermediate electrodes. That nearest the cathode receives the signal which causes the tube to FIRE, and the other, nearer the anode and termed the SHIELD GRID, receives a potential which determines the value of control grid voltage at which the tube shall fire. See Fig. G-1.

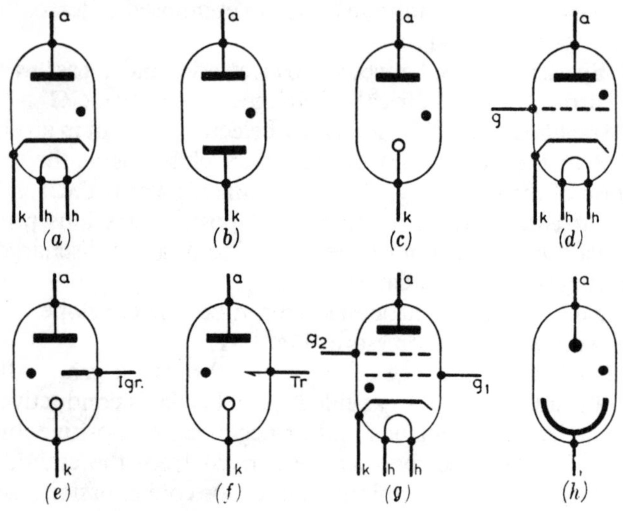

FIG. G-1.—GRAPHICAL SYMBOLS FOR TYPICAL GAS-FILLED ELECTRON TUBES.
The gas-filling is indicated by a black dot.
(a) Gas-filled thermionic diode;
(b), (c) Alternative symbols for cold-cathode diodes;
(d) Gas-filled thermionic triode (thyratron);
(e) Cold cathode triode (with igniter electrode);
(f) Cold cathode triode (with trigger electrode);
(g) Gas-filled thermionic tetrode;
(h) Gas-filled photocell.

Gas Triode. Three-electrode gas-filled electron tube, containing a cathode, an anode and a control grid. Operating conditions are so adjusted that, if the potential applied to the control grid is less than a certain value, the tube will remain non-conductive. A positive-going potential applied to the grid causes the tube to fire when the grid potential reaches a pre-determined value (Fig. G-1). See THYRATRON.

Gas-filled Photocell. Photo-emissive cell, the envelope of which contains an inert gas at low pressure. Ionization of the gas atoms by collision with photo-electrons increases the current through the tube (Fig. G-1). See GAS AMPLIFICATION.

Gas-filled Rectifier. Rectifier valve the envelope of which is filled with inert gas. The cathode may be of the thermionic type or a pool cathode, and the anode current may or may not be controlled by a third electrode.

Gas-filled Tube. General name for an electron tube the envelope of which contains an inert gas at low pressure.

Gate. Part of an electric circuit, and particularly, but not necessarily, of a computer circuit, which permits current to pass only when certain electrical conditions are fulfilled. In the simple basic circuit of Fig. G-2(a), for example, suitable choice of the various

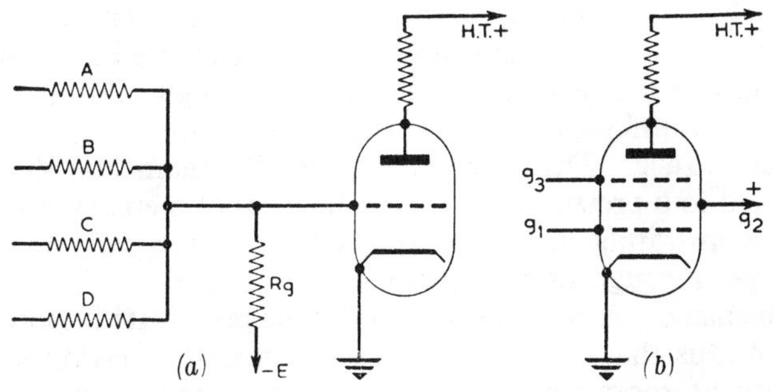

FIG. G-2.—TWO BASIC FORMS OF SIMPLE GATING CIRCUIT.

(a) Valve is conductive (or non-conductive) according to the number of input circuits (A . . . D) to which signals are applied, and to the value and polarity of the voltage − E.
(b) Valve remains non-conductive unless suitable voltages are applied to grids 1 and 3.

resistors and of the grid-bias voltage E could cause the valve to remain non-conductive (or conductive) unless suitable signals are applied to the grid via each of the resistors A, B, C and D. Again, in the circuit of Fig. G-2(b) it could be arranged that no current will flow to the anode unless suitable signals arrive simultaneously at both the grids g_1 and g_3.

Gauge (Ionization). Device for measuring very small gas pressures. Actually what is measured is the ion current in a triode the envelope of which is connected to the space the pressure in which it is desired to determine. See IONIZATION GAUGE.

Gauss. The c.g.s. unit of magnetic flux density or magnetic induction, and equal to one maxwell/sq. cm.

Gee. Radar navigational aid in which a group of fixed ground stations transmit synchronized pulses which are picked up by the aircraft or ship and displayed on the screen of a cathode-ray tube in such a way that the time intervals between receipt of the signals from the different stations can be determined, and thus the differences of the distances from the transmitters. From these readings, with the help of special charts, the position of the craft can be worked out.

Geiger–Müller Tube. Electron tube forming an IONIZATION CHAMBER, and used as a radiation counter or meter. A wire mounted axially in the tube forms the anode, and is surrounded by a co-axial cylindrical cold cathode, the intervening space being filled with gas at a low pressure. The voltage between anode and cathode is adjusted to a value just below the IONIZATION VOLTAGE of the gas filling. The radiation to be measured, e.g. alpha or beta particles or gamma rays, enters the tube and causes momentary ionization of the gas so that a current pulse flows through the tube. These pulses are transferred to a suitable counter circuit.

Geissler Tube. Discharge tube, often of ornamental shape, and exhausted to a pressure of a few millimetres of mercury. Intended for demonstrating the luminous effects accompanying electric discharges through rarefied gases.

Germanium. A tetravalent metallic element. Its importance in electronics is that the metal is a semiconductor, having low conductivity at room temperature and increasing conductivity with rising temperature. When alloyed with very small but accurately-controlled proportions of trivalent or pentavalent metallic impurities, thus producing P-TYPE or N-TYPE germanium respectively, it is used in the manufacture of CRYSTAL DIODES and TRANSISTORS.

Germanium Crystal Diode. Combination of a crystal of p-type or n-type germanium and a cat's whisker, or in some cases the junction of a p-type and an n-type zone in a single crystal. The arrangement possesses a high degree of asymmetric conductivity and can be used as a rectifier.

Getter. Quantity of a volatile element such as barium, incorporated in a high-vacuum electron tube, and evaporated, after the tube has been evacuated as completely as possible by pumping. The volatilized getter combines with any residual gas, thus perfecting the vacuum within the tube. The getter remains active throughout the life of the tube, absorbing any further quantity of gas which may be released from the electrodes, etc., due to the heat generated during operation.

Ghost Images. Additional but relatively faint images produced on the screen of a television receiver and slightly to the right of the true image (see Fig. G-3). Caused by signals reflected from a neighbouring obstacle, such as a tall building or some topographical feature (see Fig. G-4). Also termed DOUBLE IMAGE.

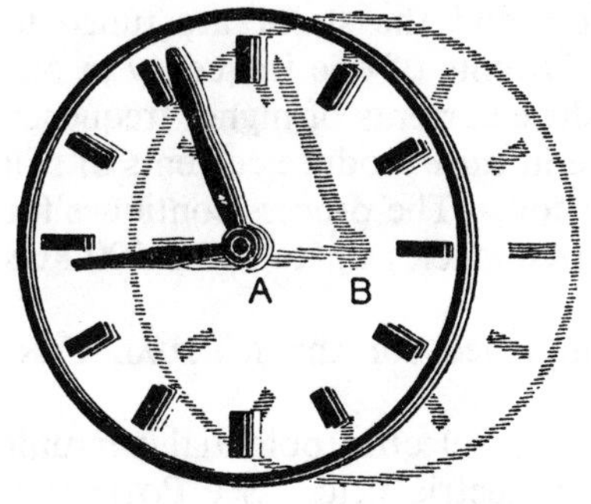

FIG. G-3 (*left*).—GHOST IMAGE.

FIG. G-4. (*below*).—PRODUCTION OF GHOST IMAGE DUE TO REFLECTED WAVES.

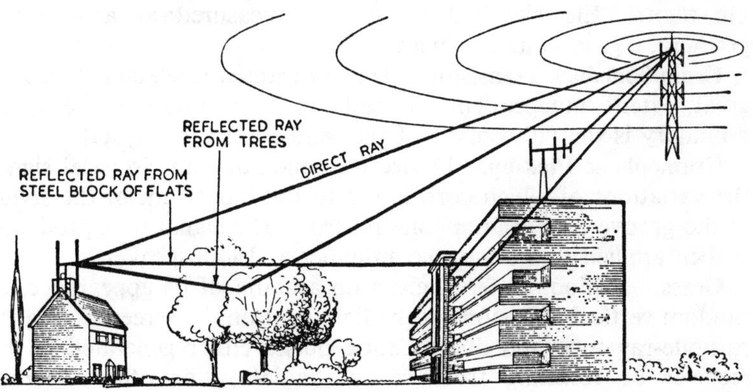

Giga. Prefix denoting 10^9.

Gilbert. The c.g.s. unit of MAGNETO-MOTIVE FORCE. Equal to $10/4\pi$ AMPERE-TURNS.

Giorgi System of Units. Another name for the METRE–KILOGRAMME–SECOND or m.k.s. system of units.

Glow Discharge. Silent electric discharge through gas, the whole of the gas exhibiting luminosity but without appreciable volatilization of the electrodes.

Gluing of Wood. Important application of DIELECTRIC LOSS HEATING, largely employed in the manufacture of plywood and in furniture making. The pieces to be joined, dressed with a suitable thermo-setting glue, are clamped between electrodes and an oscillating electric field with a frequency in the order of 10–20 Mc/s is applied.

Goldschmidt Alternator. Dynamo–electric a.c. generator for producing currents of high frequency. A number of windings arranged alternatively on the rotor and the stator are tuned to successively higher frequencies. Currents of one frequency in one of the coils, say, on the rotor, produce currents of higher frequency in one of the stator coils, and these in turn produce currents of still higher frequency in the next rotor coil. The process continues for the complete series of coils, and frequencies up to some 100 kc/s can be produced.

Goodness. Term sometimes employed for the MUTUAL CONDUCTANCE of a thermionic valve.

Gradient, Potential. The change of electric potential per unit length along a conductor or in an electric field. See POTENTIAL GRADIENT. Electric field strength is measured as a potential gradient, e.g. in volts per metre.

Grain-boundary Transistor. Type of transistor which is to a very great extent independent of ambient temperature. The grain boundary is the (100) plane of the semi-conductor crystal.

Gramophone Pick-up. Device for generating an electrical signal the variations of which correspond to the movement of the stylus in the groove of a gramophone record. The signal thus produced is then applied to a electronic amplifier and loudspeaker.

Grass. Colloquial term, given on account of its appearance, to random vertical deflexions of the light spot on the screen of a radar cathode-ray tube and due to noise pulses either generated in the receiver or resulting from cosmic radiation or other external sources.

Grid. One form of electrode employed in thermionic valves and tubes. It consists of a spiral of fine wire, or other mesh-like metallic structure, located between the cathode and anode so that electrons leaving the region of the cathode must pass through the grid meshes. A tube may have one or more grids. By applying suitable potentials to these electrodes the intensity of the electron stream can be controlled or MODULATED. Typical grids are illustrated in Fig. G-5.

Grid Base. The value of negative voltage (negative grid bias) which must be applied to the control grid of a thermionic tube in order to reduce the electron current to zero, i.e. to produce CUT-OFF. See Fig. G-6.

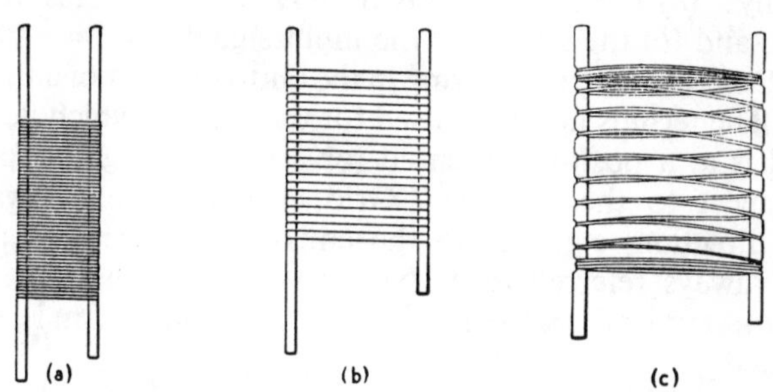

FIG. G-5.—TYPICAL GRID ELECTRODES.
(a) Control grid. (b) Screen grid. (c) Suppressor grid.

Grid Bias. Steady negative potential applied to the control grid of a thermionic valve or other tube in order to pre-set the no-signal value of the cathode current. See Fig. G-6.

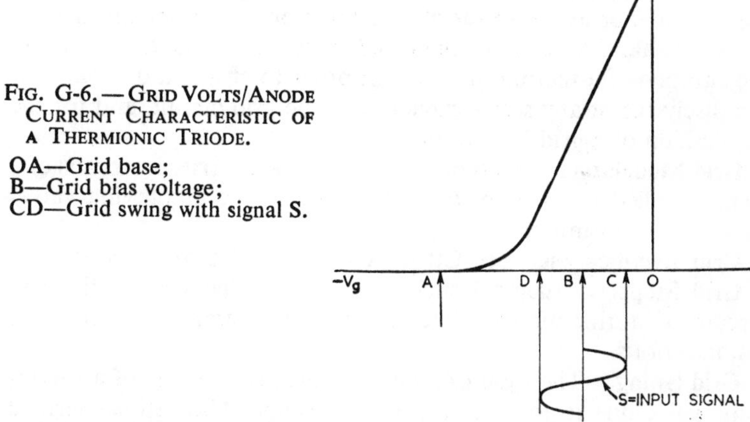

FIG. G-6.—GRID VOLTS/ANODE CURRENT CHARACTERISTIC OF A THERMIONIC TRIODE.
OA—Grid base;
B—Grid bias voltage;
CD—Grid swing with signal S.

Grid-bias Resistor. Resistor connected between the cathode of a thermionic tube and the negative terminal of the h.t. supply in order to produce AUTOMATIC GRID BIAS.

Grid Circuit. The various components connected between the control grid and the cathode of a thermionic tube. It comprises essentially: (*a*) means for applying any necessary bias voltage to the grid, and (*b*) the source of the input signal.

Grid Current. Current flowing in the GRID CIRCUIT of a thermionic valve. The term is normally used for the current which flows when the grid is at a positive potential (or a slightly negative potential) with respect to the cathode. Grid current which flows in the reverse direction, e.g. due to the emission of electrons from the grid, is always referred to as NEGATIVE GRID CURRENT, REVERSE GRID CURRENT or BACKLASH. The last-mentioned term is, however, deprecated.

Grid-current Characteristic. Graph showing the relation between the grid current and the grid potential of a thermionic valve, the potentials of all other electrodes being maintained at constant values.

Grid Detector. Thermionic triode or other multi-electrode valve so operated that rectification occurs in the circuit of the effective diode formed by the cathode and control grid. See CUMULATIVE GRID RECTIFICATION.

Grid Emission. Emission of electrons from the control grid of a thermionic valve as the result of heating of the grid by radiation from the cathode, or as the result of electronic or ionic bombardment.

Grid Leak. A resistor connected between the control grid and the cathode of a thermionic valve in order to ensure a d.c. path for the discharge of any series capacitor in the grid circuit, and for the application of a grid-bias voltage.

Grid Modulation. Method of modulating a carrier by means of a signal applied to the control grid of one of the amplifying valves in a radio transmitter.

Grid Rectification. See CUMULATIVE GRID RECTIFICATION.

Grid Stopper. Element such as a resistor, included in the grid circuit of a thermionic valve in order to damp out PARASITIC OSCILLATIONS.

Grid Swing. The total excursion of the grid voltage of a thermionic valve due to the application of a signal. Sometimes termed the grid sweep. See Fig. G-6.

Grid Voltage. The potential of the grid of a thermionic valve with respect to that of the cathode. In the case of a multi-grid valve it is necessary to specify the grid concerned, e.g. the control-grid voltage, screen-grid voltage, etc.

Ground. Alternative term for EARTH.

Ground-controlled Approach. (G.C.A.) Radar system whereby the controller at a ground station can determine accurately, and in three dimensions, the position of an approaching aircraft with respect to the correct touch-down point on the landing runway, and can thus give the pilot precise verbal instructions for navigating his aircraft up to the final touch-down.

Grounded Base Operation. See COMMON BASE operation of a transistor.

Grounded Cathode. See EARTHED CATHODE operation of a thermionic valve.

Grounded Collector Operation. See COMMON COLLECTOR operation of a transistor.

Grounded Emitter Operation. See COMMON EMITTER operation of a transistor.

Grounded Grid. See EARTHED GRID operation of a thermionic valve.

Ground Wave. See DIRECT WAVE.

Guard Ring. Metal ring so located in an electric field as to ensure uniformity of the field over a certain region by eliminating fringe

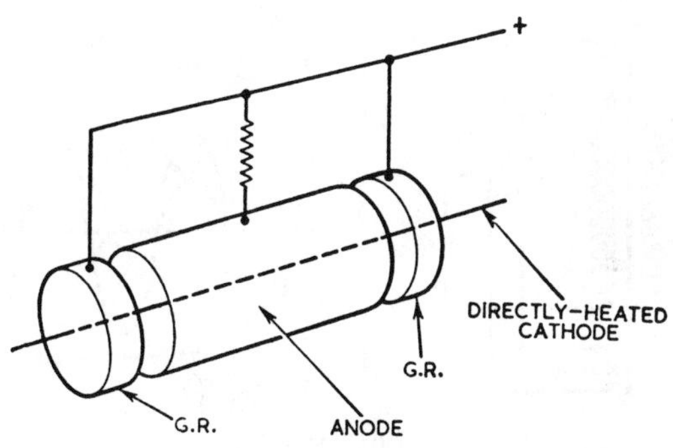

FIG. G-7.—DIODE SYSTEM WITH GUARD RINGS.

effects. In the diode electrode system of Fig. G-7 the guard rings GR are connected to the h.t. supply and ensure that the electric field between anode and cathode is uniform.

Guide, Wave. See WAVEGUIDE.

Gun, Electron. See ELECTRON GUN.

H

H-aerial. Aerial array comprising a DIPOLE and one reflector.

H-mode. A particular field configuration in waveguide technique. See MODE.

H-type Waves. Waves propagated in the H-mode, i.e. in which there is a magnetic field component in the direction of propagation but no electrical field component in that direction.

Half-life. Time taken for the activity of a radioactive substance to decay to one-half of a given initial value. This may range from a few milliseconds to thousands of millions of years. Also called the half-value period.

Half-wave Aerial. Aerial the electrical length of which is approximately half the wavelength of the signal it is designed to receive. The physical length of an aerial is slightly less than the electrical length.

Half-wave Dipole. A DIPOLE aerial having an electrical length equal to one-half of the signal wavelength. It is the most usual type of aerial for television reception, for which purpose it is often used in conjunction with a reflector and/or directors.

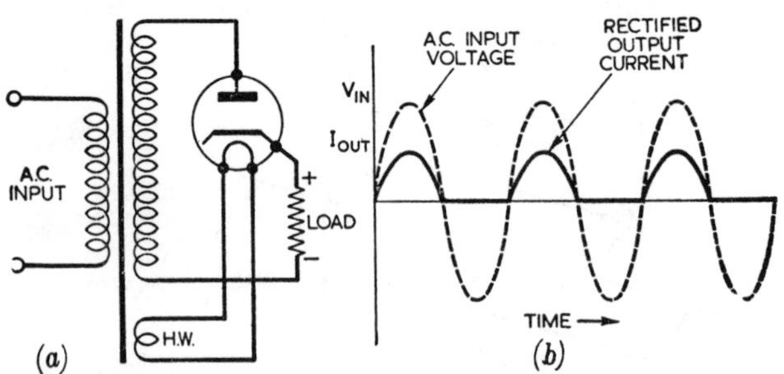

FIG. H-1.

(a) Basic circuit of a half-wave rectifier employing a thermionic diode.
(b) A.C. input voltage (broken line) and unidirectional output current (heavy line) plotted against time.

Half-wave Rectification. Method of RECTIFYING an alternating current in which current flows only during alternate half cycles of the input voltage. See Fig. H-1.

Hall Effect. When a piece of conductor material with a current flowing through it is subjected to a magnetic field perpendicular to the current flow a voltage proportional to the product of the magnetic field and the electric current appears across the faces of the material perpendicular to the current flow.

Hard Tube (Hard Valve). An electron tube the envelope of which is exhausted to a high degree of vacuum, in contrast to a SOFT TUBE which contains an appreciable quantity of residual gas.

Hard X-rays. X-rays of relatively high frequency and of relatively great penetrating power.

Harmonic Aerial. An aerial which, together with its associated circuit, is designed to operate at a frequency which is a harmonic of the natural frequency of the aerial itself.

Harmonic Analyser. See WAVE-FORM ANALYSER.

Harmonic Distortion. Occurrence of harmonics in the output waveform of an amplifier or other network, and produced as a result of the non-linear characteristics of the network or of an individual component thereof. For example, the non-linearity of the anode current/grid volts characteristic of a thermionic valve introduces amplitude distortion which can be shown to correspond to the introduction of second, third and higher harmonics. See Fig. H-2.

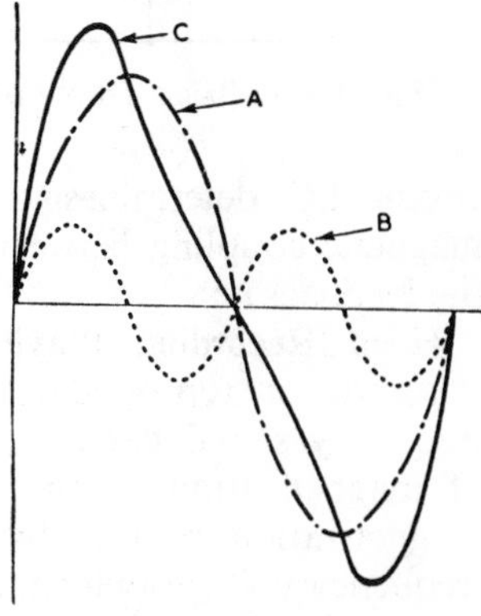

FIG. H-2.
(A) A fundamental wave;
(B) Its second harmonic;
(C) Distorted wave produced by combining A and B.

Harmonic Generator. Another term for FREQUENCY MULTIPLIER.

Harmonic Selective Signalling. System used in telephony in which each of a number of subscribers on a party line has apparatus tuned to a different frequency. It is thus possible to ring a particular subscriber by using the frequency allotted to him and to him alone.

Harmonics. Oscillations the frequency of which are whole multiples of the frequency of the FUNDAMENTAL. Harmonics are designated second, third, fourth harmonics, etc., i.e. harmonics having twice, three times, four times, etc., the fundamental frequency. See Fig. H-2.

Hartley Oscillator. Thermionic oscillator comprising a triode with an oscillatory circuit connected between anode and grid, and inductive coupling between the anode and grid circuits, via a tapping on the inductive element of the tuned circuit. One form of Hartley oscillator is illustrated in Fig. H-3. The tuning of the

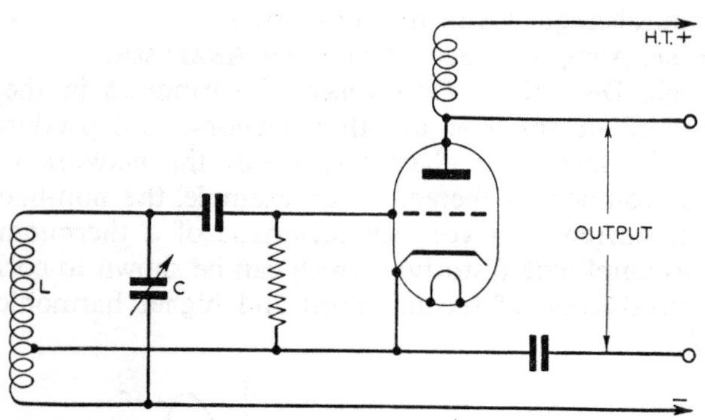

FIG. H-3.—BASIC DIAGRAM OF ONE FORM OF HARTLEY OSCILLATOR.

circuit LC determines the frequency of the oscillations, while magnetic coupling between the two sections of the coil L provide the feedback.

Head (Recording, Playing, Erasing Head). Part of a TAPE RECORDING or reproducing apparatus in which either the audio-frequency signal derived from a microphone produces variations of magnetization along the tape, or in which the variations of magnetization previously imparted to the tape produce audio-frequency voltages which, applied to an amplifier and loudspeaker, reproduce the original sounds, or in which magnetic signals previously recorded are expunged.

Head Amplifier. Video-frequency amplifier mounted on or near a television camera.

Heading Marker. A luminous radial line displayed on the screen of the cathode-ray tube in a PLAN-POSITION INDICATOR and corresponding to the dead-ahead direction of the ship. It allows the observer to determine whether an object shown on the screen lies to port or to starboard.

Hearing Aid. Preferred term for DEAF AID. Consists of a combination of microphone, audio-frequency amplifier and telephone receiver, the latter of miniature dimensions which is comparatively inconspicuous when worn in the ear. The development of SUB-MINIATURE VALVES made possible great reductions in the size of the amplifying unit, and still greater reductions have been made possible by the adoption of TRANSISTORS in place of thermionic valves.

Heart-shaped Reception. Reception of radio signals using an aerial having a CARDIOID polar diagram.

Heart, Tuning. Sub-assembly of a radio receiver, incorporating all the tunable high-frequency circuits.

Heat Sink. A relatively large mass of material which is a good conductor of heat, and preferably of such form and so located that it can also radiate a considerable amount of heat rapidly. Small pieces of apparatus or components which generate heat during operation, e.g. transistors and sub-miniature valves, may be mounted in contact with a heat sink in order to limit their temperature rise.

Heat Treatment. General term embracing any process in which a metal has to be heated, e.g. hardening, tempering, etc. Many heat-treatment operations can be performed by HIGH-FREQUENCY INDUCTION HEATING.

Heater. A high-resistivity wire, usually tungsten, located inside the cathode tube of an indirectly-heated thermionic valve, and heated by the passage of a l.t. current, thus raising the temperature of the cathode material to a value at which electrons are emitted.

Heater Chain. Network consisting of the heaters of the various valves in a mains-operated equipment, connected in series (or in series–parallel).

Heater Circuit. Circuit comprising the heaters of the indirectly-heated valves in an equipment, together with the source of the heater current.

Heater Current. (Symbol I_h) (1) The current flowing in the heater circuit of a valve-operated equipment.

(2) The rated current at which the heater of a particular indirectly-heated tube is designed to operate.

Heater Voltage. (Symbol V_h) (1) The voltage applied to the heater circuit of a valve-operated equipment.

(2) The rated voltage on which the heater of a particular indirectly-heated tube is designed to operate.

Heater Winding. The secondary winding of a POWER TRANSFORMER which provides the heater current for indirectly-heated valves.

Heating, Dielectric Loss. See HIGH-FREQUENCY HEATING and also DIELECTRIC LOSS HEATING.

Heating, Induction. See HIGH-FREQUENCY HEATING and also INDUCTION HEATING.

Heating Time. See VALVE HEATING TIME.

Heaviside Layer. The E-layer of the IONOSPHERE. Also known as the Kennelly–Heaviside layer.

Hectometric Waves. Radio waves having wavelengths between 100 and 1000 m, corresponding to frequencies between 3000 and 300 kc/s, i.e. the MEDIUM WAVEBAND.

Height Control. Means incorporated in a television receiver for adjusting the height of the picture by increasing the amplitude of the vertical timebase.

Helical Aerial. Aerial array composed of a conductor wound in the form of a helix, the circumference of each turn being equal to a whole number of wavelengths.

Helix. A wire wound to a circular spiral with all the turns of the same diameter.

Henry. (Symbol H) Unit of inductance (plural henrys). An inductor has an inductance of one henry if an electro-motive force of one volt is induced when the current changes at the rate of one ampere per second.

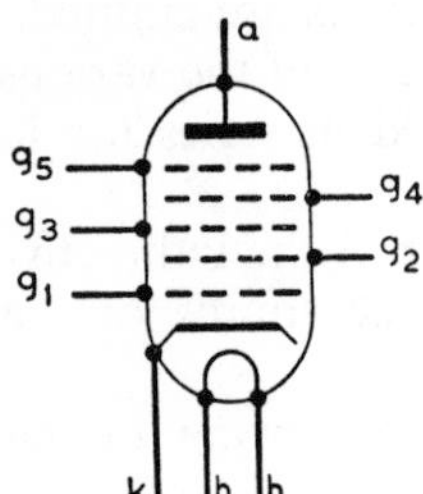

FIG. H-4.—GRAPHICAL SYMBOL FOR A HEPTODE.

Heptode. High-vacuum thermionic valve having seven electrodes, namely an anode, a cathode and five grids. Heptodes are used mainly as FREQUENCY-CHANGERS. See Fig. H-4.

Hertz. Term for unit frequency (abbreviation Hz), i.e. one cycle per second. Employed mainly on the continent of Europe. Frequencies in excess of 1000 c/s are usually expressed in kilo-hertz or in mega-hertz.

Hertzian Waves. Name sometimes given to electromagnetic waves of frequencies up to some 10,000 Mc/s.

Heterodyne. The process whereby two oscillations of different frequencies are combined to produce other oscillations, and particularly oscillations having a frequency equal to the difference between the frequencies of the two original oscillations. See BEAT.

Heterodyne Frequency. See BEAT FREQUENCY.

Heterodyne Frequency Meter. See HETERODYNE WAVEMETER.

Heterodyne Interference. Interference experienced in radio receivers due to the simultaneous reception of two signals the difference between the carrier frequencies of which falls within the audio range.

Heterodyne Oscillator. See BEAT-FREQUENCY OSCILLATOR.

Heterodyne Reception. See BEAT RECEPTION.

Heterodyne Wavemeter. Oscillator the frequency of which can be varied, the adjustment being calibrated either in frequencies or in wavelengths or in both. The output is connected to the source of the signal of which the wavelength is to be measured, and the instrument is adjusted until the heterodyne or beat note falls to zero. Also termed a heterodyne frequency meter.

Heterodyne Whistle. Continual high-pitched note heard in the loudspeaker and resulting from the beating of two oscillations of slightly different frequencies.

Hexode. High-vacuum thermionic valve having six electrodes, namely an anode, a cathode and four grids. Frequently employed as a MIXER in conjunction with a triode oscillator in a FREQUENCY CHANGER. The hexode system and the triode system are usually enclosed in a common envelope, to form a TRIODE-HEXODE.

Hi-Fi. Colloquialism for HIGH FIDELITY sound reproduction.

High Definition. Applied to television systems in which the picture is scanned in a number of lines exceeding 200.

High Fidelity. The sound output of an amplifier and loudspeaker combination is said to be of high fidelity when it is a reasonably faithful reproduction of the quality of the original sound.

High Frequency. (h.f.) (1) A general term used to distinguish signals of radio frequency from those of audio frequency.

(2) A relative term used to describe frequencies at the upper end of a particular frequency band.

(3) Term of specific application to radio waves in the frequency range between 3 and 30 Mc/s, i.e. of wavelengths from 100 m down to 10 m.

High-frequency Amplifier. Thermionic amplifier designed for magnifying signals of radio frequency.

High-frequency Choke. Inductor having a high impedance to currents of high frequency.

High-frequency Heating. Process of heating materials by placing them in a high-frequency electric or magnetic field. When a metal is to be heated it is placed in the magnetic field produced by a coil carrying a high-frequency current, and is heated by the circulation of eddy currents. This is known as high-frequency INDUCTION HEATING. In the case of non-conductors the material to be heated is placed between metallic electrodes connected to the output terminals of a high-frequency oscillator. The material is then heated as the result of DIELECTRIC LOSSES.

High-frequency Resistance. Resistance of a conductor measured when high-frequency current is flowing. This value is greater than the resistance measured under d.c. conditions, as a result of the skin effect, and eddy-current and other losses.

High-frequency Transformer. Static transformer designed to operate at high frequencies. A high-frequency transformer may have an air core, or a core of IRON DUST or of one of the MAGNETIC FERRITES.

High-level Detection. Detection of radio signals by means of a thermionic diode, with sufficient pre-detection amplification to reduce to insignificance the effect of the non-linearity of the diode characteristic at low input levels.

High-level Modulation. See HIGH-POWER MODULATION.

High-pass Filter. A FILTER network which permits the passage of currents having frequencies exceeding a specified value, and attenuates all other frequencies. Typical filters of this type are illustrated in Fig. H-5.

High-power Modulation. Modulation of a carrier by introducing the signal information into the anode circuit of the final amplifying valve of a radio transmitter.

High-stability Components. Circuit components the values or electrical characteristics of which do not appreciably change with changing conditions such as of temperature or age.

High Tension. (h.t.) Comparative term used in electronics to denote voltages of the order of those applied to the anode and other accelerating electrodes of an electron tube, in contrast with the LOW TENSION supplies for cathode heating.

High-tension Battery. Primary or secondary battery which supplies energy at high tension to the anodes and other accelerating electrodes of electron tubes.

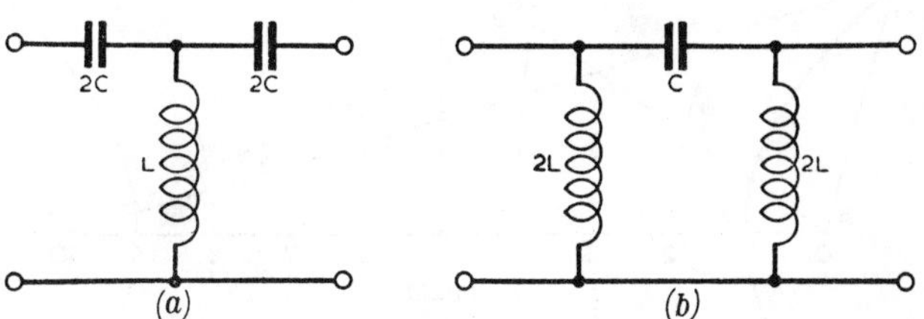

FIG. H-5.—TYPICAL FORMS OF HIGH-PASS FILTER: (a) T-SECTION; (b) π-SECTION.

Either filter will pass a continuous band of frequencies above the critical frequency $1/4\pi\sqrt{LC}$, and attenuate all lower frequencies.

High-tension Supply. The h.t. supply for electron tubes is obtained either from batteries or from the electricity mains. In the case of a.c. mains, some form of RECTIFIER is needed, together with a RIPPLE FILTER.

High-vacuum Tube. Thermionic or photo-emissive tube the envelope of which has been exhausted to a high degree of vacuum.

Hill and Dale Recording. Method of producing gramophone records wherein the sound track is formed by the vertical movement of the cutting stylus. This method is virtually obsolete, having been replaced by that in which the movement of the stylus is approximately radial but has been revived for stereo recording.

Hold Control. Control provided in the timebase circuit of a television receiver for adjusting the free-running frequency of the timebase generator to a value at which the synchronizing pulses transmitted by the television station can maintain synchronism. Two such controls are fitted, one, the vertical or frame hold, and the other, the horizontal or line hold.

Hole. Concept of a positive charge carrier in P-TYPE semiconductor material and representing the deficiency of a valency electron in an atom of ACCEPTOR impurity.

Horizontal Deflexion. Deflexion of the electron beam, and hence of the light spot in a cathode-ray tube, in a horizontal direction. In television this corresponds to the line scan.

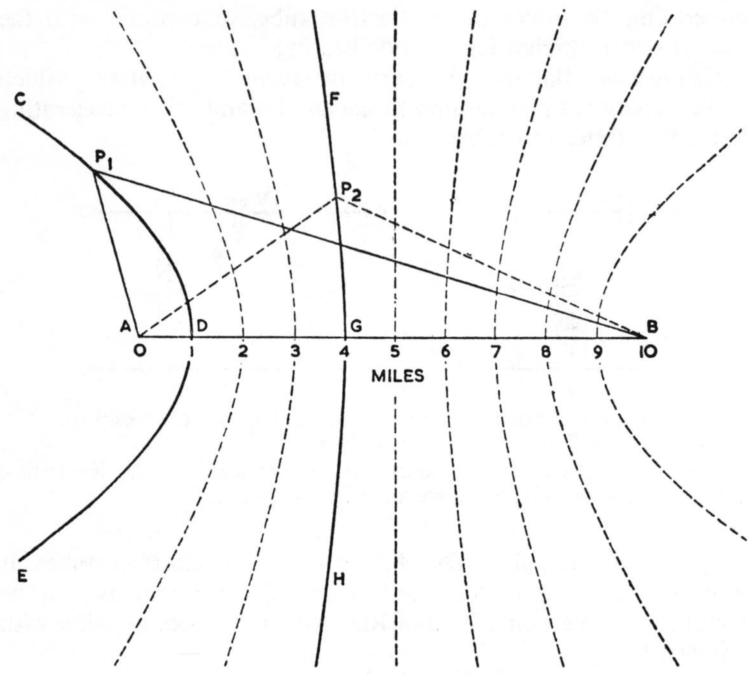

FIG. H-6.—PRINCIPLE OF THE HYPERBOLIC CHART.

Transmitting stations A and B are assumed to be 10 miles apart. The difference between the distances of any point on a particular curve from the two stations is constant. Thus, for hyperbola CDE the difference factor is 9 − 1 = 8 miles; for hyperbola FGH the difference factor is 6 − 4 = 2 miles.

Horizontal Hold. The HOLD CONTROL of the horizontal (line) timebase in a television receiver.

Horizontally-polarized Wave. Radio wave in which the direction of the electric field is horizontal; cf. VERTICALLY POLARIZED WAVE.

Hot Cathode. See THERMIONIC CATHODE.

Hot-cathode Discharge Lamp. A GAS DISCHARGE LAMP in which a thermionic cathode is employed when the tube is switched on, so as to provide sufficient free electrons to facilitate the initiation of the main discharge.

Hot-cathode Tube. Electron tube employing a thermionic cathode.

Hot Spot. In electron tubes employing a POOL CATHODE the discharge takes place between the anode and a hot spot developed at the surface of the liquid cathode.

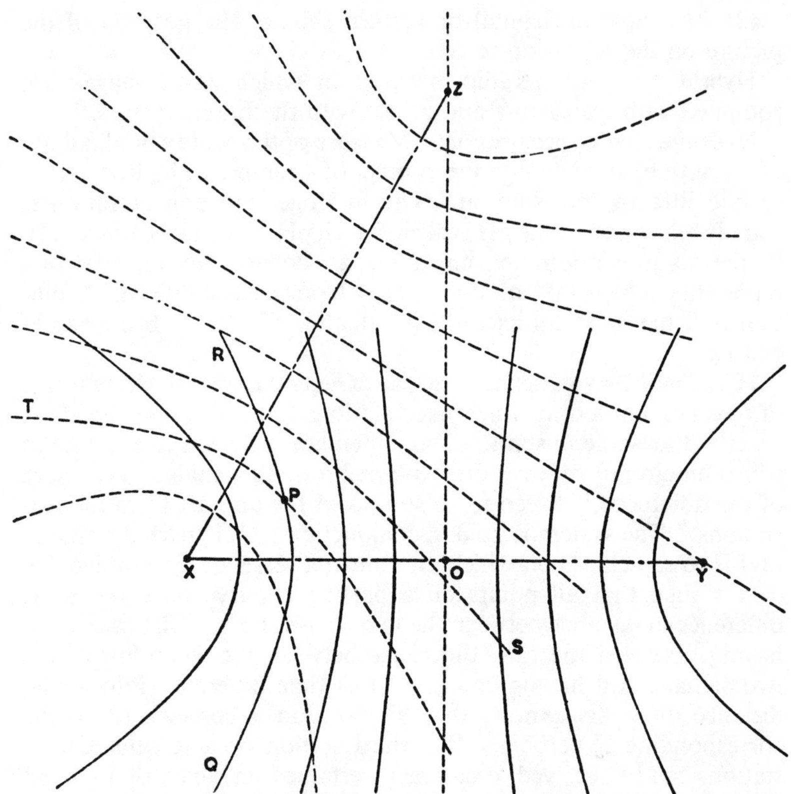

FIG. H-7.—SUPERIMPOSED HYPERBOLIC CHARTS IN RESPECT OF TWO PAIRS OF TRANSMITTERS: X, Y AND Y, Z.

Howl-back. Mechanical feedback at audio frequency, between the loudspeaker and the microphone or some other MICROPHONIC component in a sound reproducing system, whereby uncontrolled oscillations are built up.

Hum. Unwanted components of the sound output of a receiver or amplifier, corresponding to frequencies equal to the electricity mains frequency or to twice that frequency, and due either to insufficient smoothing of the rectified h.t. supply or to induction from conductors carrying alternating current (e.g. from the cathode heater circuit).

Hunting. (1) General term for rhythmic variation of the speed of a machine, or in the difference between the speeds of two machines operated in parallel.

(2) Rhythmic horizontal or vertical shift of the position of the picture on the television screen.

Hybrid Receiver. Radio receiver in which some stages are equipped with transistors and others with thermionic valves.

Hydrogen-ion Concentration. Measure of the acidity or alkalinity of a solution, and equal to the number of grammes of hydrogen ions in one litre of the solution. The hydrogen-ion concentration is usually expressed in the pH scale in which $pH = \log(1/H^{\cdot})$, where $H^{\cdot}$ is the hydrogen-ion concentration as defined above. $pH = 7$ represents a neutral solution, $pH = 0$ an exceedingly acid solution and $pH = 14$ an exceedingly alkaline solution. See also pH METER.

Hyperbolic Navigational Systems. General name for those forms of navigational aid in which fixed stations transmit pulse signals at exactly the same instant. The difference between the times at which an aircraft receives the two synchronized signals is a measure of the difference between the distances of the aircraft from the two stations. The system is used in conjunction with hyperbolic charts, that is to say charts on which are drawn a series of hyperbolae, i.e. curves such that all points on a particular curve have the same difference in distance between the two transmitters. The navigator, having observed the time difference between the reception of the two signals, and having converted this time difference into actual distance difference, knows that his position is somewhere on the corresponding hyperbola. If a third station or a second pair of stations can be received, it can be ascertained on which of a second set of hyperbolae the position of the aircraft is situated. By superimposing the two hyperbolic charts the actual position of the aircraft can be found. Fig. H-6 shows a hyperbolic chart for the stations A and B situated 10 miles apart. Fig. H-7 shows the two sets of hyperbolae for the pairs of stations X-Y and X-Z.

Hysteresis. Phenomenon whereby the quantitative effect of a given change in an applied force depends upon whether the change represents an increase or a decrease. For example, the curves representing the relation between the magnetic induction and the magnetizing force for increasing and decreasing values of the magnetizing force do not coincide. See MAGNETIC HYSTERESIS.

Hysteresis Loop. Graph showing the relation between the magnetic induction and the magnetizing force over a complete cycle comprising gradual magnetization in one direction, demagnetization, magnetization in the reverse direction and final demagnetization. Owing to the hysteresis effect, the graph is a closed figure, a typical form being illustrated in Fig. H-8.

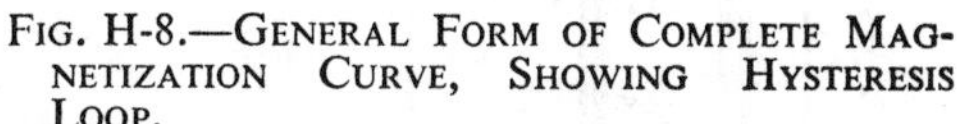
FIG. H-8.—GENERAL FORM OF COMPLETE MAGNETIZATION CURVE, SHOWING HYSTERESIS LOOP.

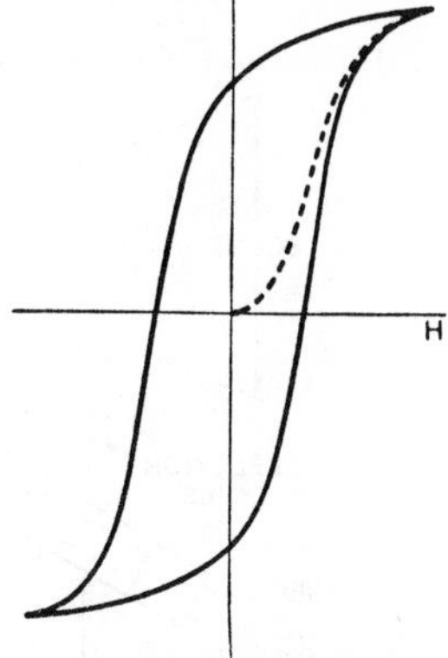

Hysteresis Losses. The energy expended in taking a piece of ferromagnetic material through a complete magnetizing cycle. The power loss is proportional to the area enclosed by the hysteresis loop. See Fig. H-8.

I

I-core. One of the standard shapes of core material for transformers and inductors. It is either a narrow rectangular iron lamination, or a rectangular block of one of the MAGNETIC FERRITES. Cf. E-, T-, and U-cores, and see also INDUCTOR CORES.

Iconoscope. Type of television camera tube in which an image of the scene to be televised is projected on a mosaic consisting of granules of photo-emissive material. Emission of photo-electrons from each granule in proportion to the amount of light falling upon it results in the formation of a CHARGE IMAGE on the mosaic. Each granule, together with the conductive plate behind the mosaic, forms a small capacitor, all these capacitors having a common plate. The capacitors are discharged in succession when the mosaic is scanned by an electron beam projected from an electron gun, and the resulting changes of potential at the metal plate constitute the picture signal. See Fig. I-1.

Ignite. A gas-filled tube is said to ignite when, owing to ionization of the gas filling, the tube becomes fully conductive. This condition is accompanied by a luminous glow at the cathode.

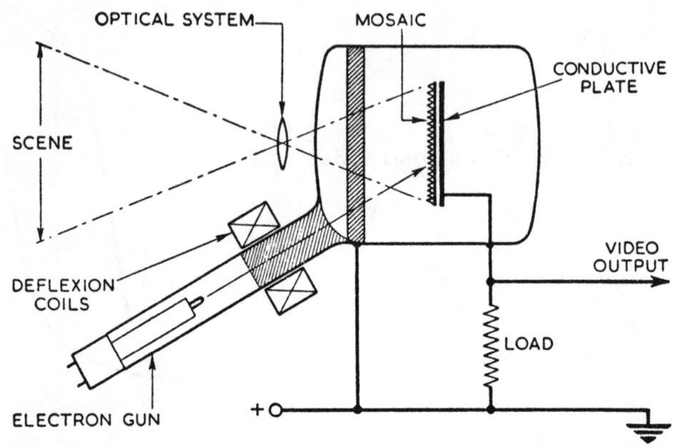

FIG. I-1.—DIAGRAMMATIC SECTION OF THE ICONOSCOPE.

Ignition Interference. The effect in a radio or television receiver of spurious signals resulting from the discharge at the sparking plugs (and to a less extent at the distributor) of an automobile engine. In a radio receiver it is manifest as noise; in a television receiver as bright spots on the screen.

Ignition Rectifier. Mercury arc rectifier with a pool cathode, the cathode hot-spot being initiated by a voltage pulse applied between the cathode and an igniter electrode which dips into the mercury pool. See IGNITRON.

Ignition Voltage. The voltage which must be applied between the anode and cathode of a gas-filled discharge tube in order to initiate the discharge.

Ignitron. Discharge tube consisting of a steel envelope enclosing a mercury-pool cathode, an anode and a pointed ignition electrode of refractory material such as boron carbide, which dips into the mercury pool but is not wetted thereby. See Fig. I-2. A positive potential applied to the ignition electrode causes a small arc between this electrode and the mercury, thus producing a cathode hot spot and initiating the main discharge. The tubes are designed to handle large currents, and the steel envelope has double walls for the circulation of cooling water. Their main applications are as high-power rectifiers, and in automatic welding control.

Image. In addition to its familiar optical application, the term " image " is also applied to the charge pattern (charge image), i.e. a distribution of electric charge over a surface such as a photo-emissive mosaic or a target in a television camera, the charge per elemental area being proportional to the brightness of the corresponding area of the original scene. The term image is also used in connexion with a particular form of radio interference. See IMAGE INTERFERENCE.

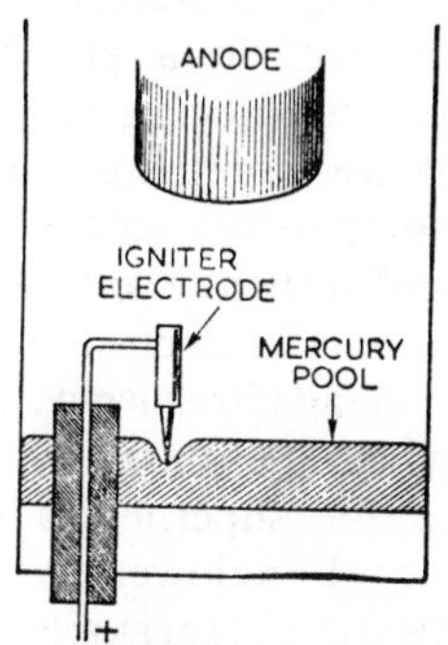

FIG. I-2.—DIAGRAMMATIC SECTION OF PART OF AN IGNITRON, SHOWING IGNITION ARRANGEMENT.

Image Converter. Electron tube in which an applied image, which may or may not be visible, produces an equivalent image in visible light. In the simple diagram of Fig. I-3 the original image, which may, for example, be composed of infra-red radiation and

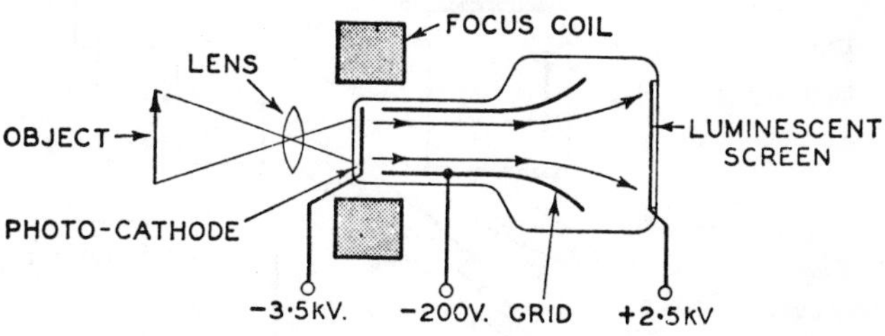

FIG. I-3.—FUNCTIONAL DIAGRAM OF AN IMAGE CONVERTER.

therefore invisible, is focused on a photo-emissive cathode which emits photo-electrons from each elemental area in proportion to the amount of radiation falling upon it. These electrons are accelerated along the tube by an electric field and ultimately strike a luminescent screen at the distant end, where a visible image is produced. In some image converters a control electrode is fitted between the photo-cathode and the viewing screen. This enables the electron beam to be suppressed at will. By applying suitable voltage pulses to the control electrode, it acts as a high-speed shutter so that photographs of the final image may be taken at very short exposure.

Image Dissection. Process of scanning the charge image in a television camera tube.

Image Dissector. Camera tube in which an image of the scene is focused on a photo-emissive cathode, the photo electrons thus produced being accelerated to form a beam, the intensity of which at any point is proportional to the brightness of the corresponding point in the scene. The beam is then deflected both horizontally and vertically so that each elemental area is scanned by a fixed anode of small dimensions.

Image Frequency. Carrier frequency of an unwanted radio signal which is as much higher (or lower) than the local oscillator frequency of the superheterodyne receiver as the frequency of the wanted signal is lower (or higher) than the oscillator frequency. See IMAGE INTERFERENCE.

Image Iconoscope. Camera tube related to the ICONOSCOPE, but the target on which the charge image is formed is separate from the

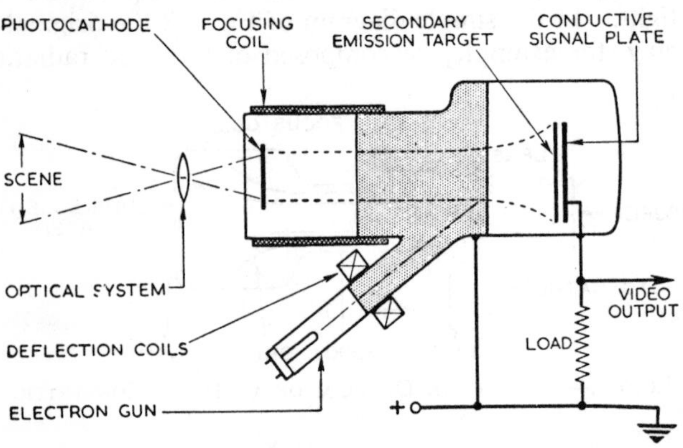

FIG. I-4.—DIAGRAMMATIC SECTION OF THE IMAGE ICONOSCOPE.

photo-emissive cathode. An optical image of the scene is focused on a photo cathode, and the photo electrons emitted therefrom are accelerated and focused on a target composed of some material such a mica which has a high SECONDARY EMISSION FACTOR, resulting in the production of a charge image. The target is scanned by a high-velocity electron beam, thus progressively discharging the charge image, and the resulting potential variations at the conductive layer at the rear of the target forms the basis of the picture signal. See Fig. I-4.

Image Intensifier. Electron tube operating on a similar principle to that of the IMAGE CONVERTER but specially designed to produce a small but very bright final image. In one form used in RADIOGRAPHY the primary image is formed by X-rays on a fluorescent screen situated at one end of the tube, and the light so produced causes the emission of electrons from a layer of photo-emissive material in intimate contact with the fluorescent screen. The photo-electrons are accelerated and focused by an electron optical system on a small luminescent screen, and the very bright image thus produced can be examined by means of a microscope, or photographed with a cine-camera.

Image Interference. Interference experienced in a superheterodyne receiver due to beating between the local oscillation and an unwanted signal, the frequency of which is as much above (or below) the oscillator frequency as the frequency of the wanted signal is below (or above) the oscillator frequency. Both signals therefore produce the same intermediate frequency, and their respective modulations interfere with each other. Also termed SECOND-CHANNEL INTERFERENCE.

Image Orthicon. Camera tube of extreme sensitivity. The optical image of the scene is focused on the rear of a photo-emissive cathode (Fig. I-5) which emits photo-electrons at each point in proportion to the amount of light falling upon it. The photo-electrons are accelerated and focused on a metal target, producing secondary emission so that a positive charge image is formed on the target. The rear of the target is scanned by a low-velocity electron beam which supplies the target with just sufficient electrons to progressively neutralize the charge image, the remaining electrons, now forming a beam modulated in accordance with picture brightness by reason of the electrons imparted to the target, returning towards the electron gun along a path parallel to that of the outward beam, and striking the first DYNODE of a multi-stage ELECTRON MULTIPLIER, the output of which forms the basis of the picture signal.

Impedance. (Symbol Z) The total opposition offered by a circuit to the flow of alternating current, and equal to the ratio of the r.m.s. value of the applied voltage to the r.m.s. value of the current. Impedance is a complex property, having three components: (*a*) the resistance of the circuit, (*b*) a reactive component due to the inductance of the circuit, and (*c*) a further reactive component due to the capacitance of the circuit, the last two being frequency-dependent. If the resistance in ohms is R, the inductance in henrys is L and the capacitance in farads is C, the impedance in ohms is $Z = [R^2 + (2\pi fL - 1/2\pi fC)^2]^{\frac{1}{2}}\ \Omega$, for a given frequency f.

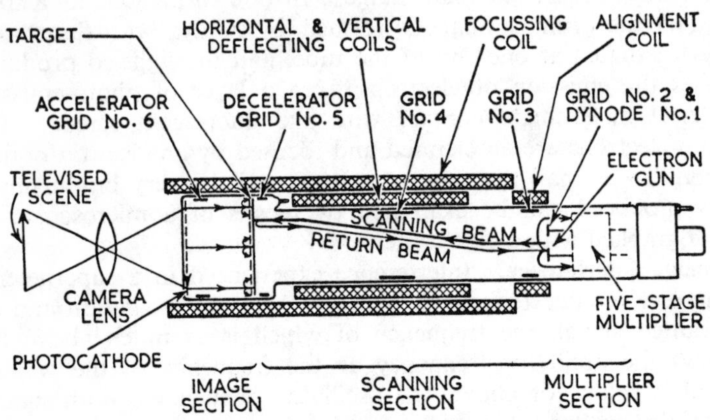

FIG. I-5.—DIAGRAMMATIC SECTION OF THE IMAGE ORTHICON CAMERA TUBE.

Impulse. A unidirectional flow of current of very short duration, which may or may not be superimposed upon a steady direct current.

Impulse Noise. Another name for interference due to spurious signals such as the pulses radiated by ignition systems, producing a crackling noise in sound receivers and bright spots or even streaks in television pictures. Ideally, pulse interference should be countered by suppression at the source, but where this is impracticable some form of NOISE LIMITER must be employed in the receiving apparatus.

In Phase. Said of two alternating currents or voltages which are not only of the same frequency but reach their positive and negative maxima at the same instant of time.

Independently Heated Cathode. See INDIRECTLY HEATED CATHODE.

Independent-sideband Transmission. A logical development from the basic s.s.b. transmission is independent-sideband operation (i.s.b.) whereby a second, but completely independent, sideband is also associated with the same pilot carrier and radiated on the opposite side of it, thus allowing simultaneous transmission of two or more speech channels.

Indirect Ray. Path of a radio wave which reaches the receiver after having been reflected from the IONOSPHERE.

Indirectly Heated Cathode. Thermionic cathode consisting of a metal tube, the external surface of which is coated with emissive material, and heated by the current flowing in a heater wire located within the tube but electrically insulated therefrom. Also termed an independently heated cathode or an equipotential cathode.

Indirectly Heated Valve. Thermionic valve employing an indirectly heated cathode.

Inductance. (Symbol L) The property of a circuit whereby an electro-motive force is generated by reason of a change in the magnetic flux through the circuit. If the change of flux is due to a change in the current flowing through the circuit itself, the inductance is more properly termed SELF-INDUCTANCE; if by a change in the current flowing in a neighbouring circuit, the inductance is termed MUTUAL INDUCTANCE. Unit the HENRY.

Inductance–Capacitance Filter. Network for removing the ripple frequency component of a unidirectional current. A basic circuit is given in Fig. I-6, in which the inductor and the capacitor form

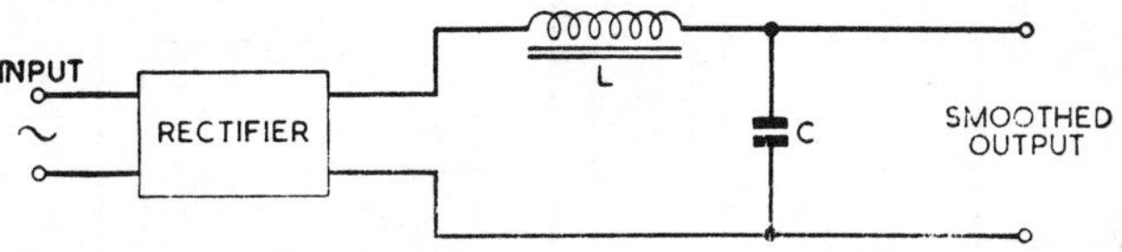

FIG. I-6.—BASIC CIRCUIT OF AN INDUCTANCE–CAPACITANCE RIPPLE FILTER.

a voltage divider across the input terminals. The inductor has a low impedance to direct current but a high impedance to the alternating component, while the capacitor has a high impedance to direct current and a low impedance to the alternating component.

Inductance Coupling. COUPLING between two circuits due to a component possessing inductance and common to both circuits.

Induction. (1) The production of an electro-motive force in a circuit possessing the property of INDUCTANCE.

(2) The magnetic flux density or intensity of the magnetic field at a given point. Symbol B; unit the GAUSS.

Induction Heating. Method of heating metal objects by induced (eddy) currents generated in the material when placed in an alternating magnetic field. In high-frequency induction heating the oscillating magnetic field is produced by an alternating current of suitable frequency in the range of about 20 kc/s to about 1 Mc/s, generated by a thermionic oscillator and flowing in a water-cooled coil. If the metal to be heated is ferromagnetic, the heating is due partly to eddy currents and partly to hysteresis effects until the temperature of the material rises to the CURIE POINT, after which any further heating is due solely to eddy currents. Among the industrial applications of high-frequency induction heating are metal hardening and other heat-treatment processes, soldering and brazing metal melting and the drying of paint on metallic surfaces.

Inductive. Said of a circuit or circuit element which possesses the property of inductance, or of a phenomenon which occurs by reason of induction.

Inductor. A component included in a circuit in order to exploit its inductance. It consists essentially of a coil of wire, the interior of the coil being either an air space or a core of ferromagnetic material.

Inductor Cores. Inductors may be air-cored or have cores made of a ferromagnetic material. For low-frequency inductors the core is usually built up of thin steel laminations, but in order to reduce

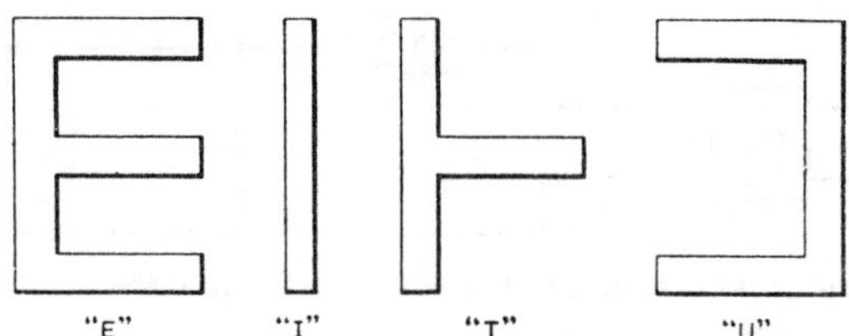

FIG. I-7.—PRINCIPAL STANDARD SHAPES OF INDUCTOR CORE STAMPINGS.

eddy-current losses in cores for high-frequency inductors, either IRON-DUST CORES or cores of one of the magnetic ferrites are used. Cores are usually built up of standard shapes, of which the E-, I-, T- and U- cores illustrated (Fig. I-7) are the most common, and which, in combination, permit a wide variety of core shapes.

Industrial Television. In addition to the use of television for entertainment purposes, the art, and also other related methods of picture reproduction, are finding increasing application in industry, in scientific research and in commerce. One large group of such applications concerns the examination of objects and processes under conditions which preclude direct vision. For example, conditions within industrial furnaces or within the danger range of radioactivity and the readings of instruments in inaccessible positions or in dangerous locations are now commonly viewed by television, often on closed circuit. Sensitive submergible television cameras carrying their own lights are used to facilitate deep-sea salvage and similar operations at depths down to at least 1200 ft. See UNDER-WATER TELEVISION. Use of the TELEVISION MICROSCOPE is less fatiguing to the observer than that of the optical microscope, and also permits the object to be viewed by many observers at the same time. Closed-circuit television, often in colour, has made it possible for large numbers of doctors and students to watch surgical operations, and the television camera may well revolutionize methods of making cinematograph films. See ELECTRONIC METHODS OF FILM MAKING. The IMAGE CONVERTER, which combines many of the features of the television camera and of the cathode-ray tube, opens up new fields in high-speed photography.

Infra-red. Infra-red radiation (heat waves) consists of electromagnetic radiation of wavelengths shorter than those of the super-high-frequency (centimetric) radio waves and longer than 7600 Å, corresponding to the red end of the visible spectrum.

Injection. The application of a signal to a circuit, and in particular the introduction of the local oscillation into the signal-frequency of a superheterodyne receiver.

Input Capacitance. The capacitance between the control grid and the cathode of a thermionic valve when all other electrodes are connected to the cathode by paths of negligible impedance.

Input Impedance. The input impedance of a thermionic valve is the impedance offered by the combination of the resistive and reactive paths between the control grid and cathode.

Input Signal. The incoming signal applied to a receiver or an amplifier.

Input Transformer. A static transformer to the primary winding of which is applied the input signal, the secondary winding being connected to the input terminals of the receiver or other apparatus. Employed for isolating the apparatus from any direct voltage in the signal source, or to provide a degree of voltage step-up.

Input Voltage. The voltage derived from the signal source and applied to the input of a receiver or other apparatus.

Instability. Generation of unwanted and sustained oscillations in an amplifier circuit, due to excessive positive feedback or to negative resistance effects.

Instantaneous Frequency. The INSTANTANEOUS VALUE of the frequency of a current or voltage when, as for example in the case of a frequency-modulated signal, the frequency is not constant.

Instantaneous Value. Value of an electrical current, voltage, etc., at some particular instant of time, as distinct from its mean value, its r.m.s. value or its peak value, etc.

Instrument Landing System. (Abbreviation i.l.s.) Method of assisting the pilot of an aircraft to land successfully under conditions of poor visibility at the airfield. Working without the services of a ground operator, the equipment gives the pilot continuous information as to his altitude above the landing path, his direction with respect to the course which he should follow and also advises him when he passes each of three radio beacons at various distances from the commencement of the runway. See also LOCATOR BEACON, LOCALIZER and MARKER BEACONS.

Insulation. Non-conductive material surrounding or supporting a conductor, and thus restricting the flow of electric current to a desired path.

Insulator. (1) In general a NON-CONDUCTOR of electricity.

(2) A structure made of porcelain, glass or some other non-conducting material and used to support a current-carrying conductor.

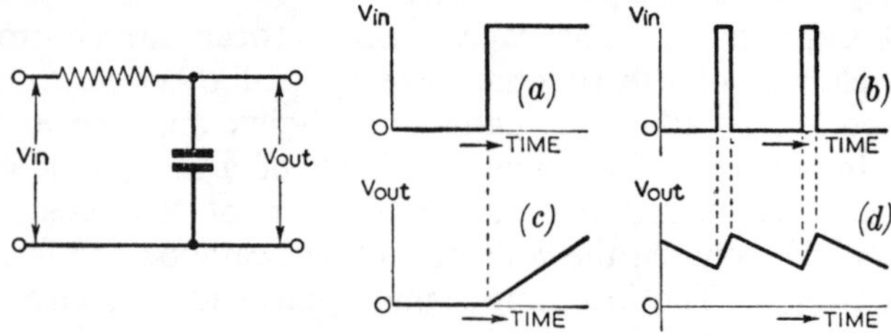

FIG. I-8.—(*left*) BASIC INTEGRATING CIRCUIT. (*right*) (a) AND (b) ARE A STEP INPUT AND A PULSED INPUT VOLTAGE RESPECTIVELY. (c) AND (d) ARE THE CORRESPONDING OUTPUT VOLTAGES.

Integrating Circuit. Circuit in which a capacitor is progressively charged by a series of current pulses, the constants of the circuit being so chosen that the capacitor is not fully discharged during the time intervals between successive charging pulses (Fig. I-8).

Intelligence. The information contained in a signal.

Inter-carrier Amplification. Method of amplification which can be employed in television receivers when the vision signal is amplitude-modulated and the sound signal frequency-modulated. Both vision and sound signals are amplified both at radio frequency and at intermediate frequency by the same chain of amplifying valves and are applied to the video detector, which, however, detects only the amplitude-modulated video signal. The frequency-modulated sound signal is filtered out of the video chain, and transferred first to further amplifying stages and then to the frequency-modulation detector.

Inter-electrode Capacitance. The capacitance between any two electrodes or groups of electrodes in a thermionic valve.

Interference. The effect in a radio or television receiver of the simultaneous reception of the wanted signal and one or more unwanted signals of sufficient strength to be reproduced in the output. Interference may be due to signals radiated by stations other than that which is radiating the wanted signal, or to radio-frequency impulses produced by natural means (atmospherics) or by electrical machinery or other equipment, such as electric motors, medical apparatus and the ignition systems of automobiles. Inter-station interference must be combated by improving the selectivity of the receiving equipment or by the use of filters or wavetraps. Most forms of " man-made " interference can be eliminated or greatly reduced by fitting suppression devices to the offending apparatus. Some interfering signals reach the receiver via the electricity mains, and it may be necessary to fit suppressor devices at the point where the mains enter the building in which the receiver is located.

Interference Inverter. Device for reducing the size and brightness of the white spots on the screen of a television receiver caused by interference, and particularly by ignition interference. It consists essentially of a diode which conducts only when an interference pulse is received. The output of the diode is applied to the grid of the picture tube in such a sense that the area of the interference white spots is increased, while for stronger interference pulses the brightness of the interference spots is reduced and they may, for very severe interference, become black.

Interference Suppressor. Filter or attenuator fitted to apparatus which is capable of radiating interference signals, or to the terminals of the electric supply which might be a source of interference.

Interlaced Scanning. Method of scanning employed in television systems whereby the scene to be transmitted, and also the screen in the picture tube, is scanned in horizontal lines in such a way that the odd-numbered lines are scanned in succession to form one FRAME and the even-numbered lines are scanned in succession to form the succeeding frame.

Intermediate Frequency. Carrier frequency produced in a superheterodyne receiver by the beating of the local oscillation with the carrier of the incoming signal. The intermediate frequency, which is normally much lower than the signal frequency, carries the original signal modulation, and is amplified by one or more pre-tuned amplifier stages before detection.

Intermediate-frequency Amplifier. Thermionic valve and its associated circuit which amplifies the intermediate-frequency signals in a superheterodyne radio receiver.

Intermediate-frequency Transformer. Intervalve transformer which forms the coupling between the mixer and the first intermediate-frequency amplifier, or between two intermediate-frequency amplifier stages, or between the final intermediate-frequency amplifier and the detector in a superheterodyne receiver. Usually both the primary and the secondary windings are pre-tuned to the intermediate frequency.

Internal Capacitance. See INTER-ELECTRODE CAPACITANCE. The term is, however, often applied specifically to the capacitance between the anode and cathode of a thermionic valve.

Internal Impedance. Total opposition to the flow of alternating current offered by a component or piece of apparatus which is included in a circuit not for the sole purpose of introducing impedance. The internal impedance of a thermionic valve comprises the parallel connexion of its differential anode resistance and the reactance corresponding to its internal capacitance.

Internal Resistance. Resistance offered by a component or piece of equipment included in a circuit not for the sole purpose of introducing resistance.

International Units. Physical units based upon internationally accepted values of fundamental units and of certain derived units.

Interrupted Continuous-wave Telegraphy. System of wireless telegraphy in which CONTINUOUS WAVES, modulated at audio frequency, are broken up (KEYED) into short and long periods (dots and dashes) in accordance with a telegraphic code. After rectification at the receiver, the signals are audible in a telephone instrument.

Inter-station Interference. Interference manifest in a radio receiver and due to the simultaneous reception of two signals—the wanted signal and the signal radiated by another station operating on the same or an adjacent frequency.

Inter-valve Coupling. Network whereby the output of one valve is applied to the control-grid circuit of the following valve in a radio receiver or amplifier.

Inter-valve Transformer. Static transformer the primary winding of which is included in the anode circuit of one thermionic valve and the secondary winding in the grid circuit of the following valve, thus forming the inter-valve coupling.

Inverse Voltage. Voltage appearing between the anode and cathode of a thermionic tube in the direction opposite to that which would result in anode current flow in the normal direction. See also PEAK INVERSE VOLTAGE.

Inverted-L Aerial. Aerial consisting of an elevated horizontal conductor insulated at both ends, and with a down lead at one end connected to the aerial terminal of the receiver. (See Fig. A-2.)

Ion. Atom or group of atoms in which there is a surplus or deficiency of ELECTRONS so that the system exhibits an electric charge. A surplus of electrons produces a negative ion (anion) and a deficiency of electrons produces a positive ion (cation). See ATOM, STRUCTURE OF. Strictly speaking, a free electron must also be considered as a negative ion.

Ion Burn. Partial destruction of the luminescent properties over a particular area of the screen of a cathode-ray tube due to bombardment of the phosphor by negative ions mainly produced at the cathode, and accelerated in the direction of the screen by the electron gun. It is avoided in modern tubes by incorporating an ION TRAP in the design of the gun.

Ion Focusing. See GAS FOCUSING.

Ion Trap. Feature of the electron-gun system of a modern television picture tube whereby negative ions, produced at the cathode, are prevented from reaching the luminescent screen and so causing ION BURN. A typical construction is illustrated in Fig. I-9. Electrons emitted from the cathode, together with any negative ions present, are accelerated in the direction WX and, if undeflected, would strike the anode as shown. However, a small permanent magnet, M, mounted on the neck of the tube, produces a field which tends to deflect negative charge carriers. The electrons in the beam are, in fact, so deflected and move axially along the tube in the direction Z, ultimately reaching the luminescent screen, but the field is not strong enough to deflect the relatively massive ions, which continue along the path shown and are collected by the anode.

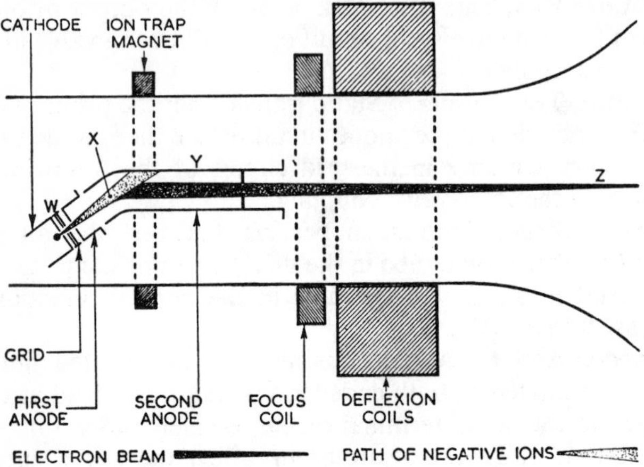

FIG. I-9.—ION-TRAP GUN ASSEMBLY OF A TELEVISION PICTURE TUBE.

Ionic Bombardment. Impact on the cathode of a gas-filled electron tube of positive ions formed by ionization of the gas within the tube. The impact may be sufficiently severe to eject electrons from the cathode material. Some of these electrons may combine with the positive ions to produce neutral atoms; others travel towards the anode, thus helping to maintain the anode current, and also ionizing by collision other gas atoms.

Ionization. The production of IONS from electrically neutral atoms or groups of atoms by the addition or removal of electrons. Removal of an electron leaves the atom or atom group positively charged, i.e. it becomes a positive ion; addition of an electron gives the atom or atom group a negative charge, i.e. it becomes a negative ion.

Conduction in a solid conductor can be explained by considering that the material is in an ionized or partly ionized condition, that is to say the atoms have parted with one or more electrons and are, in fact, positive ions, the released electrons being free to move in the inter-atomic space. The dissociation of an electrolyte into positive and negative ions is a special case of ionization.

Of chief importance in electronics is the ionization of gases, which can be brought about in a number of ways. A gas may be ionized to a greater or less degree by the action of light, ultra-violet radiation, X-rays, gamma rays, etc., and by the passage of charged particles through it. If a gas-filled chamber having two electrodes is exposed to an ionizing influence, but no difference of potential is applied between the electrodes, movement of the ions due to normal thermal agitation will result in the re-combination of practically all the positive and negative ions. If, however, a potential difference exists between the electrodes, the negative ions will be accelerated in the direction of the anode and the positive ions in the direction of the cathode, and a proportion of these ions will be collected by the electrodes before they have had time to re-combine. With increase of potential the proportion of ions which are collected in this way increases until at the " saturation " voltage practically all the ions are collected as fast as they are produced. At still higher field strengths the production of ions is greatly increased by the collisions which occur between swiftly moving electrons and neutral gas atoms—a process termed IONIZATION BY COLLISION. Ionization by collision thus produces increase of current through the tube or chamber, this increase being termed GAS AMPLIFICATION.

Ionization by Collision. In a gas discharge tube a few gas atoms will inevitably be in an ionized condition as the result of such agencies as ultra-violet rays. If an electric field of sufficient strength is created between the anode and cathode of the tube the electrons resulting from the ionization will be accelerated in the direction of the anode, and a certain number of collisions will occur between electrons and neutral gas atoms. The impact may be sufficient to expel an electron from a gas atom, thus converting the atom into a positive ion. The newly released electron (secondary electron) will now be accelerated towards the anode, possibly ionizing other atoms during its journey, while the positive ion will be attracted towards the cathode, where it will re-combine with another electron, thus regaining its original neutral condition. This mechanism explains the action not only of cold cathode tubes but also of gas-filled thermionic and photo-emissive tubes, but it will be understood that in the two last-mentioned the small initial number of free electrons resulting from ionization by ultra-violet radiation, etc., are greatly outnumbered by the electrons released from the thermionic or photo-emissive cathode.

Ionization Chamber. Gas-filled envelope containing two electrodes intended for operation under conditions in which ionization by collision does not occur. (See IONIZATION.) Ionization chambers are used in radiation and particle counters.

Ionization Gauge. Device for measuring very small gas pressures. A small triode is so mounted that there is a passage for gas between its envelope and the enclosure within which the gas pressure is to be measured. The grid of the triode is held at a positive potential and the anode at a negative potential with respect to the cathode, so that normally no anode current would flow. Due, however, to the presence of gas atoms in the envelope, which are ionized by collision in the field existing between the grid and cathode, positive ions will flow through the tube to the anode, and the anode current will be a measure of the gas pressure.

Ionization Time. The time taken for the anode current in a thyratron operated under specified conditions to rise to 90 per cent of its rated peak value after the CRITICAL GRID VOLTAGE has been applied.

Ionization Voltage. The potential which an electron must traverse before it attains sufficient kinetic energy to ionize by collision an atom of a specified gas. The ionization voltage is characteristic of the particular gas, typical values being about 10·4 V for mercury vapour and 24·5 V for helium.

Ionosphere. Region of the upper atmosphere and extending over altitudes from about 50 km to about 600 km, in which exist layers of ionized gas, the ionizing agency being ultra-violet and other solar radiations. The ionosphere consists of several vaguely defined layers, the duration, altitude, depth and electron concentration of which vary throughout the day, and from season to season, and are also affected by changing conditions such as sun-spot activity.

Radio waves entering the ionosphere penetrate it to a depth dependent on their frequency. While within the ionized region the path of the wave is progressively refracted or bent. If the frequency, and hence the depth of penetration, is below a critical value, determined by the intensity of the ionization, progressive refraction causes the wave to emerge from the ionosphere and travel back to earth, as illustrated in Fig. I-10. Waves of frequencies above the critical frequency are not reflected back to earth but pass right through the ionosphere and are then lost in outer space.

The lowest layer of the ionosphere, known as the D layer, is a weakly ionized region, the ionization existing only during daylight hours. The D layer absorbs most of the energy of the sky-wave of medium-frequency transmissions. This accounts for the fact that there is practically no FADING of signals in the medium waveband during the day. Above the D layer, at an altitude of about 100 km, is the E or Kennelly–Heaviside layer, which has a critical frequency in the neighbourhood of 3 Mc/s. This layer tends to become de-ionized at night, but sufficient ionization persists in the hours of darkness to cause reflexion of medium-frequency waves, which, due to the disappearance of the D layer, can reach the E and higher layers. This accounts for medium-frequency fading at night.

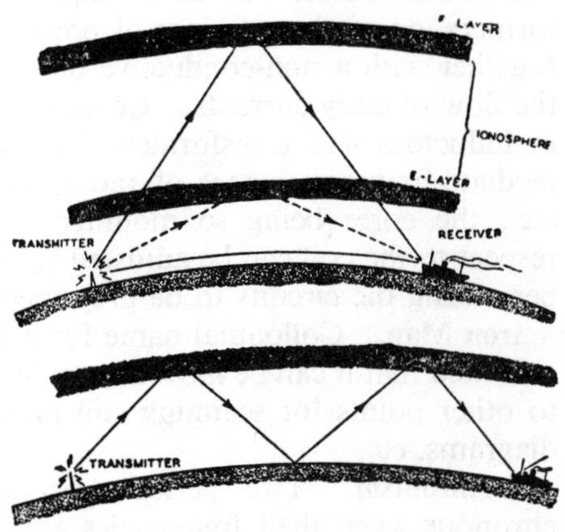

FIG. I-10.—(*above*) REFLEXION OF RADIO WAVES BY THE E AND F LAYERS OF THE IONOSPHERE. (*below*) REPEATED REFLEXION.

At a higher altitude, in the region of 200–400 km, is the F or Appleton layer, with a critical frequency ranging from 3 to 12 Mc/s. This comprises the F1 layer at 200 km, and the F2 layer at an altitude varying with time of day and season from about 280 to 400 km. It is reflexion from the F2 layer which makes possible long-distance short-wave radio communication.

Iron Cores. The inductance of a coil is not only dependent upon its geometry but is also directly proportional to the permeability of the material through which the magnetic flux passes, i.e. the permeability of the core. The inductance of a given coil can therefore be increased by the use of a ferromagnetic core. Such a core, however, tends to introduce losses due to hysteresis and to the circulation of eddy currents induced in the core material. For low-frequency operation these losses are minimized by building up the core from thin laminations of special grades of steel having low hysteresis, and by coating one side of each lamination with insulating material to restrict the flow of eddy current. In high-frequency applications in which these losses would be much greater, laminations can be replaced by IRON-DUST CORES, or by solid cores composed of one of the non-conductive MAGNETIC FERRITES. In addition to minimizing losses, a ferromagnetic core, by concentrating the magnetic field into the region immediately surrounding the coil, minimizes the risk of unwanted magnetic coupling between the coil and other parts of the circuit. Furthermore, it is possible to vary the inductance of the coil by adjusting the position of the core.

Iron-dust Cores. Cores for high-frequency inductors and transformers, consisting of slugs of powdered magnetic material bound together with a non-conductive binder, e.g. resin, thus minimizing the flow of eddy currents. Cores of this type are widely employed in inductors and transformers for the radio-frequency and intermediate-frequency stages of radio, television and radar equipment, etc., the cores being so mounted that their axial position with respect to the coil can be adjusted by means of a screw-thread, thus permitting the circuits to be pre-tuned.

Iron Man. Colloquial name for a television camera which is so mounted that it can be moved from its normal position in the studio to other points for scanning still pictures such as caption boards, diagrams, etc.

Isochronism. Two periodic phenomena are said to be isochronous when their frequencies are equal. They need not, however, be in phase. Cf. SYNCHRONISM.

Isotopes. Atoms of a chemical element which, while containing the same number of protons in their nuclei and the same number of orbiting electrons, contain different numbers of neutrons so that they have different atomic weights. The various isotopes of a given element have identical properties except for their atomic weights and those properties which are determined by their mass. See also RADIOACTIVE ISOTOPES.

J

J-aerial. Aerial of the dipole type consisting of a three-quarter wavelength vertical portion and a quarter-wavelength portion parallel to it, the feeding points being equidistant from the junction.

Jack. A socket having two or more contacts to which connexions can be made by inserting a mating plug called a jack plug. The contacts can be so arranged that insertion of the plug either makes or breaks particular circuits. Used for connecting pieces of apparatus together.

Jamming. Very severe interference deliberately produced to make it impossible to understand the wanted signal.

Johnson Noise. Unwanted voltage variations, manifest in a radio receiver as NOISE, and in other types of apparatus as spurious signals in the output, and due to the random motion of electrons in a conductor. This agitation of the electrons increases with temperature, and the effect is therefore often termed THERMAL AGITATION.

Joule. A practical unit of energy, equal to 10^7 ergs or one-watt-second.

Jumper. A conductor, i.e. a wire or cable, used to make a temporary connexion in a circuit or between two circuits.

Junction Power Rectifier. Germanium or silicon pn junctions are being increasingly used as power rectifiers. As with selenium and copper-oxide rectifiers, rectification takes place at a junction between dissimilar materials, but the junction of a germanium or silicon rectifier exists inside a single crystal of the semiconductor. This difference results in current densities of 100 A/sq. cm for germanium, compared with 0·25 A/sq. cm for selenium. Because of their small size, high efficiency and low heat dissipation, semiconductor power rectifiers offer considerable advantages over the equivalent thermionic-valve or dry-plate rectifiers. They do not require heater supplies, and the forward resistance does not alter greatly with age. The voltage drop across the rectifier is usually less than 10 per cent of that across a valve or dry-plate rectifier.

A wide range of germanium and silicon power rectifiers is now available. Generally, germanium junction rectifiers which have a lower forward resistance are used for high currents, and silicon rectifiers for applications of under about 1 A. A typical silicon rectifier for 200 mA might be the size of a small resistor.

Junction Power Transistor. In order to deliver a power output of 1 W or more a large amount of heat has to be dissipated. This transistor is welded to a copper plate which takes away the heat and also serves as an electrode.

Junction Transistor. TRANSISTOR consisting either of a zone of n-TYPE semiconductor sandwiched between two p-TYPE zones, or a zone of p-type semiconductor sandwiched between two n-type zones.

K

K-aerial. A form of dipole aerial intermediate in design between the H-AERIAL and the X-AERIAL.

K-band. Frequency band from 10,900 to 36,000 Mc/s (wavelengths of the order of 1 cm) employed in radar.

***K*-series.** The shortest group of wavelengths in the X-ray section of the electromagnetic spectrum, and corresponding to radiations associated with electrons in the *K*-SHELL.

***K*-shell.** The innermost of the hypothetical shells or spherical regions surrounding the nucleus of an atom, each shell containing one or more orbital electrons. The *K*-shell can accommodate a maximum of two electrons only. See ATOM, STRUCTURE OF.

Kathode. Alternative spelling for CATHODE.

Kation. Alternative spelling for CATION.

Kelvin Scale of Temperature. (Symbol ° K) Temperature scale in which the absolute zero of temperature (−273° C) is represented by 0° K, the value of the degree K being equal to that of the degree C. See ABSOLUTE TEMPERATURE.

Kennelly–Heaviside Layer. The " E " layer of the IONOSPHERE.

Kenotron. A high-voltage thermionic diode rectifier.

Kerr Cell. Device in which, by applying an electric field to an optically transparent medium, the plane of polarization of plane-polarized light can be rotated.

Key. A form of switch, usually spring-loaded, used for interrupting an electric current in order to produce a series of pulses in accordance with a telegraphic code.

Keying. The process of interrupting and restarting a current in order to produce telegraphic signals.

Keystone Distortion. Distortion of the shape of a rectangular image or raster in a television camera tube or television picture tube when the screen or target is set at an angle to the axis of the scanning beam so that a given angular deflexion of the beam subtends different distances at different points on the screen. In the case of a camera tube the rectangular shape is restored by suitable timing circuits. In a television receiver keystone distortion is usually the result of the two halves of a deflexion coil being unequal.

Keystone Scanning. Method of correcting keystone distortion in a television camera by modulation of the horizontal timebase waveform with a part of the vertical timebase waveform.

Kill. Colloquial expression for switching off studio lights or for suppressing an unwanted oscillation.

Kilo. (Symbol k) Prefix signifying one thousand. Thus, a kilo-ohm is 1000 ohms and one kilocycle per second (kc/s) is a frequency of 1000 cycles per second.

Kilometric Waves. Radio waves having wavelengths between 1000 and 10,000 m, corresponding to frequencies between 300 and 30 kc/s. The low-frequency or long-wave band.

Kinescope. Name employed, mainly in America, for a cathode-ray tube used in a television receiver. A television picture tube.

Kinetic Energy. The energy possessed by a body by virtue of its motion. If the mass of a body is m and its velocity v, its kinetic energy is $\frac{1}{2}mv^2$.

Kinetic Theory of Gases. Hypothesis which explains the behaviour of gases by assuming that they consist of perfectly elastic molecules in continual motion, the kinetic energy of each molecule depending upon its temperature. The molecules collide with each other and with the walls of the enclosing vessel, the latter collision being the cause of the gas pressure.

Kink. More or less abrupt departure, at some point on a graph, from the general form of the curve. A notable example is the negative resistance kink in the anode current/anode volts characteristic curve of a TETRODE.

Kirchhoff's Laws. Statement of certain fundamental facts concerning the voltages and currents in an electric circuit, namely that the algebraic sum of the electro-motive forces in a closed circuit or network is equal to the algebraic sum of the products of the resistance of each individual part of the circuit and the current flowing through that part, and that the algebraic sum of the currents meeting at any point in a circuit is zero.

Klystron. Thermionic tube suitable for use as a microwave amplifier or oscillator, in which the electron stream is velocity-modulated. The basic construction is shown in Fig. K-1. Electrons emitted from the heated cathode at one end of the tube are accelerated as the result of the positive potential applied to the accelerator grid, and proceed axially along the tube towards the collector electrode or anode, at the farther end. On the way they pass through a BUNCHER consisting of two grids connected to the two ends of a resonant circuit to which, in the amplifying klystron, the incoming signal is applied. The mean potential of the buncher grids, however, is made equal to that of the accelerator grid so that the signal causes the instantaneous potential at each grid to vary alternately above and below the accelerator grid potential. At the instant when the first buncher grid is at a potential greater than the accelerator potential, electrons approaching the first buncher will

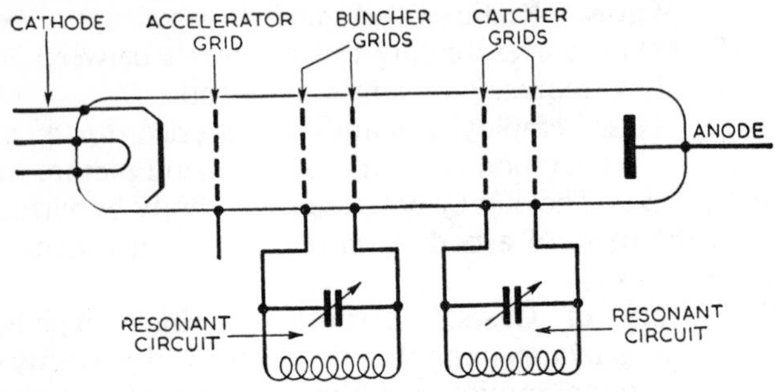

FIG. K-1.—DIAGRAMMATIC SECTION OF A KLYSTRON.

be accelerated but electrons which have just passed this grid will be retarded. Simultaneously, the second buncher grid will be at a potential lower than that of the accelerator grid, so that electrons which have passed the first buncher grid and are approaching the second buncher grid will be further retarded, but electrons which

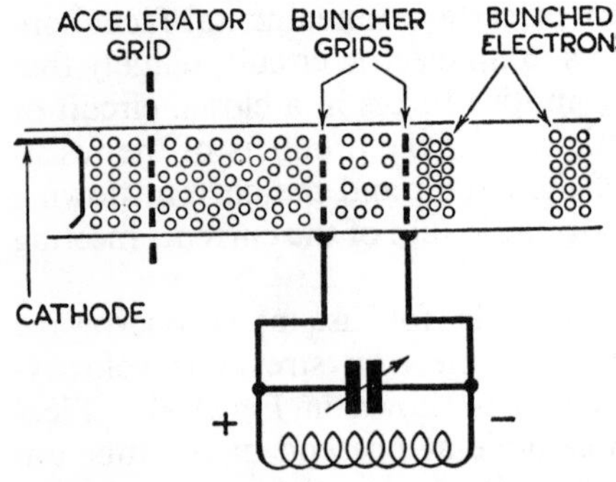

FIG. K-2.—MODULATION OF VELOCITY OF ELECTRONS BY AN ALTERNATING FIELD BETWEEN A PAIR OF BUNCHER GRIDS IN A KLYSTRON.

have already passed the second buncher grid will be accelerated. The effect of these alternate accelerations and retardations is to cause the electron stream to break up into a series of " bunches " in accordance with the signal voltage modulation (Fig. K-2). The bunches now approach the CATCHER, which, like the buncher, consists of two grids connected to the two ends of a further resonant circuit tuned to the same frequency as the buncher, the mean potential of the catcher grids being again maintained at the same value as that of the accelerator grid. The uniformly-spaced bunches of electrons leaving the buncher and approaching the catcher are

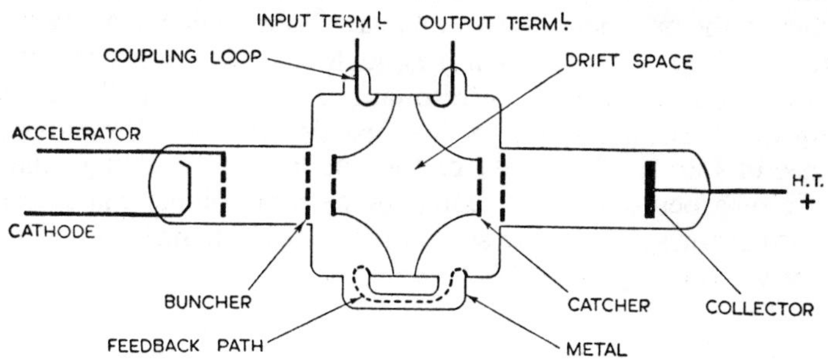

FIG. K-3.—DIAGRAMMATIC SECTION OF A CAVITY RESONATOR KLYSTRON.

therefore subjected to similar retarding forces. The distance between the first and second catcher is such, and the working conditions are so arranged, that the TRANSIT TIME of the electrons in passing through the catcher is equal to one-half of the periodic time of the oscillation to which the catcher is tuned and that each

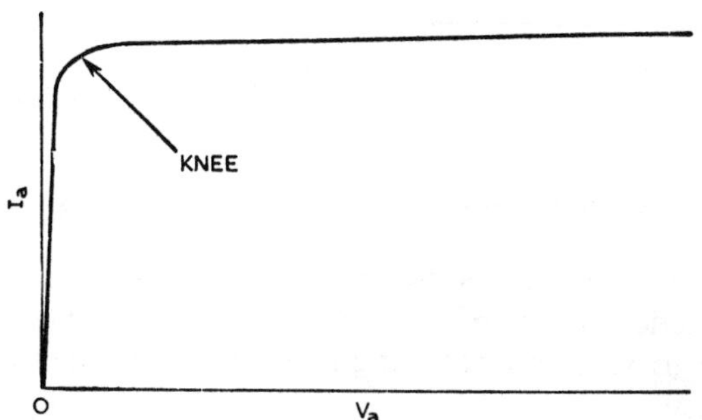

FIG. K-4.—GENERAL FORM OF THE ANODE VOLTS/ANODE CURRENT CHARACTERISTIC OF A THERMIONIC PENTODE, SHOWING KNEE.

bunch reaches the first catcher grid when that electrode is at peak negative potential so that the electrons are retarded. Since the transit time of the bunches between the two catcher grids is exactly half a period, each bunch will reach the second catcher grid when that electrode is a peak negative potential, so that there will be further retardation. It is seen, therefore, that the buncher produces a net increase in the kinetic energy of the electrons, while the catcher, in retarding the electrons, abstracts energy from them. In the amplifying application this energy is the basis of the output signal. In the oscillator klystron the energy is fed back from the catcher to the buncher. Klystrons have been made for operation at frequencies up to more than 10,000 Mc/s. In klystrons for the highest frequency ranges the resonant circuits are usually resonant cavities as indicated in Fig. K-3. See also REFLEX KLYSTRONS.

Knee of Curve. That part of the anode current/voltage characteristic of a pentode or the collector current/voltage characteristic of a transistor at which the slope of the curve changes more or less abruptly. See Fig. K-4.

L

L-band. Frequency band 390 to 1550 Mc/s employed in radar.

L-network. Network consisting of two elements possessing impedance and connected in series, their free ends being connected to one pair of terminals, and one free end and their junction to another pair of terminals. See Fig. L-1.

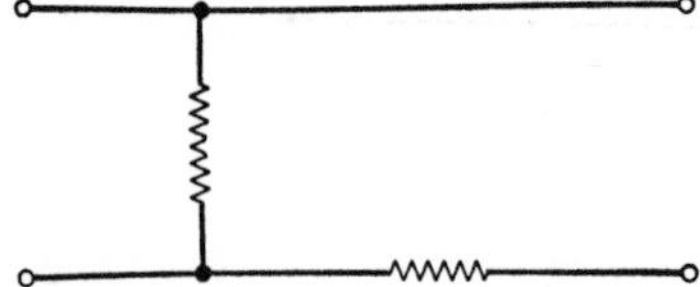

FIG. L-1.—L-NETWORK.

***L*-series.** Group of wavelengths in the X-ray section of the electromagnetic spectrum, and longer than the *K*-SERIES. They correspond to radiation resulting from the transitions of electrons to the *K*-shell.

***L*-shell.** One of the hypothetical "SHELLS" surrounding the nucleus of an atom, and situated immediately beyond the innermost or *K*-shell. It can accommodate a maximum of eight orbital electrons. Electrons in the *K*- and *L*-shells are concerned in the production of X-rays.

Lagging. Said of an alternating current which, owing to the inductance of the circuit, reaches its peak value at an instant of time later than the voltage producing it. In a purely inductive circuit, i.e. one having no resistance or capacitance, the amount of lag would be a quarter of a cycle, or, vectorially speaking, the angle of lag would be 90°. The current and voltage are then said to be in QUADRATURE.

Lambert. Unit of brightness, corresponding to the brightness of a perfectly reflecting surface when emitting or reflecting one LUMEN per square centimetre.

Laminated. The iron cores of electromagnets, inductors or transformers for operation on low-frequency alternating current are built up of laminations, insulated on one side, thus restricting the circulation of eddy currents and the resultant losses.

Lamination. A sheet iron, steel or alloy stamping used for constructing laminated iron cores.

Lamps. See EXCITER LAMPS, FLASH TUBE, GAS DISCHARGE LAMPS.

Landing Aids. Radio navigational aids for facilitating the safe landing of aircraft on the runway under conditions of poor visibility, etc. See GROUND CONTROLLED APPROACH SYSTEM and INSTRUMENT LANDING SYSTEM.

Large-screen Television. Reproduction of television pictures of sizes greater than can be produced on the screen of a cathode-ray tube. A very brilliant image is first produced on the screen of a comparatively small tube, and this is optically magnified and projected on to a large viewing screen. See PROJECTION TELEVISION.

Lash-up. Colloquial term for a temporary or extemporized assemblage of apparatus for the purpose of experiment or to tide over an emergency.

Lateral Inversion. Said of an optical image, e.g. a television picture, which has been reversed so that the right-hand side appears on the left, and vice versa. Usually due to the connexions to the horizontal scanning coils being reversed.

Lattice, Crystal. The pattern of atoms in a crystal.

Lattice Chart. Chart showing the positions of, say, three fixed radio transmitters radiating synchronized pulses, and marked with a series of hyperbolae, i.e. lines any point on which has a fixed difference of distances from two of the transmitters. Used in PULSE-MODULATED NAVIGATIONAL SYSTEMS for determining the position of an aircraft or a ship. See also HYPERBOLIC NAVIGATIONAL SYSTEMS.

Lattice Network. Network consisting of four elements possessing impedance connected as shown in Fig. L-2 to form a closed circuit, one pair of non-adjacent junctions being connected to the input terminals and the other pair to the output terminals. Also termed a BRIDGE NETWORK.

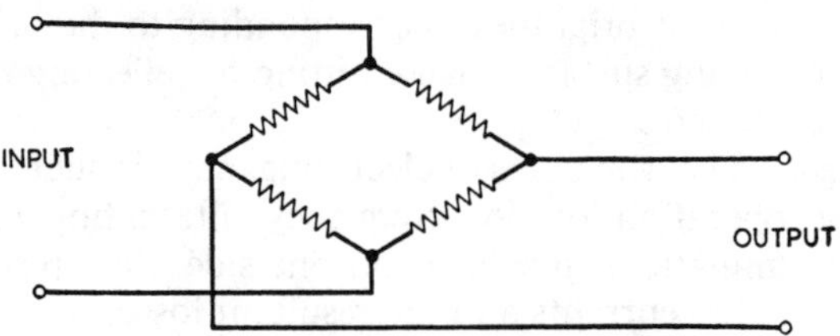

FIG. L-2.—LATTICE OR BRIDGE NETWORK.

Law. A scientific " law " is a general statement which, within the limits of experimental observation, faithfully describes a phenomenon or a relationship which will always occur under specified conditions.

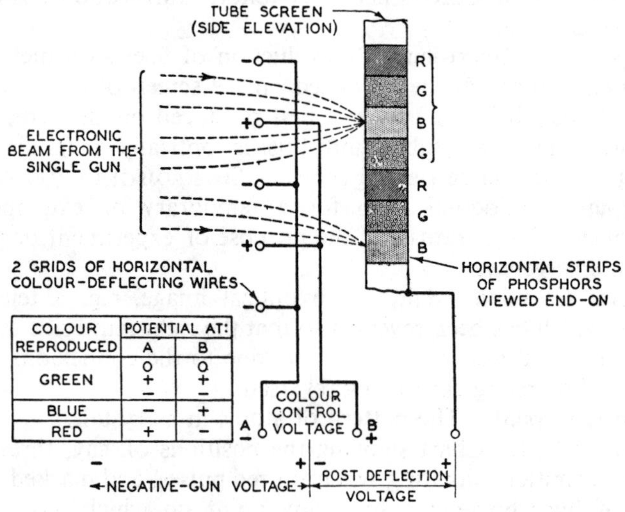

COLOUR REPRODUCED	POTENTIAL AT: A	B
GREEN	O + −	O + −
BLUE	−	+
RED	+	−

FIG. L-3.—DIAGRAMMATIC REPRESENTATION OF A COLOUR TELEVISION SYSTEM EMPLOYING A PICTURE TUBE OF THE LAWRENCE TYPE.

Lawrence Tube. A form of picture tube for colour television, having a single electron gun, the beam from which scans the luminescent screen in horizontal lines, each line consisting of three closely-spaced lines of three phosphors producing red, green and blue luminescence respectively. The beam is deflected to the line of appropriate colour by information contained in the signal waveform. See Fig. L-3.

Lead. Wire or cable used to connect two pieces of apparatus together. Thus, the wires connecting a loudspeaker to a receiver or amplifier are spoken of as the loudspeaker leads.

Lead-in. (1) Lead connecting an aerial to the aerial terminal of a receiver.

(2) The lead-in wires of an electron tube are wires connected internally to the various electrodes and passing through the envelope of the tube by means of gas-tight seals. The outer ends of the leads are usually connected to rigid contact pins which can be plugged into a mating socket for connexion to the external circuit. In some of the smaller types of tube the lead-in wires are soldered directly into the circuit wiring.

Lead Inductance. The lead-in wires of a thermionic valve possess a small but definite amount of inductance. At low frequencies their reactance is small and of no particular consequence, but at the higher frequencies it is appreciable and is one of the factors which limit the upper frequency at which the valve will operate satisfactorily.

Leading. Said of an alternating current which, owing to the capacitive reactance of the circuit, reaches its peak value at an instant of time before the voltage producing it. In a purely capacitive circuit, i.e. one possessing no resistance and no inductance, the amount of lead will be one-quarter of a waveperiod or, vectorially speaking, the angle of lead will be 90°. The current and voltage are then said to be in QUADRATURE.

Leading Edge of a Pulse. That part of the waveform of a PULSE which occurs first in time. See Fig. L-4.

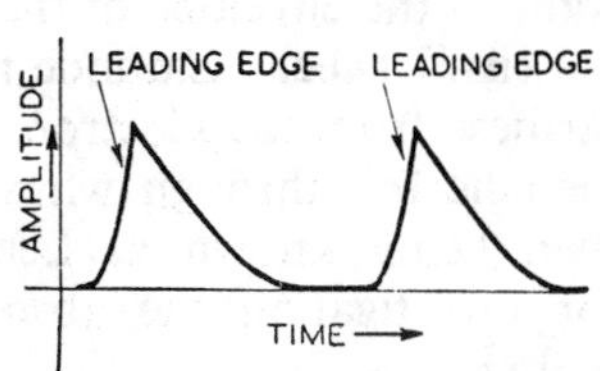

FIG. L-4.—PULSE WAVEFORM, INDICATING LEADING EDGE.

Leak. A high-resistance path such as may be deliberately included in a circuit to permit the gradual discharge of a capacitor; or an unwanted path of high resistance through which current can flow between two conductors which are intended to be insulated from each other, or between one conductor and earth.

Leak, Grid. See GRID LEAK.

Leakage Current. Electric current which flows from a point of high potential to a point of lower potential via a (usually unwanted) high-resistance path.

Leakage Flux. That part of the magnetic flux which is not confined to the desired path, e.g. that part of the flux in a transformer which does not link with the secondary winding. Leakage flux may cause unwanted electromotive forces to be induced in other parts of a circuit.

Leakance. The reciprocal of the insulation resistance, that is to say, the reciprocal of the resistance, measured under specified conditions, between two conductors nominally separated by insulating material.

Leaky Grid Detector. See CUMULATIVE GRID RECTIFICATION.

Lecher Wires. Tunable resonant circuit consisting of two stretched parallel wires, along which a short-circuiting strip can slide. It is used in microwave techniques as a tuned circuit, as an impedance matching device or as a choke, and also in wavelength measurement. In the latter application a meter is connected to the two wires at one end, the outer ends being left free. The signal whose wavelength is to be measured is induced into the loop represented by the two wires and the short-circuiting link, and the link is moved until resonance is achieved, indicated by a kick in the meter. There are two positions of the link at which resonance is indicated, and the electrical distance between these points is one-quarter of the wavelength. It should be noted that the electrical length is a few per cent more than the measured distance.

Lenard Rays. CATHODE RAYS which have passed through the walls of the envelope of the tube in which they were produced.

Lenard Tube. Cathode-ray tube in which the end of the envelope farthest from the electron gun is provided with a window of thin metallic foil through which the cathode rays may pass, the rays then being known as Lenard rays. Used, among other things, for investigating the absorption and scattering of electrons by matter.

Lens (Electron). An electric or magnetic field of such configuration that it produces a focusing effect upon a beam of electrons similar to that of an optical lens on a beam of light. See ELECTRON LENS and ELECTRON OPTICS.

Lens, Electrostatic. An ELECTRON LENS comprising an electric field of suitable configuration.

Lens, Magnetic. An ELECTRON LENS comprising a magnetic field of suitable configuration.

Lenticular. Shaped like, or acting as, a double convex lens.

Level. A reference value for a particular quantity. See BLACK LEVEL and REFERENCE LEVEL.

Light. Electromagnetic radiation of wavelengths between approximately 4000 and 7000 Ångström units, and producing the sensation of vision. The different colours are represented by different wavelengths as indicated in the spectrum shown in the accompanying table.

WAVELENGTHS OF LIGHT

Wavelengths (Ångström Units)	Colour
Below 3600	Ultra-violet and other invisible radiation
3600–4300	Violet
4300–4550	Indigo
4550–4920	Blue
4920–5500	Green
5500–5880	Yellow
5880–6470	Orange
6470–7600	Red
Above 7600	Infra-red invisible radiation including heat and radio waves

Light, Ambient. The amount of illumination prevailing at a particular location.

Light Quantum. A single and coherent train of light waves representing a QUANTUM of radiant energy and equal to $h\nu$, where ν is the frequency of the radiation in cycles per second and h is PLANCK'S CONSTANT ($6{\cdot}624 \times 10^{-27}$ erg-seconds).

Light, Velocity of. Like all forms of electromagnetic radiation, light travels at a mean velocity of $2{\cdot}9978 \times 10^8$ metres per second (say 3×10^8 m/sec).

Light-sensitive Cell. A device in which incident light produces the emission of electrons, or a change of electrical resistance, or the production of an electromotive force. See PHOTO-ELECTRIC CELL.

Lighthouse Valve. Thermionic valve of American design, corresponding to the British disk-seal valve, and so called on account of its general shape. It has planar electrodes of small dimensions, closely spaced, and components such as resistors and capacitors are included inside the envelope, as indicated in Fig. L-5.

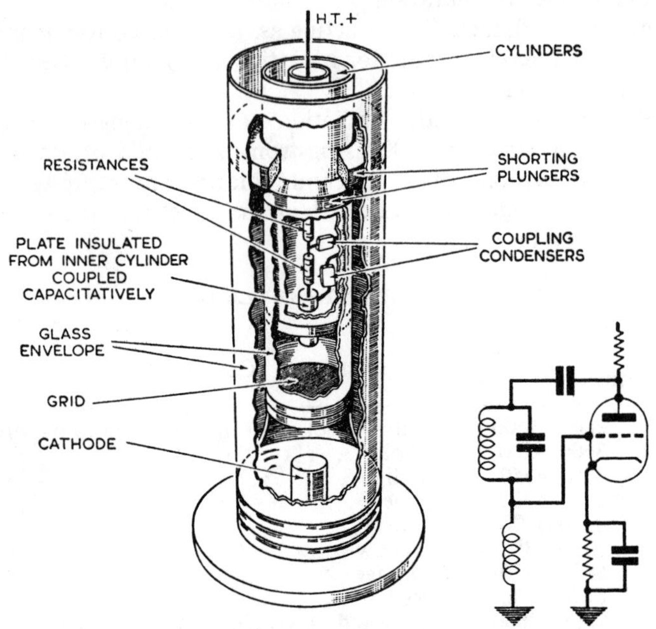

FIG. L-5.—GENERAL CONSTRUCTION AND EQUIVALENT CIRCUIT OF A LIGHTHOUSE VALVE.

Lightning. Spark discharge of electricity between two charged clouds or between a charged cloud and earth.

Lightning Arrester (Protector). Device for protecting apparatus from damage by lightning discharge. See SURGE ARRESTER.

Limb of Core. Part of the magnetic core of a transformer or inductor which is surrounded by the winding. See Fig. L-6.

Limiter Valve. In general, a thermionic valve operated in such a way that it suppresses certain parts of a signal, and more particularly those parts which exceed a certain amplitude. Specifically, a limiting valve in a receiver for frequency-modulated transmissions to remove any amplitude-modulated component present in the signal before it reaches the detector valve. Other applications of limiter valves are for reducing the amplitude of interfering (noise) pulses (see NOISE LIMITER), and in pulse-shaping circuits.

Limiting Values. In published valve data, maximum (or minimum) values specified for circuit parameters and operating conditions (voltages, etc.) which must be observed in the interest of performance and/or valve life.

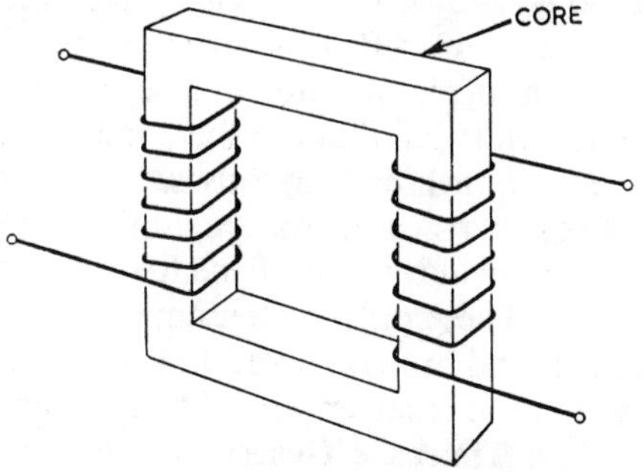

CORE

FIG. L-6.—THE WINDINGS OF AN INDUCTOR OR TRANSFORMER ENCIRCLE THE "LIMBS" OF THE CORE.

Line. (1) A conductor (wire, cable, etc.) connecting two pieces of apparatus, e.g. the wires from a telephone subscriber's instrument to the telephone exchange.

(2) In television a line is a very narrow horizontal strip of picture produced by one horizontal sweep of the electron beam across the screen of the picture tube. In the British television system the picture transmission occupies 405 line periods, of which 377 correspond to actual picture information, the remaining periods being utilized for transmitting the frame synchronizing pulses.

Line Blanking. Reduction of the amplitude of the television video signal to below black level at the end of each line period to permit the transmission of the line synchronizing pulses.

Line Flyback e.h.t. Method of producing the extra-high-tension supply in a television receiver by rectifying high-voltage pulses generated in the line output transformer when the horizontal scanning current, having reached its peak value, decays rapidly during the flyback period.

Line Frequency. The number of horizontal scanning periods (line periods) occurring in one second in a television transmission. Since in the British system there are 405 line periods per complete picture and 25 complete pictures are transmitted per second, the line frequency is $405 \times 25 = 10{,}125$ lines per second.

Line of Force. Imaginary line drawn in an electric or a magnetic field such that the direction of the line at any point is the direction of the electric (or magnetic) force at that point.

Line Output Transformer. The transformer whereby the output of the line timebase generator in a television receiver is transferred to the horizontal scanning coils.

Line Output Valve. The final amplifying valve in the line timebase generator of a television receiver.

Line Scan. Process of sweeping the picture area in a television camera or picture tube in a series of horizontal lines, one below the other, thus building up the complete picture.

Line Synchronizing Pulses. Series of negative-going pulses in the BLACKER-THAN-BLACK region of the television waveform and occurring at the end of the line scan, following the picture information. These pulses, after amplification, are separated from the video signal and are employed to synchronize the line timebase generated within the receiver with the scanning in the television studio.

Line Timebase Generator. A device consisting of one or more thermionic valves and their associated circuits, and producing a current of sawtooth waveform at line frequency for application to the deflexion coils for horizontal scanning in the television receiver.

Line Up. To adjust the constants of a number of circuits or networks so that they operate in the desired manner. For example, the adjustment of the primary and secondary circuit of one or more intermediate-frequency transformers in a radio receiver so that they are all accurately tuned to the intermediate frequency.

Line Voltage. The voltage existing between the two lines of an electric supply, and more particularly those of the public electricity mains.

Linear. Said of the relationship between two quantities when the value of one quantity is strictly proportional to the value of the other, so that the graph representing their relationship is a straight line.

Linear Accelerator. Device for accelerating charged particles to very high velocities in a straight line. In the travelling-wave linear accelerator high-power pulsed waves, generated in a MAGNETRON, travel along a corrugated waveguide into which is also injected a high-velocity electron beam produced by an ELECTRON GUN. Electrons gain energy from the wave, and achieve final velocities closely approximating to the speed of light. The accelerated electrons may be directed on a target for the production of high-energy X-rays for medical or industrial purposes, or may be allowed to pass through a window for use in various research processes.

Linear Amplifier. Amplifier in which the output is strictly proportional to the input voltage.

Linear Detector (Linear Rectifier). Detector (rectifier) in which the instantaneous value of the unidirectional output current is directly proportional to the instantaneous value of the alternating input voltage.

Linear Network. A network the electrical constants (resistance, inductance and capacitance, etc.) of which are independent of the current flowing in the network.

Linear Resistance. Resistance such that the current flowing through it is always strictly proportional to the voltage applied, all other conditions, e.g. temperature, remaining constant. In other words, a resistance which obeys Ohm's Law.

Linear Timebase. A timebase of such waveform that, when it is applied to the deflexion system of a cathode-ray tube, the light spot traverses the luminescent screen at constant velocity during the STROKE, returning to the starting position rapidly during the FLYBACK period.

Linear Variable Resistor. A variable resistor, the change of resistance of which is directly proportional to the angle through which the control knob is turned. Cf. LOGARITHMIC RESISTOR.

Linearity. The degree to which the relationship between two variable quantities is LINEAR.

Linearity Control. A variable component included in the circuit of a timebase generator to permit the user to correct any slight incidental departure from linearity in the timebase waveform.

Linearity Correction. The adjustment of one or more constants in a timebase generator circuit to ensure linearity of the timebase waveform.

Linkage. (1) Chemical bonding, and more particularly covalency bonding between atoms.

(2) Condition when magnetic flux passes through the turns of a coil, a change in the linkage resulting in the production of an electromotive force.

Lissajous Figures. Patterns produced on the screen of a cathode-ray rube when two sinusoidal voltages of different but simply-related frequencies are applied to the horizontal and vertical deflecting systems. See Fig. L-7.

Litzendraht. (Abbreviation Litz.) Composite conductor designed for use in high-frequency circuits, and composed of a large number of fine wires, each separately insulated, and interwoven in a special way. This construction ensures a high ratio of surface area per unit length to cross-sectional area, and thus reduces the SKIN EFFECT, i.e. the increase of the a.c. resistance of a conductor due to the tendency for high-frequency currents to travel along the surface of the wire.

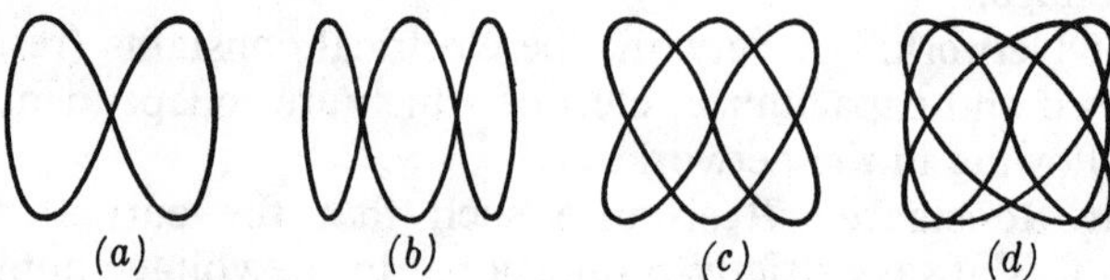

FIG. L-7.—TYPICAL LISSAJOUS' FIGURES, CORRESPONDING TO FREQUENCY RATIOS (a) 2 : 1, (b) 3 : 1, (c) 3 : 2, (d) 4 : 3.

Load. That part of an electric circuit in which the output is developed, or that part of an electrical apparatus in which the output is applied.

Load, Anode. Load included in the anode circuit of a thermionic valve. See ANODE LOAD.

Load Line. A line drawn across the family of anode current/anode voltage characteristics of a thermionic valve to represent the

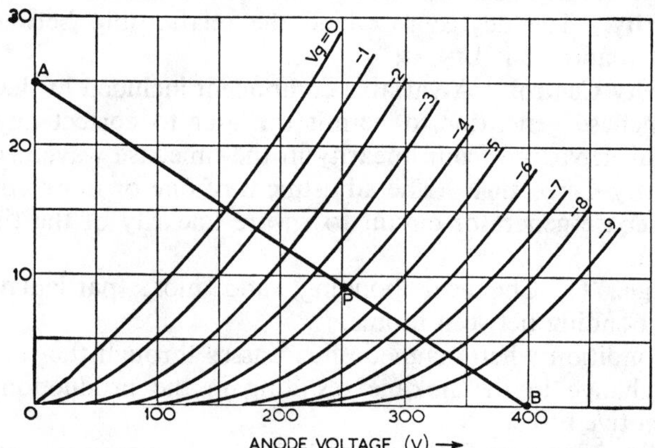

FIG. L-8.—FAMILY OF ANODE VOLTS/ANODE CURRENT CHARACTERISTICS FOR A TYPICAL HIGH-VACUUM TRIODE, SHOWING LOAD LINE AB CORRESPONDING TO AN ANODE LOAD OF 16 kΩ AND OPERATING POINT AT P.

relationship between the anode current and anode voltage for a given anode load and with variations of control-grid voltage. Its slope is determined by the load impedance, and its position by the steady or rest value of the anode voltage and the steady value of the grid bias. See Fig. L-8.

Loading. The addition of inductance to a circuit as, for example, to an aerial in order to increase its natural frequency, or to a transmission line in order to reduce the attenuation of signals within a specified frequency band.

Loading Coil. A coil included in a circuit in order to increase the inductance of the circuit.

Local Oscillation. Radio-frequency oscillation generated in a radio receiver of the supersonic heterodyne type, and used to BEAT with the incoming signal and thus to produce the intermediate-frequency carrier.

Local Oscillator. Thermionic oscillator used in a supersonic heterodyne receiver for generating the local oscillation. It may be an independent valve, usually a triode, or it may be a triode electrode system incorporated with a MIXER valve in the same envelope, or it may be certain electrodes in an electron-coupled FREQUENCY CHANGER VALVE.

Localizer. A form of radio beacon used in INSTRUMENT LANDING SYSTEMS for aircraft. Located about 750 ft beyond the "stop" end of an airfield runway, it radiates two signals of different frequencies from two aerials whose POLAR DIAGRAMS overlap in such a way that their signals are of equal strength along the centre of the runway. In the receiving equipment fitted in the aircraft the two signals are applied to a centre-zero instrument. When the indicating pointer of the instrument is in the central (zero) position the pilot knows that he is correctly aligned with the runway.

Location (Radiolocation). Original term for the process later known as RADAR, i.e. the determination of the position of objects by radio.

Locator Beacon. Form of radio beacon installed at an airfield and radiating a Morse identity signal and a continuous signal for operating a radio compass. The pilot of an aircraft can "home" on this beacon until he is near enough to the airfield to pick up the instrument landing system LOCALIZER signals.

Locking. (1) Effect whereby two thermionic oscillators operating at slightly different frequencies are pulled into synchronism by coupling between them.

(2) Adjustment of one part of a circuit to ensure that incidental variations in other parts of the circuit do not greatly affect the output. For example, adjustments (hold controls) are provided in

the vertical and horizontal timebase circuits of a television receiver in order to correct variations of scanning frequency which are too great to be dealt with by the normal synchronizing pulses.

Lodge Valve. Early form of cold-cathode rectifier tube.

Loft Aerial. A receiving aerial suitable for erection in the loft of a house, and in particular a television aerial of this type. A common form consists of two quarter-wave rod aerials mounted at an angle of 45° in the form of an inverted V.

Logarithmic Decrement. Characteristic quantity for an oscillation the amplitude of which decays in geometrical progression. It is given by the Naperian logarithm of the ratio of the peak values in the same direction of two successive oscillations.

Logarithmic Resistor. A variable resistor in which the resistance remaining in circuit is directly or indirectly proportional to the logarithm of the amount by which the variable contact is moved. Potentiometers and variable capacitors can also be obtained with logarithmic characteristics.

Long-tailed Pair. Arrangement of two similar thermionic valves operated with equal anode loads and with a common cathode bias resistor (Fig. L-9). A.C. inputs of equal amplitude and in phase,

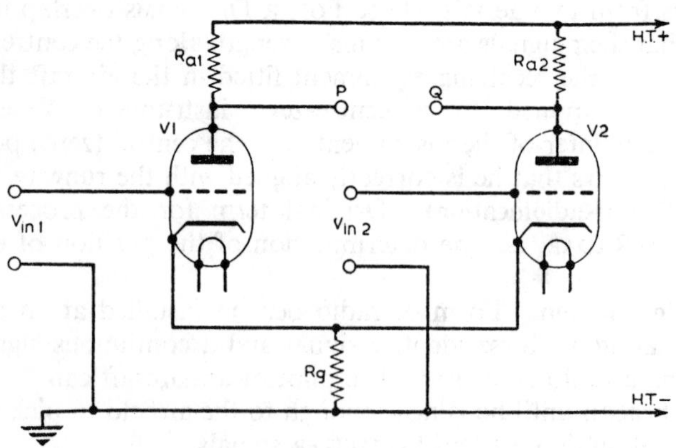

FIG. L-9.—BASIC CIRCUIT OF A LONG-TAILED PAIR.

or equal d.c. signals applied to the two control grid circuits produce no output voltage between terminals P and Q. A.C. signals of equal amplitude but having a phase difference, or unequal d.c. signals, produce a difference of potential between terminals P and Q

Long Waves. Radio waves having wavelengths between 1000 and 10,000 m, corresponding to frequencies from 300 kc/s down to 30 kc/s. The low-frequency or kilometric waves.

Loop. A circuit with " go " and " return " conductors.

Loop Aerial. Another term for FRAME AERIAL.

Loose Coupling. Coupling between two circuits such that the COUPLING COEFFICIENT is small, i.e. the rate at which energy is transferred from one circuit to the other is low. Also termed weak coupling.

Loran. Radio navigation system of the HYPERBOLIC TYPE and developed in America chiefly for long-range navigation over the sea. Chains of transmitters radiate high-power 50 μsec pulses on frequencies in the order of 2 Mc/s. Adjacent transmitters use the same pulse-repetition frequency, but each pair of transmitters uses different pulse-repetition frequencies. Each transmitter except those at the ends of the chain is a double transmitter, forming part of two adjacent pairs.

Loss. Loss of power (attenuation) occurring in a transmission system, expressed in decibels. Negative gain.

Loss, Dielectric. Power dissipated as heat in a dielectric when in an oscillating field.

Loudspeaker. A telephone receiver instrument capable of radiating a large volume of sound. Electromagnetic speakers employ a vibrating reed or a balanced armature to drive a diaphragm; condenser loudspeakers operate by electrostatic action; crystal loudspeakers by piezo-electric action, and in moving-coil loudspeakers or electrodynamic speakers a small flexibly-mounted coil carrying the audio-frequency current moves longitudinally in a strong magnetic field and drives a cone-shaped diaphragm.

Low-definition Television. Television system in which the picture area is scanned in less than 200 lines.

Low Frequency. (1) A relative term used to distinguish waves or oscillations of a particular frequency or band of frequencies from those of higher frequency.

(2) More specifically applied to radio waves of frequencies between 30 and 300 kc/s, corresponding to the LONG WAVE range.

(3) The term is also loosely applied to the audio-frequency signals in a radio receiver to distinguish them from the " high frequency ", i.e. the radio- and intermediate-frequency signals.

Low-frequency Amplifier. Amplifier for magnifying audio-frequency signals.

Low-level Modulation. Modulation of a radio-frequency carrier in a stage prior to the final amplifier stage.

Low-pass Filter. A FILTER CIRCUIT which will transmit only signals the frequency of which is below a specified value. See Fig. L-10.

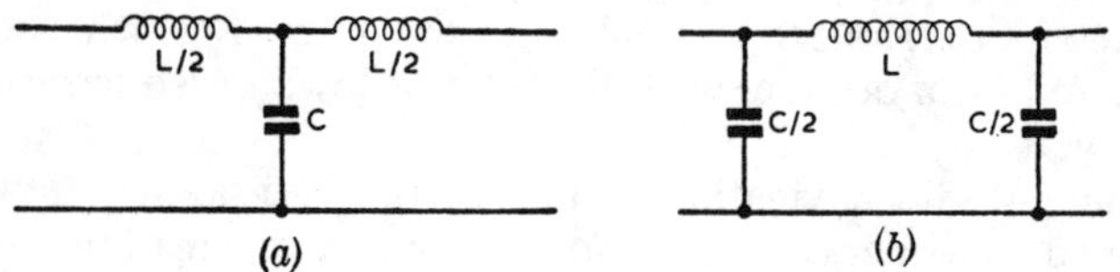

FIG. L-10.—TWO TYPICAL FORMS OF LOW-PASS FILTER, (a) T-NETWORK AND (b) π-NETWORK.

In each case the filter will pass all frequencies below f = $1/\pi\sqrt{LC}$ where is in c/s, L in henrys and C in farads.

Low-power Modulation. Another term for LOW-LEVEL MODULATION.

Low Tension. (l.t.) Term used to denote the circuits concerned in the heating of the cathodes of thermionic valves, and the voltages and currents in those circuits.

Low-tension Battery. Battery which supplies the heating current for the filaments of thermionic valves.

Lumen. Unit of LUMINOUS FLUX, equal to the amount of light emitted per unit solid angle by a standard international candle. One lumen thus falls upon unit area at unit distance from a standard candle.

Luminescence. The emission of light as the result of any stimulus other than heat. If the stimulus is heat the emission of light is termed incandescence.

Luminescent Screen. Surface in a cathode-ray rube coated with a PHOSPHOR which emits light when bombarded with high-velocity electrons.

Luminous Flux. The amount of light emitted from a light source.

Luminous Intensity. Amount of light flux emitted by a point light source into a unit solid angle.

Lux. Luminous intensity equal to one lumen per square metre.

M

m-derived Filters. Filters in which the attenuation, phase and image impedance vary differently with frequency, derived from a constant-k prototype filter, usually to obtain more desirable impedance characteristics.

Magnadur. A ceramic material used for making permanent magnets. It consists basically of sintered oxide of iron and oxide of barium, and is therefore non-metallic, although possessing ferromagnetic properties. Because of its ceramic structure it is a good insulator and can therefore be used in an alternating field without appreciable eddy-current loss. Mechanical shock or normal temperature variations do not affect a magnadur permanent magnet. Magnadur is often used for permanent-magnet focusing units for television picture tubes.

Magnet. A piece of one of the so-called ferromagnetic materials which has been " magnetized ", that is to say has acquired, either permanently or temporarily, the power of attracting or repelling other pieces of similar material and of exerting a mechanical force on a neighbouring conductor carrying an electric current. See also MAGNETISM, PERMANENT MAGNET and ELECTROMAGNET.

Magnet, Sintered. Permanent magnet made from an alloy or mixture in powder form, moulded to shape and welded into a homogeneous mass by heat and pressure. This process is used for making large numbers of identical small magnets of complex shape.

Magnet Poles. Regions in a magnet from which the magnetic effects appear to emanate.

Magnet Yoke. Strictly, that part of the magnetic circuit of an electromagnetic system, such as a transformer, which does not carry the windings. However, the term is frequently applied to the magnetic circuit as a whole.

Magnetic Amplifier. Device consisting of one or more ferromagnetic cores with windings so arranged and connected that the alternating current flowing in one winding can be modified by causing saturation of the core by means of direct or low-frequency alternating current flowing in a further winding.

Magnetic Circuit. The path, consisting of ferromagnetic material, possibly with a small air-gap, through which MAGNETIC FLUX passes.

Magnetic Component. That component of an electromagnetic radiation which has the properties of an oscillating magnetic field.

Magnetic Deflexion. Deflexion of the electron beam in a cathode-ray tube, and hence of the light spot on the screen, by the application of a transverse magnetic field. See also article on CATHODE-RAY TUBES.

Magnetic Elongation. The small increase in the length of magnetic materials when magnetized. See also MAGNETOSTRICTION.

Magnetic Ferrites. Group of ferrites having magnetic properties and also a ceramic structure which renders them good insulators. Certain of these materials, e.g. barium ferrite, are suitable for the manufacture of permanent magnets. The majority, however, such as manganese–zinc ferrite, nickel–zinc ferrite and magnesium–manganese ferrite, are suitable for use as core material for transformers, inductors, etc. Due to their insulating properties, eddy-current losses are negligible, and the materials can therefore be used in high-frequency applications, such as for the cores of radio-frequency and intermediate-frequency transformers, television line-output transformers and deflexion yokes, wide-band transformers, inbuilt radio aerials (see FERRITE-ROD AERIALS) and in computer circuits.

Magnetic Field. Region in the neighbourhood of a magnet or of a conductor carrying an electric current, over which the magnetic forces can be detected.

Magnetic Field Strength. (Symbol H) See MAGNETIZING FORCE.

Magnetic Flux. (Symbol Φ) Concept of the magnetic properties of a magnet as appearing to " flow " along definite paths termed lines of magnetic force, the total number of such lines of force issuing from a particular magnet pole being the magnetic flux. The m.k.s. unit is the weber. If the flux linking one turn in a circuit changes by one weber in one second an electromotive force of one volt will be induced in that turn. The c.g.s. unit was the maxwell; one weber $= 10^8$ maxwells.

Magnetic Flux Density. (Symbol B) Also termed the magnetic induction. The magnetic flux passing through unit area of a magnetic field normal to the direction of the magnetic force. It is expressed in terms of webers per square metre, or in terms of the c.g.s. unit the gauss (one gauss $= 10^{-4}$ webers per square metre).

Magnetic Focusing. Use of a magnetic lens to focus the beam in a cathode-ray tube. In Fig. M-1 is shown the path of a divergent electron E, before entering the magnetic field, while passing through the field, and after leaving the field. It will be understood that a divergent beam of electrons, starting from P, would be brought to a focus at F. The path of each electron is the result of three forces —the acceleration imparted by the electron gun, the radial force due to the mutual repulsion of the electrons forming the beam and the force due to the magnetic lens. The three forces are mutually

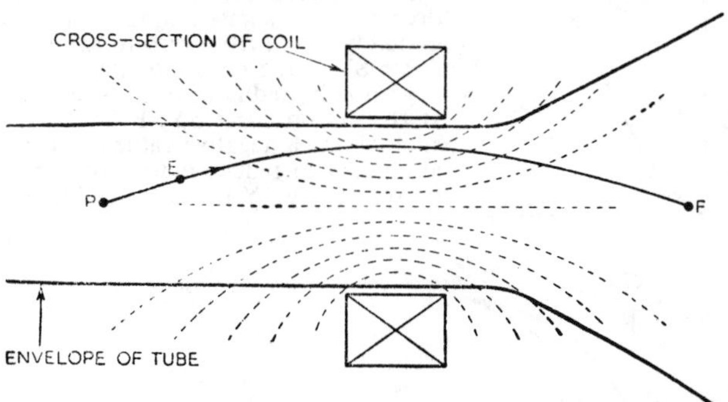

FIG. M-1.—EFFECT OF A MAGNETIC FOCUSING FIELD ON A DIVERGENT ELECTRON E.

The broken lines represent the magnetic field and the heavy line the path of the electron.

at right angles, and this fact, combined with the contour of the magnetic field, renders the final trajectory a spiral of decreasing radius.

Magnetic Hysteresis. Effect observed when a piece of magnetic material is gradually magnetized and the magnetizing force then progressively reduced. The magnetization curve under conditions of decreasing magnetizing force is not coincident with the curve for increasing magnetizing force. See Fig. M-2.

Magnetic Hysteresis Loop. Graph showing the relationship between the magnetizing force H and the magnetic induction B over a complete magnetizing cycle in which H is progressively increased from zero to a maximum in one direction, reduced to zero, reversed and increased to a maximum in the reverse direction, and then decreased to zero again. The graph is a closed figure of the form indicated in Fig. M-3.

Magnetic Hysteresis Loss. The power lost in taking a mass of magnetic material through a complete magnetizing cycle. The loss is proportional to the area enclosed by the hysteresis loop.

Magnetic Induction. See MAGNETIC FLUX DENSITY.

Magnetic Leakage. That part of the magnetic flux which leaves the desired magnetic path and can therefore affect nearby apparatus or circuits.

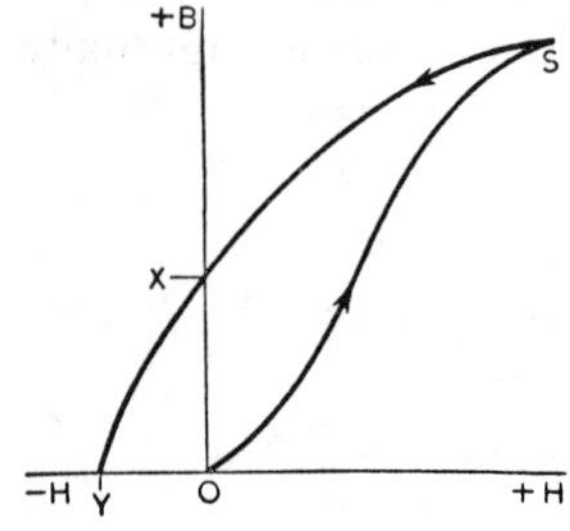

FIG. M-2.—MAGNETIC HYSTERESIS EFFECT.

Curve OS is the relation between magnetizing force H and magnetic induction B when H is gradually raised from zero to saturation value. Curve SY is the corresponding curve when H is gradually reduced from saturation value. At H = O on curve SY, B has still a positive value X, and a negative value of H (= Y) must be applied to reduce B to zero. X is termed the retentivity; Y the coercive force.

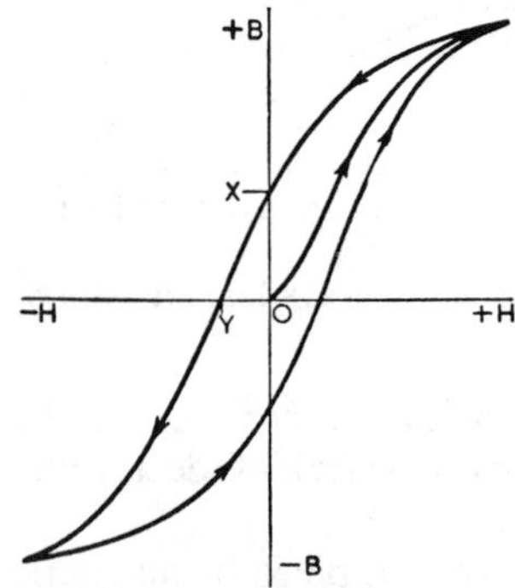

FIG. M-3.—GENERAL FORM OF THE MAGNETIC HYSTERESIS LOOP.

Magnetic Lens. Magnet or system of magnets producing a field which has a similar effect on a beam of electrons as an optical lens has on a beam of light. See MAGNETIC FOCUSING.

Magnetic Lines of Force. Concept of a magnetic field as being filled with non-material, non-intersecting lines of force, each line leaving the magnet at one pole and re-entering the magnet at the opposite pole. The direction of the magnetic force at any point is along the line of force passing through that point.

Magnetic Oxide. Certain oxides of iron possess ferromagnetic properties. When mixed in powder form with other substances the resultant material is suitable for the production of efficient and very light permanent magnets. Manufacturing techniques include grinding, mixing, pressing to shape and heat treatment.

Magnetic Permeability. (Symbol μ) Ratio of the magnetic flux density B to the magnetizing force H. The absolute permeability of free space, μ_0, in the electromagnetic system of units is unity. The relative permeability of a material or medium is the ratio of the flux density produced by a given magnetizing force to that produced in a vacuum by the same magnetizing force.

Magnetic Pole, Unit. A unit magnetic pole is one such that, if located 1 cm away from an exactly similar pole *in vacuo* the mutual force of repulsion would be 1 dyne.

Magnetic Screen. Barrier made of permeable material and used to prevent or limit the penetration of a magnetic field into a given region. For example, a cathode-ray tube is often fitted with a Mu-metal screen in order to prevent interference by the magnetic fields of components such as transformers.

Magnetic-tape Recorder. Apparatus for recording electrical signals of audio or video frequency as variations of magnetic strength along a wire or tape of magnetic material. See TAPE-RECORDING.

Magnetism. Name given to a group of phenomena resulting from the special properties of certain substances known as magnetic substances. Under certain conditions a mass of magnetic substance becomes " magnetized ", that is to say, it acquires, either temporarily or more or less permanently, the power to attract other pieces of magnetic material. It is then called a magnet. A magnet exerts a force of attraction or repulsion on another piece of magnetized material, and when freely suspended a magnet tends to orient itself in the north–south direction. The properties of a magnet appear to emanate from two regions called the poles of the magnet, and it is the line joining these poles which points north–south when a magnet is suspended. The poles are therefore known as the " north " or north-seeking and the " south " or south-seeking poles. Like poles, i.e. two north or two south poles, repel each other; unlike poles attract each other. A magnet also exerts a mechanical force on a conductor carrying an electric current, and conversely a conductor carrying an electric current behaves in many respects as a magnet.

Magnetism, Theories of. Many theories, or rather, hypotheses, have been advanced from time to time to account for the phenomena of magnetism. In one of the earliest a magnet was envisaged as emitting an impalpable medium or fluid—hence the somewhat archaic terms MAGNETIC FLUX, PERMEABILITY, etc. In the later

" molecular " theory of magnetism each molecule of a magnetic substance was considered to be a small permanent magnet, the molecular magnets normally arranging themselves in closed mag-

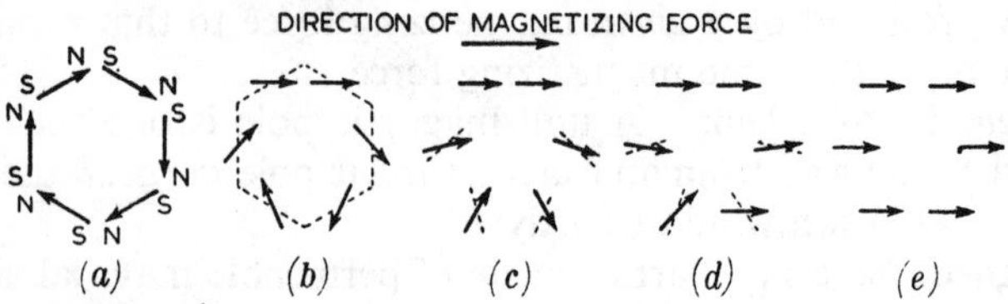

FIG. M-4.—REPRESENTATION OF PROGRESSIVE STAGES OF MAGNETIZATION, BASED ON THE CONCEPT OF MOLECULAR MAGNETS.

At (a) there is no magnetizing force and the magnetic chains are closed. From (b) to (e), re-orientation of molecular magnets results in increasing values of H.

netic chains as suggested in Fig. M-4(a), so that the net effect of each chain was nil. On the application of a magnetizing force or field the closed chains are ruptured, and the molecular magnets tend to re-orient themselves in the general direction of the applied field

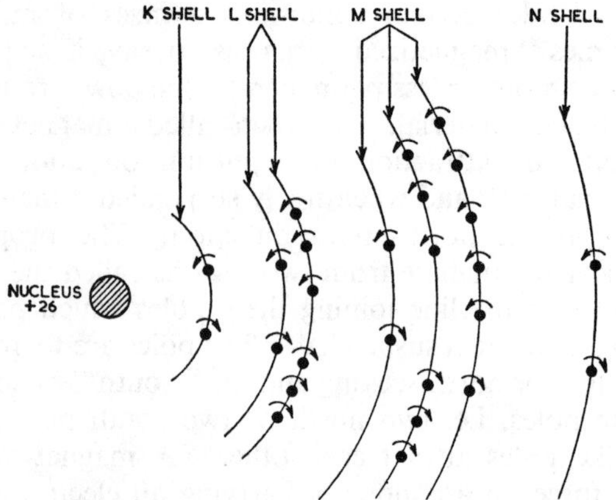

FIG. M-5.—ELECTRON ARRAY IN THE IRON ATOM SHOWING INEQUALITY BETWEEN THE NUMBER OF ELECTRONS WITH POSITIVE SPIN AND THE NUMBER WITH NEGATIVE SPIN IN THE M SHELL.

as (b)–(e) indicate. In the more modern theory, magnetism is explained as resulting from the movement of electrons within the atom. The rotation of an electron about the nucleus of a given atom is equivalent to an electric current flowing in a path of the same size and shape as the orbit of the electron, and therefore sets up a magnetizing force. However, the combination of two or more atoms to form a molecule may result in the magnetizing forces produced by the several electrons cancelling each other out. But in addition to its orbital revolution, each electron spins on its own axis, and thus sets up a magnetizing force of its own. Some electrons spin in one direction (positive spin) and others in the reverse direction (negative spin). In non-magnetic substances all the spins cancel each other out; in magnetic substances, however, the number of electrons with positive spin is not equal to the number with negative spin (see Fig. M-5). However, it is not merely the unbalance of positive and negative spins in individual atoms or molecules which determines whether a substance is magnetic or non-magnetic but the net effect of a number of atoms or molecules in a small but finite region of the crystal lattice. These regions are called " domains ", and it is thought that even when a mass of a magnetic substance is not actually magnetized, the domains themselves behave as though they were magnets. In other words, the modern theory is very similar to the molecular theory, but " domains " are substituted for the molecular magnets.

Magnetization. The process of converting a piece of magnetic material into a magnet, either permanently or temporarily.

Magnetization Curve. Graph showing the relation between the magnetic flux density B and the magnetizing force H. The general form of such curves is shown in Fig. M-6. At low values of H, B

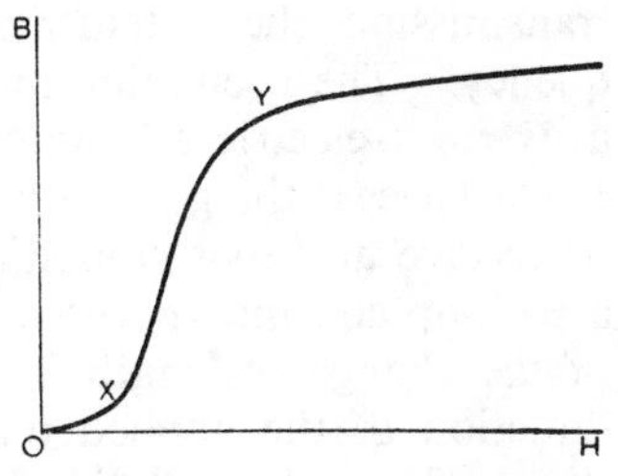

Fig. M-6.—General Form of Magnetization Curve for a Ferromagnetic Material.

increases slowly with increase of H as shown at X. Over the region XY, B rises rapidly with increase of H. Beyond Y is the saturation region in which increase of H produces very little increase of B.

Magnetizing Coil. Coil carrying an electric current and surrounding a mass of magnetic material. The current circulating in the coil magnetizes the material.

Magnetizing Current. The current in a magnetizing coil required to produce the magnetic flux in the core.

Magnetizing Force. (Symbol H) The force which produces the flux density at a given point. It is equal to the force which would be exerted on a unit magnetic pole situated at that point. Unit the oersted in the c.g.s. system. The m.k.s. unit of magnetizing force, for which no name has been decided at present, is defined as the field strength at the centre of a circular turn of wire 1 m in diameter, when a current of 1 A is flowing in the wire. The conversion factor, oersteds to m.k.s. units is $10^3/4\pi$.

Magneto-motive Force. (Symbol F) The line integral of the magnetizing force along a given path. For a closed magnetic circuit carrying a magnetizing coil of T turns, the magnetomotive force is $4\pi AT/10$, where A is the magnetizing current in amperes. Unit, the gilbert.

Magnetostriction. Small changes in the length of a piece of magnetic material which accompany the process of magnetization.

Magnetostrictor. More correctly, a magnetostrictive transducer, is a device for converting electrical oscillations to mechanical oscillations by employing the property of magnetostriction. It consists in essence of a bar of magnetic material, anchored at one point, and subjected to an oscillating magnetizing force, i.e. an oscillating current circulating in a coil carried by the magnetic member. The magnetostriction effect (change of length with change of magnetization) results in oscillating movement of the free end or ends of the bar. In order to achieve maximum energy transmission, the system must be driven at or near its natural frequency. The oscillating magnetizing current can be derived from a dynamo–electric alternator or from a thermionic generator. In the latter case the generator must either include an oscillating valve or receive an input consisting of an oscillating current induced in a pick-up coil incorporated in the transducer itself. The direction of the change of length is, in most materials, independent of the direction of the applied magnetizing force, and the frequency of the mechanical oscillations is therefore twice the frequency of the field. However, by providing a magnetic bias by means of a superimposed unidirectional field produced by a direct current flowing in the main or in an auxiliary winding, the mechanical oscillation frequency can be made equal to the field frequency. Transducers are principally employed for producing pressure waves of ULTRASONIC frequency.

Magnetron. Thermionic diode in which the MAGNETRON EFFECT is employed for the generation of electrical oscillations in the MICROWAVE range. The principle is illustrated in Fig. M-7, which shows the anode divided into two half-cylinders and an oscillatory circuit connected between the two halves, the centre-point of the oscillatory circuit being connected to the cathode via the h.t. supply. On switching on, the oscillatory circuit is excited, and a radio-frequency electric field, of frequency determined by the constants

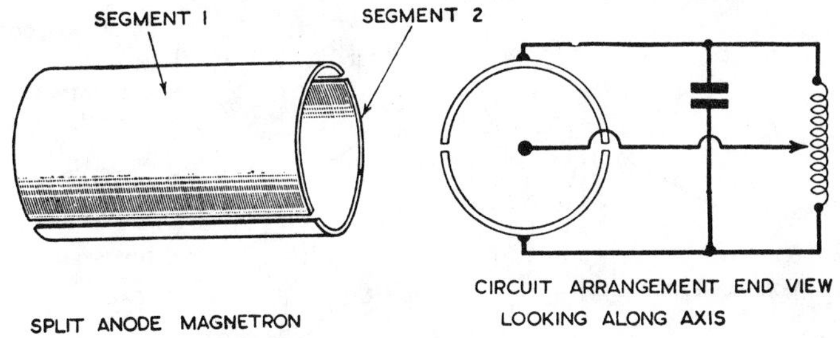

FIG. M-7.—SPLIT-ANODE MAGNETRON.

of the oscillatory circuit, is established across the gaps between the anode sections. In the presence of a constant axial magnetic field the effect of the oscillating electric field is to vary the curvature of the electron paths, i.e. the electrons are alternately accelerated and retarded. In other words, the anode current of the tube is velocity modulated, thus maintaining and building up the oscillations in the oscillatory circuit. An oscillatory output can therefore be taken by means of a tuned circuit coupled to the oscillatory circuit.

In the modern version, known as the cavity magnetron, one form of which is represented in Fig. M-8, the anode is a massive copper cylinder with a central bore or tunnel, and a number of axial cavities joined by slots to the central tunnel. The cathode is located centrally in the tunnel, leaving an annular space between cathode and anode. Each cavity with its associated slot forms, in effect, an oscillatory circuit, of which the wall of the cavity is the inductive element and the two lips of the slot with the air-space between them the capacitive element. The effective circuit corresponding to this arrangement is shown in Fig. M-9. The axial magnetic field is, of course, perpendicular to the surface of the paper. It will now be clear that an oscillatory field is set up between the two lips of each cavity in the same manner as described above for the simple

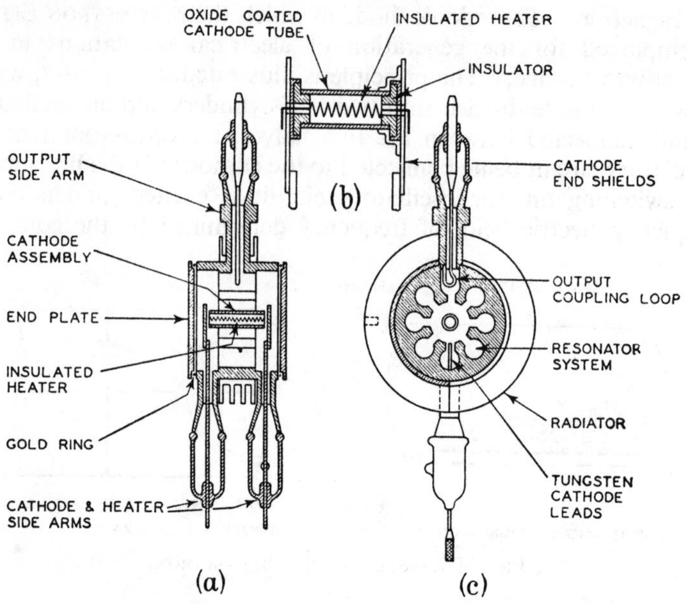

FIG. M-8.—MULTI-RESONANT CAVITY MAGNETRON.
(a) Longitudinal section.
(b) Detail of cathode and heater assembly.
(c) Cross-section.

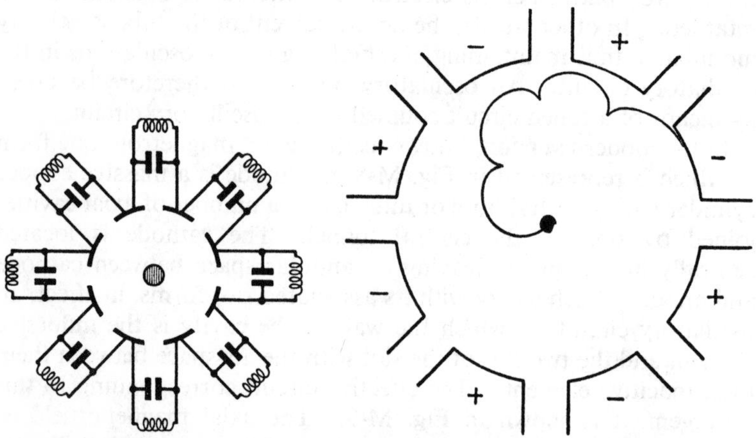

FIG. M-9 (*left*).—EFFECTIVE CIRCUIT OF A MULTI-RESONANT MAGNETRON.
FIG. M-10 (*right*).—TYPICAL ELECTRON PATH FROM CATHODE TO ANODE IN AN EIGHT-CAVITY MAGNETRON.

split-anode magnetron, and the path of each electron emitted from the cathode will be modified as the result of the reaction between the magnetic field and the oscillatory electric field. Fig. M-10 shows a typical form of path for a single electron in an eight-cavity magnetron. The radio-frequency output is taken from a pick-up loop situated within, and magnetically coupled to, one of the resonant cavities. In general, the operating frequency is fixed by the geometry of the device, but in some instances provision is made for adjusting the frequency over a small range by mechanical means.

Magnetron Effect. Deflexion of electrons emitted from a straight filamentary or thin tubular thermionic cathode and accelerated

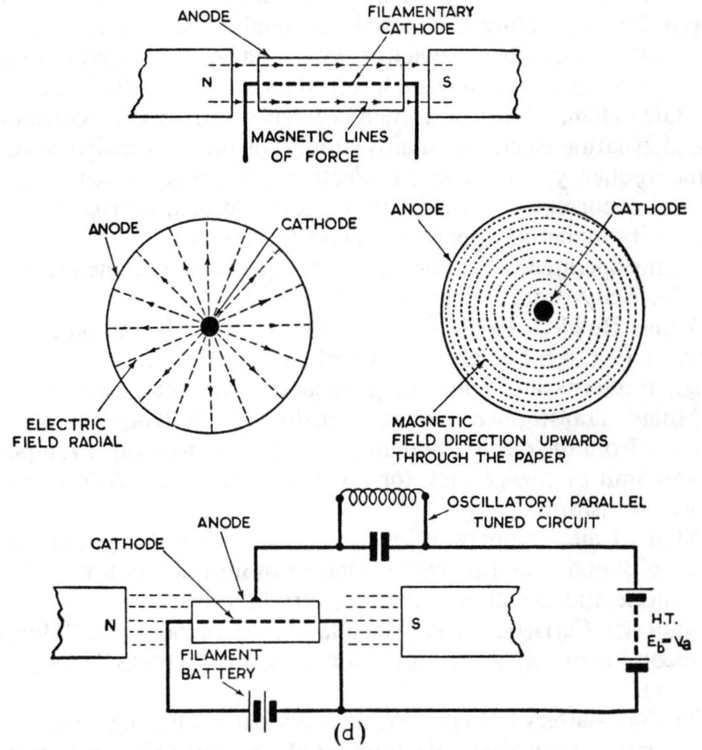

FIG. M-11.—SIMPLE FORM OF MAGNETRON, ILLUSTRATING THE MAGNETRON EFFECT.

(*Top*) Diagrammatic section of the tube.
(*Left*) Radial electric field due to the positive potential at the anode.
(*Right*) Path of electron due to radial electric field and axial magnetic field.
(*Lower*) Basic circuit.

towards a co-axial cylindrical anode, the deflexion resulting from the application of an axial magnetic field. If no magnetic field is applied, the paths of the electrons are radial; the effect of the magnetic field is to cause the electrons to follow a curved path, the shape of which is governed by the relative strengths of the electric and magnetic fields. See Fig. M-11. The effect is exploited in the MAGNETRON.

Magslip. Device for rotating a radar aerial in either direction, continuously at any desired speed, or over a small arc, or from one set position to another. Means can also be provided for indicating the position of the aerial at a remote point.

Mains Aerial. Device for using the electricity mains as a radio aerial by connecting the aerial terminal of the receiver to the electricity main via a capacitor which passes the radio-frequency signal but has a relatively high impedance at mains frequency.

Mains Hum. Note of a pitch corresponding to the frequency of the alternating electricity mains supply, or other disturbance of the same frequency, experienced in electronic equipment due to penetration of a current or an electric or magnetic field derived from the electricity mains or apparatus connected thereto.

Mains-operated. Said of electronic equipment designed to obtain its electricity supplies from the mains.

Mains Ripple. Small alternating component in the output of a rectifier (e.g. a h.t. supply unit) and representing the residue of the original alternating input not smoothed by the filter network.

Mains Transformer. Static transformer drawing its primary current from the electricity mains and forming part of, say, a power supply unit or power pack for a radio equipment. Also termed a power transformer.

Mains Unit. Apparatus obtaining an electrical input from the electricity mains and providing one or more outputs for supplying the anode and heater circuits of electronic tubes.

Majority Carriers. The principal charge carriers in a " doped " semiconductor, i.e. electrons in an n-TYPE and " HOLES " in a p-TYPE material.

Mallory Battery or Cell. Primary dry battery having a zinc anode and a cathode consisting of a mixture of mercuric oxide and graphite, the electrolyte being caustic potash. Originally developed for military applications, it is now extensively used in hearing aids on account of its compact size. Known as mercury battery.

Mansbridge Capacitor. Capacitor having metal foil plates and paper dielectric and so designed that, should the insulation break down due to puncture of the dielectric, the discharge between the plates at the seat of the breakdown oxidises the metal and thus restores the insulation resistance.

Marker Beacons. Radio beacons indicating specific points on the approach path at an airfield, and used in connexion with INSTRUMENT LANDING SYSTEMS. The outer, middle and inner markers are located at 4 miles, 2000–4000 ft, and 250 ft respectively from the commencement of the runway. They radiate beams of different frequencies, and with distinctive modulations.

Maser. Microwave Amplification by Stimulated Emission of Radiation. Device the operation of which is based upon the fact that an elemental atomic magnet in a magnetic field may have one of two energy states, i.e. parallel or anti-parallel to the field. In a complex of atomic magnets their equilibrium distribution between the two possible states is governed by the temperature, there being more in the lower energy state than in the higher energy state. If electromagnetic radiation of suitable frequency is applied to the system transitions of atomic magnets from one energy state to the other can take place, energy being absorbed if the transition is from the lower energy state to the higher, or radiated if the transition is from the higher energy state to the lower. The frequencies required to effect such transitions are in the microwave range. Employing this principle, practical amplifiers and oscillators have been produced. One valuable feature of the Maser is that it can be operated at very low temperatures at which the noise factor is extremely small. An important field of application is in radio astronomy, where the very high signal-to-noise ratio is of particular advantage.

Mask. A frame having a rectangular opening of standard television aspect ratio (4 : 3), usually with rounded corners, mounted in front of a television picture tube to block out the unused portion of the luminescent screen.

Mast Aerial. Aerial in which the oscillating currents are carried by the metallic structure of the mast itself.

Master Oscillator. Thermionic oscillator, usually of comparatively low power, the frequency of which is maintained constant between very close limits (e.g. by crystal control) and used in turn for controlling the frequency of other equipment.

Matched Load. Load connected to the output terminals of an amplifier or other equipment, and having a value such that it accepts the maximum power which the source is able to supply.

Matching, Impedance. Adjustment of the effective impedance of a load with respect to that of the source, so as to ensure maximum power transfer.

Matching Transformer. A transformer coupling a source to a load and so designed as to ensure maximum energy transfer in spite of the fact that the load impedance differs from the source impedance. For optimum matching the square of the turns ratio of the transformer should equal the ratio of the two impedances.

Mavar. With the name derived from Mixer Amplification of Variable Reactance, the Mavar is another name for the PARAMETRIC AMPLIFIER.

Maxwell. The c.g.s. unit of magnetic flux. The m.k.s. unit is the weber. One maxwell = 10^{-8} weber.

Mean Free Path (of a Molecule). The average distance travelled by a gas molecule between successive collisions with other molecules.

Mechanical Scanning. Any method of scanning in television which uses mechanical devices, such as moving apertures or mirrors, as distinct from the electronic scanning in television picture tubes and camera tubes.

Medium-frequency Waves. Radio waves having frequencies between 300 kc/s and 3 Mc/s (wavelengths from 1000 down to 100 m). The hectometric waves.

Meg or Mega. Prefix meaning one million or one million times.

Megacycles per Second. (Mc/s) A frequency of one million cycles per second.

Meissner Oscillator. A valve oscillator circuit which is derived from the Hartley but in which the oscillation circuit is coupled inductively to the grid and anode coils. There is thus no conductive coupling between the oscillator tuning circuit and the valve.

Mercury Arc Rectifier. Rectifier in which rectification takes place in an arc discharge through mercury vapour. Typical modern forms are described under IGNITRON and EXCITRON.

Mercury Pool Cathode. Type of cathode used in mercury arc rectifiers such as the ignitron and the excitron. It consists of a pool of mercury, the emission taking place from a hot-spot developed at the surface of the mercury.

Mercury-vapour Rectifier. Gas-filled diode having a conventional thermionic cathode, the envelope being filled with mercury vapour.

Mercury-vapour Tube. Any electron tube having an envelope filled with mercury vapour, but the term is more especially used for cold-cathode tubes having mercury-vapour filling.

Mesons. Charged particles observed in COSMIC RAYS, and having rest masses greater than that of an electron but less than that of a proton. The three principal types of meson are the μ-meson, the π-meson and the τ-meson, having rest masses of 215, 280 and 1000 respectively referred to the mass of an electron as unity. Other types of meson also exist. Both positive and negative mesons are known; they carry a charge equal to the charge of an electron. Neutral mesons also have been detected.

Metal Backing (Metallization) of a Cathode-ray Tube. Very thin deposit of metal, usually aluminium, on the back of the luminescent screen of a television picture tube, that is to say between the phosphor and the electron gun. Its purpose is to reflect forward much of that part of the emitted light which, in the non-metallized tube, is directed towards the back (i.e. towards the gun) and is then either absorbed and lost or is diffusely reflected in the forward direction, thus reducing picture contrast.

Metal Rectifier. Rectifier unit consisting in essence of two metal plates separated by a thin layer of a compound (usually the oxide) of one of the metals.

Metallized Valve. Thermionic valve having the external surface of the envelope sprayed with a metallic conductive coating which can be earthed to form an electrostatic screen.

Metre-kilogramme-second System. System of units based upon the metre, the kilogramme and the second as the fundamental units of length, mass and time. One of the advantages of the m.k.s. system is that it includes many of the so-called " practical " units, such as the ampere, volt, ohm, farad and henry, which are multiples or sub-multiples of c.g.s. units.

Metrosil. Proprietary name for a range of semiconductor devices containing silicon carbide and having non-linear resistance. The current through a Metrosil is proportional to about the fourth or fifth power of the applied electromotive force. In other words,

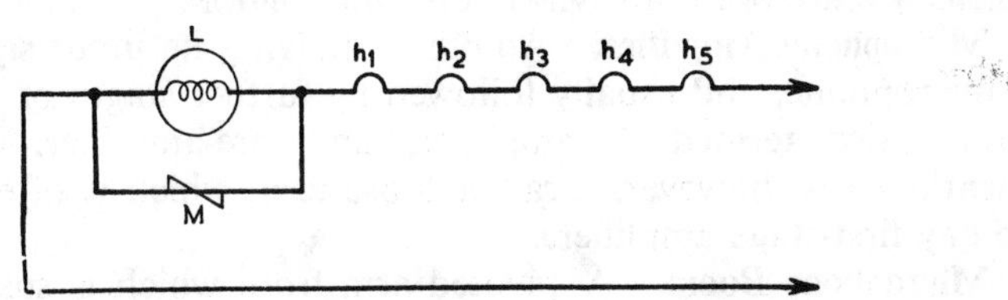

FIG. M-12.—VOLTAGE-DEPENDENT RESISTOR (METROSIL) IN PARALLEL WITH PILOT LAMP IN A SERIES HEATER CHAIN.

if the voltage applied across a metrosil is doubled the current increases by a factor of about 16. A typical application is illustrated in Fig. M-12, where a Metrosil is connected in parallel with a pilot lamp which itself is in series with the heater chain of a radio receiver. Normally, the current through the Metrosil is small and does not materially affect the operation of the lamp but, on switching on, when the cold resistance of the heater chain is low the resultant voltage surge greatly reduces the resistance of the Metrosil, which passes a heavy current, thus protecting the lamp from burn-out.

Metric Waves. Radio waves of wavelengths from 10 down to 1 m (frequencies of 30–300 Mc/s). The " very high frequency " waves.

Mho. Unit of conductance, the reciprocal of the OHM.

Mica Capacitor. Capacitor in which the dielectric consists of a plate or plates of mica.

Mica Spacer. Shaped disk of mica, pierced with holes to accommodate the ends of the electrodes of a thermionic valve or other electron tube. The electrode system is assembled between two or more such spacers, which serve to keep the system rigid and the whole assembly central in the envelope.

Micro. (Symbol μ) Prefix meaning one-millionth part—e.g. one microampere (μA) = 10^{-6} A.

Microfarad. (Symbol μF) Sub-unit of capacitance, equal to the one-millionth part of a FARAD.

Microgroove Records. " Long-playing " gramophone records with groove pitches in the order of 200–300 grooves per inch, and designed to be played at rotational speeds of $33\frac{1}{3}$ or 45 r.p.m.

Micron. (Symbol μ) Unit of length equal to the one-thousandth part of a millimetre or 10^{-6} m.

Microphone. A mechanico-electrical transducer in which the energy of sound waves is converted into electrical energy. See CONDENSER MICROPHONE, CRYSTAL MICROPHONE, ELECTROMAGNETIC MICROPHONE, MOVING-COIL MICROPHONE.

Microphone Amplifier. Amplifier deriving its input signal from a microphone, and usually followed by further stages of amplification. Also termed A amplifier, and pre-amplifier. The last mentioned is, however, a rather loose term which is often applied to any first-stage amplifier.

Microphone Boom. A pivoted arm from which is suspended a microphone, which can thus be swung to any position in a television or cinema studio, clear of scenery, lights, cameras, actors, etc.

Microphone Current. The current flowing in a microphone circuit.

Microphonic Noise. Noise in the output of an electronic equipment due to the variation of the electrical characteristics of a valve or of the constants of the circuit, resulting from mechanical vibration.

Microphonic Valve. Thermionic valve in which the electrode system is not sufficiently rigid to prevent relative movement between electrodes under prevailing working conditions. The resultant changes in the characteristics of the valve cause corresponding variations in the output.

Microphony. Rhythmic variations in the output of a circuit due to variations of its electrical characteristics or constants produced by external causes. A familiar example is the production of unwanted sounds (microphonic noise) due to changes in the characteristics of a valve resulting from relative movement between its electrodes. The immediate cause of microphony may be mechanical vibrations reaching the electrode system via the chassis and valve pins, or sound waves from the loudspeaker impinging on the envelope of the valve. Microphony in a sound-reproducing equipment manifests itself in severe distortion and often uncontrolled howling; in a television receiver it may produce variations of picture brightness and loss of picture quality. Much has been, and is still being, done by valve manufacturers to render valves less liable to microphony, by making the electrode systems more rigid and ensuring that the natural frequencies of its parts are outside the audio range. Equipment manufacturers can also do much in this direction by locating valves as far as possible from sources of vibration, and by resilient mounting of both valves and loudspeakers.

Microwave Tubes. Thermionic tubes such as the DISK-SEAL and LIGHTHOUSE VALVES, KLYSTRONS, MAGNETRONS and TRAVELLING-WAVE TUBES used for generating or amplifying oscillations in the microwave range.

Microwaves. Radio waves having wavelengths of less than 20 cm.

Midget Super-emitron Camera Tube. Television camera tube in which the scene to be televised is focused on a photo-emissive cathode, the photo-electrons emitted therefrom being accelerated and focused on a target plate, thus providing a charge image of the scene. The target is scanned obliquely by an electron beam, thus discharging the electron image spot by spot and line by line. The corresponding voltage variations at a signal plate at the rear of the target and separated from it by a dielectric constitute the video signal. See Fig. M-13.

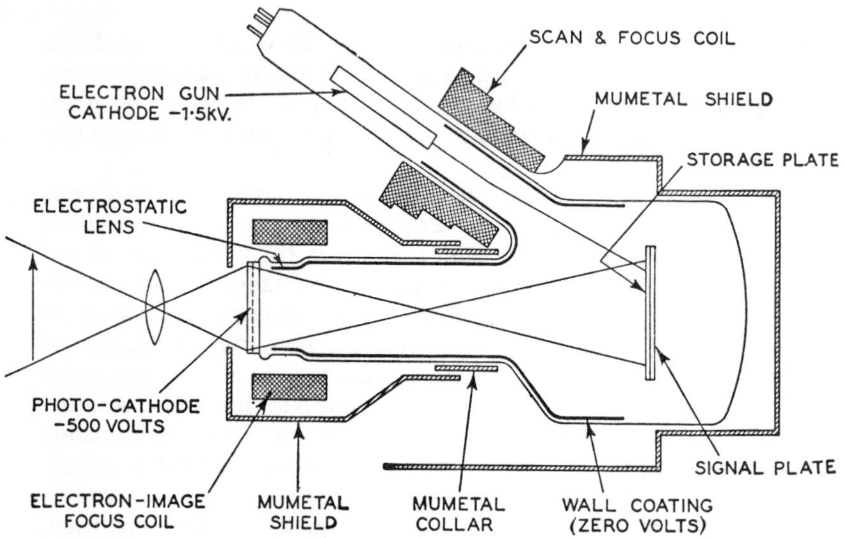

FIG. M-13.—MIDGET SUPER EMITRON.

Miller Effect. Change of input impedance of a thermionic valve resulting from variations of the effective impedance of the anode circuit due to the capacitance between the control grid and those electrodes (e.g. anode or screen grid) at which an alternating component of their potentials is produced by the alternating signal applied to the control grid.

Miller Timebase. Circuit for the generation of a sawtooth waveform based on the fact that in a pentode of high mutual conductance the suppressor grid will attract electrons and so acquire a negative charge under certain relative conditions of anode and screen voltage, and so increase the screen current at the expense of the anode current. A basic circuit is reproduced in Fig. M-14.

Milli. (Symbol m) Prefix signifying the one-thousandth part, e.g. milliampere (mA) $= 10^{-3}$ A.

Milli-micro. (Symbol mμ) Prefix meaning the one-thousandth of a millionth part, or 10^{-9}.

Milli-micron. A unit of length equal to the one-thousandth part of a micron and thus 10^{-6} mm or 10^{-9} m.

Miniature Valves. Name originally given to the range of thermionic valves in all-glass construction with the B7G or "button" base (see VALVE BASES), and having a diameter of about 20 mm and an overall height in the region of 50 mm. Still smaller valves (see SUB-MINIATURE VALVES) were later introduced.

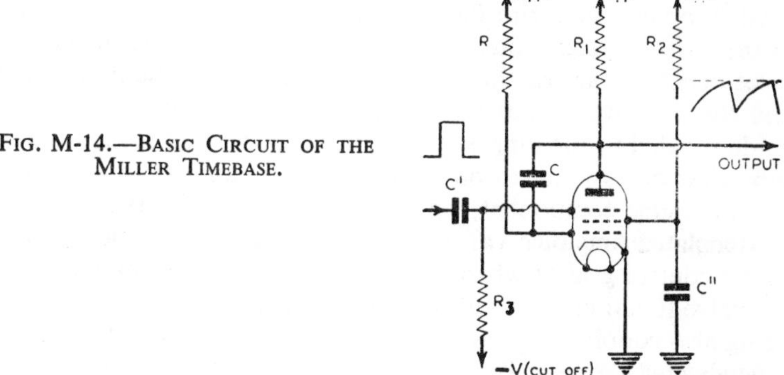

FIG. M-14.—BASIC CIRCUIT OF THE MILLER TIMEBASE.

Miniaturization. The growing tendency to design circuit components, and also complete equipments, of very small dimensions.

Minority Carriers. Charge carriers which form only a small proportion of the total number of charge carriers in a "doped" semiconductor. In p-TYPE material the minority carriers are electrons; in n-TYPE material they are "holes".

Mirror Image. Image, whether optical or electronic, in which the object is reversed (right to left) as in a mirror.

Mixer. (1) Arrangement of adjustable potentiometers whereby two or more input signals (e.g. from different microphones or gramophone pick-ups) can be combined in any desired proportions to form a composite signal. Used, for example, to introduce sound effects produced in a separate studio, or to superimpose background music on a radio programme.

(2) Thermionic valve in which two signals of different frequencies are combined. The most familiar example is the mixer portion of a FREQUENCY CHANGER, in which the incoming modulated carrier is combined with a locally generated oscillation of different frequency in order to produce a signal of intermediate frequency.

Modes. The field configurations due to guided waves (see WAVE-GUIDE). According to the British nomenclature, the letter E is used to distinguish modes in which there is a longitudinal component of the electric field but the longitudinal component of the magnetic field is everywhere zero, and the letter H to distinguish modes in which there is a longitudinal component of the magnetic field but the longitudinal component of the electric field is everywhere zero (in the American system TM modes, transverse magnetic, and TE modes, transverse electric). Modes are further distinguished by two subscript figures (zero, 1, 2, . . .), the first of which in the British system indicates the number of maxima of magnetic force occurring across the guide at right angles to the longest side, and the second the number of such maxima occurring across the guide parallel to the longest side. In the American system the two subscripts correspond to the corresponding numbers of maxima of the transverse component, whether magnetic or electric.

Modulated Amplifier Valve. In a transmitting equipment, a valve to the control grid of which the carrier frequency is applied so that the valve functions as a radio-frequency amplifier, the anode circuit being also coupled to the output of the MODULATOR VALVE.

Modulated Wave. Radio-frequency wave the amplitude, frequency or phase of which is varied in order to transmit information.

Modulation. Process of varying the amplitude, frequency or phase of a carrier wave in accordance with the sound, telegraphic or video signal it is desired to transmit.

Modulation Depth. Extent to which the amplitude of a carrier wave is modulated. Measured by the ratio of the difference between the peak and trough values and their sum. Usually expressed as a percentage.

Modulation Envelope. Outline indicating the variation of the peak values of an amplitude-modulated wave, as illustrated by the heavy line in Fig. M-15.

Modulation Frequency. The frequency of the signal with which a carrier wave is modulated.

Modulator Valve. In a transmitting equipment, a valve to the grid circuit of which the modulating signal is applied, the output of the valve being then injected into the anode circuit of the MODULATED AMPLIFIER VALVE.

Molybdenum. Metallic element having a melting point of 2450° C. It is used in the form of wire for the grid windings of thermionic valves, and for filament supports, etc.

Monad. A MONOVALENT element.

Monitor. Receiving equipment, e.g. a radio or television receiver, loudspeaker or picture tube used for sampling a transmission, for example, to check quality, without interfering with the normal service.

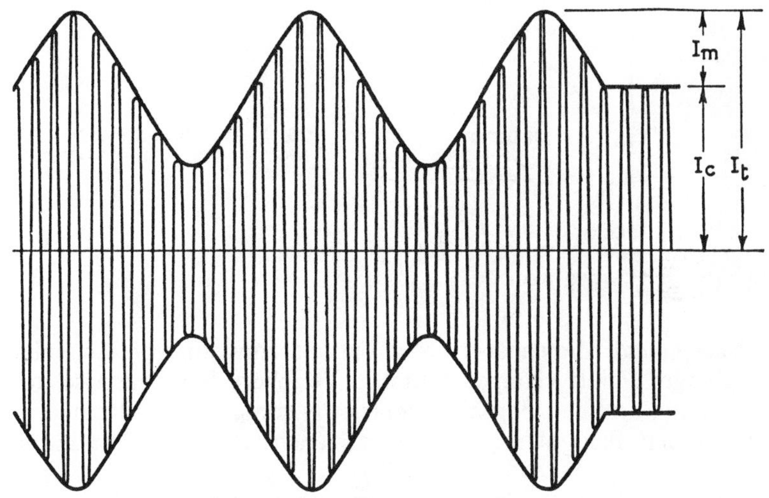

FIG. M-15.—AMPLITUDE-MODULATED WAVE (MODULATION DEPTH 50%). Modulation envelope is the heavy line.

Monoscope. Television camera mounted in a fixed position and used for televising " stills " such as test patterns.

Monovalent. Said of an atom which is capable of combining with only one atom of hydrogen or its equivalent.

Morse Code. A telegraphic code, devised by S. F. B. Morse, wherein letters, figures, etc., are represented by different arrangements of long and short pulses (dots and dashes).

Mosaic. Photo-emissive surface composed of a non-conducting plate coated on one side with a large number of very small granules of photo-emissive material insulated from each other.

Motor Boating. Form of intermittent oscillation which may arise in an amplifier due to unwanted coupling between its input and output circuits and resulting in the amplifier becoming periodically inoperative.

Moving-coil Loudspeaker. Loudspeaker in which the sound is reproduced by the axial movement of a cone-shaped diaphragm driven by a coil carrying the audio-frequency current and flexibly mounted in the annular air-gap of a magnet and thus subjected to a strong radial magnetic field. See Fig. M-16. Also termed an ELECTRO-DYNAMIC loudspeaker.

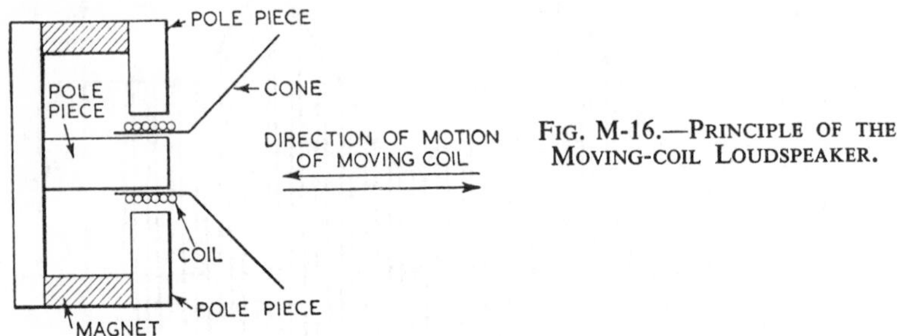

FIG. M-16.—PRINCIPLE OF THE MOVING-COIL LOUDSPEAKER.

Moving-coil Microphone. MICROPHONE consisting of a circular diaphragm rigidly clamped round its periphery but otherwise free to vibrate, and carrying a concentrically mounted coil located in the annular field of a powerful permanent magnet. The sound waves impinge on the diaphragm, the movement of which is transmitted to the coil, thus causing an audio-frequency electromotive force to be generated in the coil. See Fig. M-17.

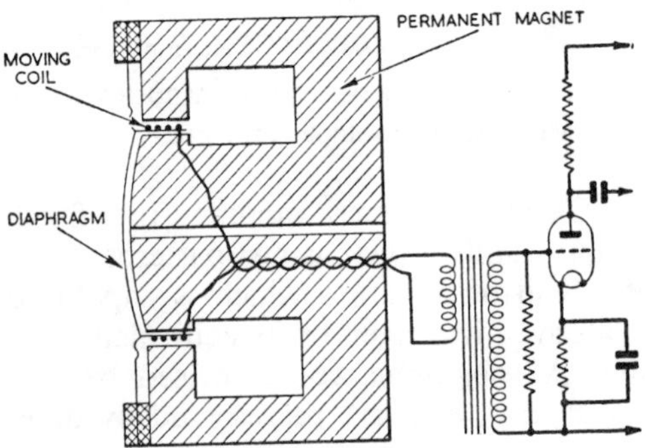

FIG. M-17.—DIAGRAMMATIC SECTION OF A MOVING-COIL MICROPHONE WITH THE BASIC CIRCUIT OF THE MICROPHONE AMPLIFIER.

Moving-iron Loudspeaker. Loudspeaker in which the sound is reproduced by the axial vibration of a conical diaphragm driven by an iron armature flexibly mounted in a magnetic field, the strength of the field being varied by the audio-frequency current circulating in a coil. See Fig. M-18.

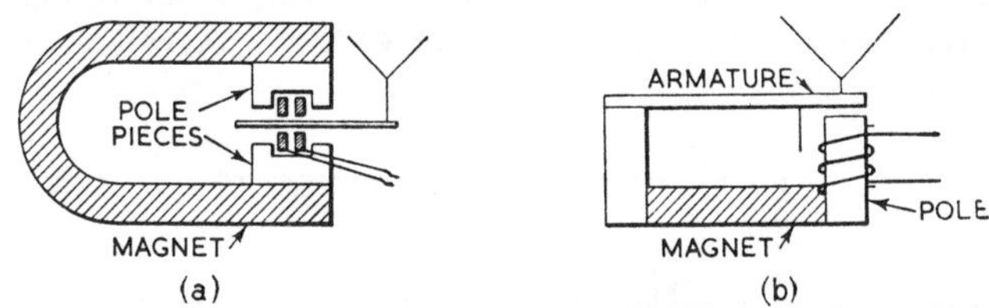

FIG. M.-18.—DIAGRAMMATIC SECTIONS OF TWO FORMS OF MOVING-IRON LOUDSPEAKER.

Moving Plate(s). The plate or plates of a variable capacitor which are mounted on a spindle capable of being rotated so as to interleave to a greater or less extent with the fixed plates, thus varying the capacitance.

Mu-metal. A nickel–iron alloy characterized by its high permeability at low field strengths and its small hysteresis losses. It is largely used for making magnetic screens for cathode-ray tubes and other apparatus.

Multi-cavity Klystron. KLYSTRON in which the oscillating circuits consist of internal or external resonant cavities.

Multi-cavity Magnetron. MAGNETRON incorporating a number of resonant cavities.

Multi-channel. Term applied to radio- or line-telecommunication systems in which more than one message or conversation can be passed simultaneously over the same link (radio or land line). This may be achieved by using a wide-band transmission and by severely limiting the frequency band occupied by each message.

Multi-mu Valve. See VARIABLE-MU VALVE.

Multiple Valve. Thermionic valve in which two or more electrode systems, sometimes with a common cathode, are enclosed in a single envelope. Common examples are the double-diode, double-triode, double-diode–triode, triode–pentode, triode–hexode and double-pentode combinations.

Multiplier. See FREQUENCY MULTIPLIER, ELECTRON MULTIPLIER and VOLTAGE MULTIPLIER.

Multi-vibrator. Thermionic oscillator in which two similar valves are resistance–capacitance coupled to each other in such a way that the grid signal for each valve is derived from the anode potential of the other valve. A basic circuit is given in Fig. M-19. On switching on, the anode current of one valve (say valve A) will inevitably rise faster than that of the other valve (valve B) due to slight differences in their characteristics. Owing to the voltage drop across R1, the potential at the anode of valve A will drop, with corresponding decrease of the potential at the grid of valve B. The

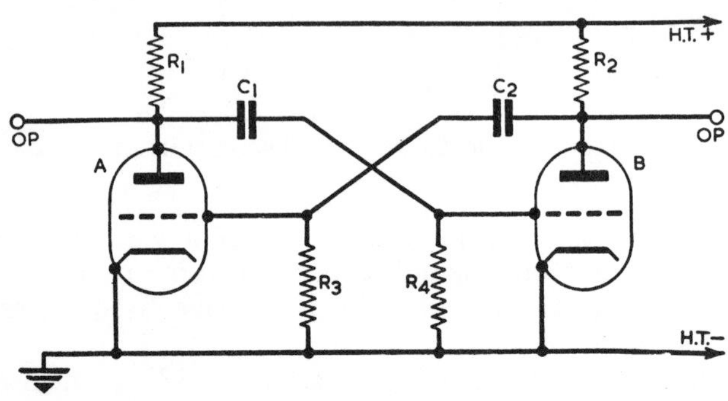

FIG. M-19.—FREE-RUNNING OSCILLATOR OF THE MULTI-VIBRATOR TYPE.

anode current of valve B therefore falls, and the potential at the anode of valve B rises, with corresponding increase of potential at the grid of valve A so that the anode current of valve A rises still further. This action is cumulative until the anode current of valve B falls to zero. The circuit has then achieved a quasi-stable state with valve A conducting and valve B cut off, which persists until the charge of capacitor C1 has been discharged via resistor R4, when a similar action takes place, the anode current of valve B rising and that of valve A falling until another quasi-stable condition is reached with valve B conducting and valve A cut off. If the valves and the corresponding coupling components are identical the cut-off periods for the two valves will be of equal duration, that is to say, the circuit will generate an approximately square waveform. If the corresponding components are unequal the durations of the two half-cycles will also be unequal, corresponding, for example, to the "stroke" and "flyback" of a timebase generator. The true or free-running multi-vibrator with two quasi-stable states is not the only form. Modification of the grid circuit of one or both valves results in the arrangement having either one stable and one quasi-stable state or two stable states. Such circuits are known respectively as "flip-flop" and "flip-and-flop" circuits. In the flip-flop circuit, a basic diagram of which is given in Fig. M-20, valve B is given a negative bias beyond the cut-off point so that in the stable-state valve A conducts and valve B is cut off. Application of a negative-going pulse to the grid of valve A causes the anode current of valve A to decrease, and its anode voltage, and thus the grid voltage of valve B, to rise so that the circuit rapidly achieves the

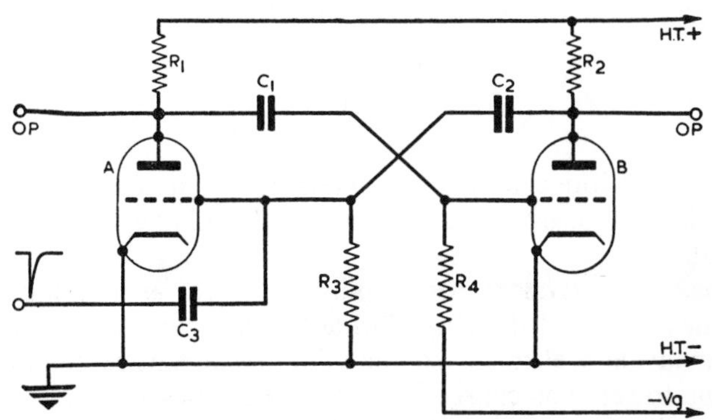

FIG. M-20.—BASIC FLIP-FLOP CIRCUIT.

Valve B has a standing bias below cut-off. Negative-going pulses applied via C3 to the grid of valve A initiate the temporary change-over from the stable to the quasi-stable state.

quasi-stable condition in which valve B conducts and valve A is cut off. However, after a short interval, dependent upon circuit values, the change-over previously described takes place, valve A becoming conductive and valve B cut off, and this condition persists until a further pulse applied to the grid of valve A produces another " flip-flop " action. In the " flip-and-flop " circuit a bias below cut-off point is applied to both valves, and the incoming pulse affects the change-over from one stable state to the other, the two valves operating alternately.

Mutual Conductance. (Symbol g_m) A figure of merit for a thermionic valve and equal to the ratio between the change of anode current brought about by a small change in control grid voltage, and the change in grid voltage itself. Mutual conductance is usually expressed in milliamperes (change of anode current) per volt (change of grid voltage). The mutual conductance is also represented by the slope of the anode current/grid volts characteristic curve of the valve, and is therefore sometimes referred to as the

" slope " of the valve. Other terms are " transconductance " and " goodness factor ". See also VALVE CHARACTERISTICS.

Mutual Induction. Production of an electromotive force in one circuit due to a change of flux linkage in that circuit resulting from a change of current in another circuit.

Myriametric Waves. Electromagnetic waves of wavelengths above 10,000 m (frequencies below 30 kc/s). The " very low " frequency waves.

N

npn. Descriptive term for a TRANSISTOR in which the emitter and collector consist of n-TYPE material and the base of p-TYPE material.

n-type. Quadrivalent semiconductor, such as germanium, to which has been added a small but accurately controlled proportion of a pentavalent element, so that the crystal lattice contains free electrons to serve as charge carriers. See TRANSISTOR.

Nano. Prefix denoting 10^{-9}.

Napierian Logarithms. See NATURAL LOGARITHMS.

Natural Frequency. Lowest frequency at which a system will freely oscillate.

Natural Logarithms. System of logarithms in which the base (e or ε) is 2·71828 . . . and not 10 as in common logarithms.

Natural Period. The time period of one complete oscillation corresponding to the natural frequency of a system.

Natural Wavelength. The wavelength of an electromagnetic wave corresponding to the natural frequency of the system.

Navigational Aids. Radio systems or installations which assist ships or aircraft to: (*a*) ascertain their bearings or position, or (*b*) to proceed with safety (homing) under conditions of poor visibility. Two main principles are employed: (1) the reception by the ship or aircraft of signals radiated from fixed transmitters; (2) the reception by the ship or aircraft of signals transmitted by the vessel and reflected back from some obstacle or target.

The principal systems are briefly described under the names by which they are known. See also DIRECTION FINDING and RADAR.

Near Infra-red. The shortest infra-red wavelengths, corresponding to radiations the wavelengths of which are nearest to the lower end of the visible spectrum.

Near Ultra-violet. The longest ultra-violet wavelengths, corresponding to radiations the wavelengths of which are nearest to the upper end of the visible spectrum.

Negative. A point or electrode is said to be at a negative potential with respect to a second point if an electric current tends to flow from the second point to the first, using the normal convention for the direction of current flow. See also POSITIVE.

Negative Charge. A body is said to have a negative charge, or to be negatively charged, when it possesses more than its normal quota of electrons.

Negative Electron. One of the fundamental constituents of an atom, and carrying a negative electric charge. Modern theories also include the conception of a positive electron of the same mass and carrying a positive charge equal to the negative charge of the negative electron. However, the positive electron is usually referred to as a POSITRON, and the negative electron is then referred to simply as an ELECTRON.

Negative Feedback. The process of applying a part of the output of an amplifier to the input, but with opposite polarity. Also

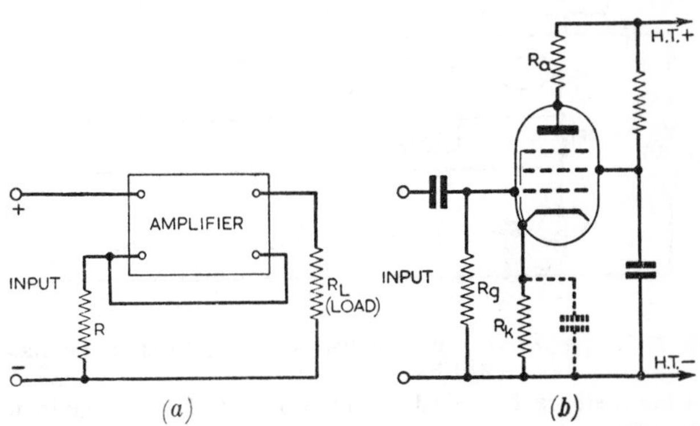

FIG. N-1.—NEGATIVE CURRENT FEEDBACK. (a) BLOCK DIAGRAM, (b) BASIC CIRCUIT.

R_a and R_k in (b) correspond to R_L and R in (a).

termed degeneration or degenerative feedback. It is obvious that negative feedback results in a reduction of the gain of an amplifier. It has, however, the advantage that the amount of feedback can be adjusted so that a large proportion of the harmonic distortion and hum is neutralized. It can also be used to assist in levelling out the frequency-response of an amplifier, or to ensure that, when the volume control is operated, the frequency response of the amplifier is modified to correspond with the frequency response of the human ear at various sound levels. In radio-frequency amplifiers, negative feedback can be applied to prevent high-gain valves being over-

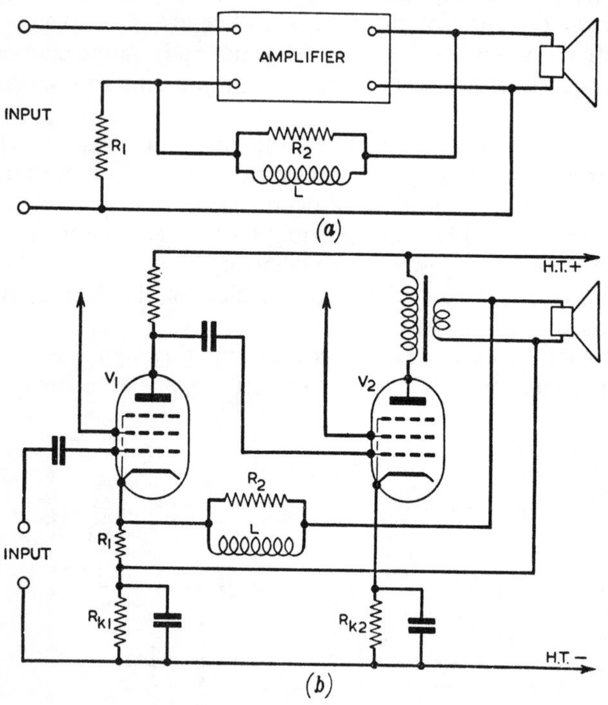

FIG. N-2.—NEGATIVE VOLTAGE FEEDBACK. (a) BLOCK DIAGRAM, (b) BASIC CIRCUIT.

In (b) the feedback is applied from the output of V2 to the input of V1. Grid leaks omitted for simplicity.

loaded by strong signals. Negative feedback can be made proportional either to the output current or to the output voltage. Fig. N-1 is a basic arrangement for current feedback, and consists simply in omitting the decoupling capacitor of the cathode-bias resistor (this capacitor is indicated in broken line in the figure). A simple arrangement for voltage feedback is shown in Fig. N-2, where R1 and R2 form a potential divider across the loudspeaker. In this particular arrangement R2 is shunted by an inductor L, the reactance of which increases with increasing frequency, thus reducing the feedback to compensate for the increase of loudspeaker impedance with rising frequency.

Negative Glow. Region in the neighbourhood of the cathode of a gas discharge tube, in which a luminous glow appears. See GAS DISCHARGE.

Negative-going. Said of a change, e.g. of current or voltage, whether gradual or a pulse, in the negative direction, i.e. from a positive value to a lower positive or to a negative value, or from zero or a negative value to a more negative value. See Fig. N-3.

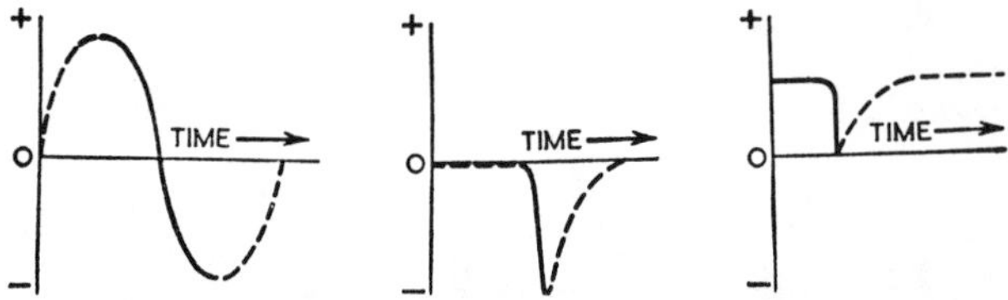

FIG. N-3.—TYPICAL WAVE AND PULSE FORMS.
The parts in full line are considered negative-going.

Negative Grid Current. Current flowing in the grid-to-cathode circuit of a thermionic valve in the direction corresponding to the loss of electrons by the grid. See also REVERSE GRID CURRENT.

Negative Image. Picture reproduction in a television receiver with the black and white areas interchanged as in a photographic negative. It can be caused by faulty adjustment of the ION TRAP of the picture tube, or by low values of e.h.t. or of heater voltage.

Negative Ion. Atom or group of atoms which, in consequence of possessing more than the normal quota of electrons, exhibits a negative charge.

Negative Modulation. System of carrier modulation used in television transmissions in America and certain European countries, such that picture highlights are represented by small amplitudes of the modulating signal and the darker portions by increasing amplitudes of the modulating signal. The British television system employs POSITIVE MODULATION, in which the instantaneous value of the amplitude of the modulating signal is directly proportional to the brightness of the picture element being transmitted. See Fig. N-4.

Negative Resistance. Property possessed by certain circuit elements, and more particularly by certain forms of thermionic valves and gas-filled tubes when operated under certain conditions, whereby an increase of current results from a reduction of the applied electromotive force. See also TETRODE.

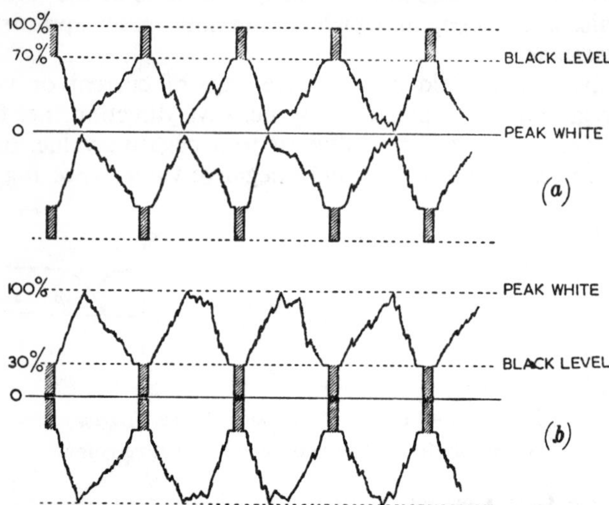

FIG. N-4.—WAVEFORMS OF TELEVISION TRANSMISSIONS CORRESPONDING TO (a) NEGATIVE MODULATION, AND (b) POSITIVE MODULATION.

In each case the synchronizing pulses are transmitted during the time intervals indicated by the shaded areas.

Negative Resistance Oscillator. Thermionic oscillator employing one or more valves operated on that part of their anode current/anode voltage characteristics over which they exhibit negative resistance. See DYNATRON and TRANSITRON.

Negative Transmission. Television transmission employing NEGATIVE MODULATION. In a negative transmission, zero carrier amplitude corresponds to peak white, 75 per cent carrier amplitude corresponds to black, and the region between 75 per cent and full carrier amplitude is used for transmitting the synchronizing pulses.

Neon. An inert gas, one of the rare components of the atmosphere, used in some forms of discharge tubes and lamps, in which it gives a characteristic red glow.

Neon Stabilizer Tube. A voltage stabilizer tube containing the gas neon.

Neper. Unit used for comparing two currents, in a similar way to the BEL or DECIBEL. If I_1 and I_2 are the two currents to be compared, N, the number of nepers, equals the natural logarithm of their ratio, i.e. $N = \log_e (I_1/I_2)$. The sub-unit is the decineper (=1/10 neper). One decibel = 0·1151 nepers or 1 neper = 8·686 dB.

Network. System of inter-connected conductors and other circuit components, usually so chosen and connected as to exhibit specific electrical characteristics.

Neutralization. The process of counteracting the effects of positive (regenerative) feedback via the inter-electrode capacitance (anode to control grid) of a thermionic valve, by applying an equal amount of feedback in anti-phase via coupling between the external anode and grid circuits. See Fig. N-5.

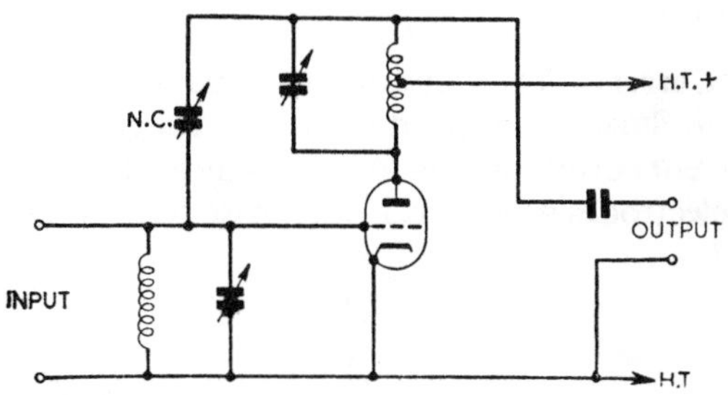

FIG. N-5.—TRIODE CONNECTED AS A RADIO-FREQUENCY AMPLIFIER.

Negative feedback from anode to grid via the neutralizing capacitor NC cancels out the positive feedback via the anode-to-grid internal capacitance of the valve.

Neutrino. A short-lived uncharged particle of zero or near-zero rest mass, which takes part in certain nuclear reactions.

Neutrodyne. Proprietary name for a particular form of neutralized radio-frequency amplifier.

Neutron. Uncharged particle, of slightly greater mass than a PROTON, and forming a constituent part of the nucleus of all atoms except hydrogen atoms, which consist of a single proton. It may be considered as the equivalent of one proton and one electron.

Nipkow Disk. Mechanical scanning device first used by Paul Nipkow in 1884, and later by John Logie Baird in his low-definition television experiments. It consists of a rotating disk having a number of holes located on a spiral path and so spaced that when the disk is rotated each aperture scans one strip of a rectangular area and that one complete revolution of the disk results in the rectangular area being completely scanned in a succession of parallel lines. See Fig. N-6.

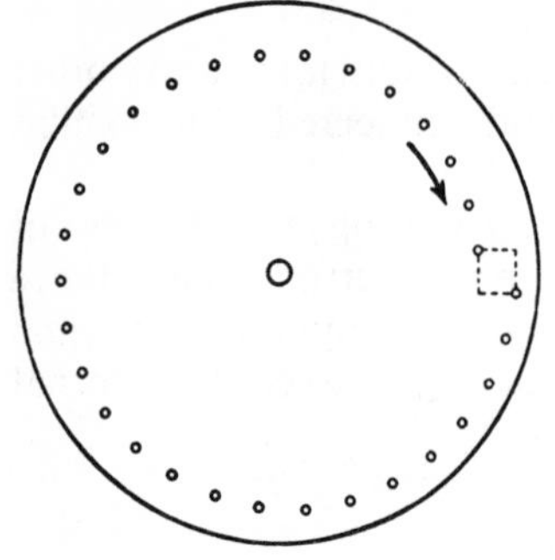

FIG. N-6.—NIPKOW DISK WITH THIRTY HOLES.

If rotated on its centre, the holes will scan a rectangular area such that shown, in thirty approximately parallel lines.

No-signal Current. The value of the anode current of a thermionic valve when no SIGNAL is applied to the control grid. It is the value of anode current corresponding to the steady grid bias, the potentials of all other electrodes being specified. Also termed the rest current. See Fig. N-7.

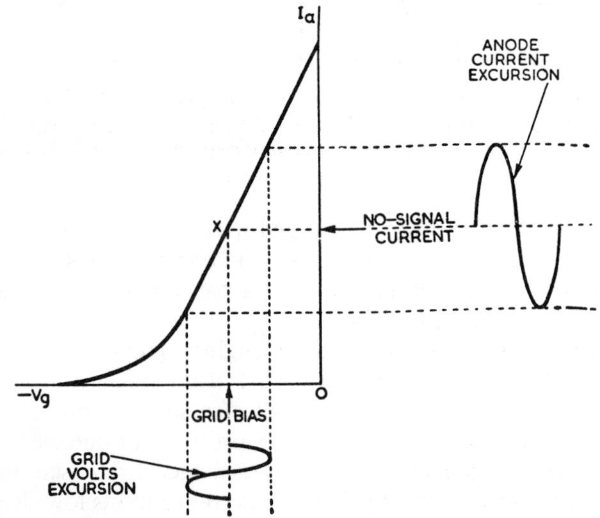

FIG. N-7.—ANODE CURRENT/GRID VOLTS CHARACTERISTIC OF A THERMIONIC VALVE SHOWING VALUE OF NO-SIGNAL CURRENT CORRESPONDING TO A FIXED VALUE OF GRID BIAS, AND THE EXCURSION OF ANODE CURRENT RESULTING FROM THE IMPOSITION OF AN ALTERNATING SIGNAL ON THE GRID BIAS VOLTAGE.

Noctovision. System of television in which the sensitive device responds to infra-red radiation, but the output is in the form of visible light.

Node. A point in a system of stationary (standing) waves at which the displacement is zero. In a high-frequency circuit, a point at which either the current or the voltage is a minimum (current node or voltage node).

Noise. In general, unwanted electrical signals, present in the input to a receiver or amplifier, or generated within the apparatus itself, which, in a sound-reproducing system, would be manifest in the output as unwanted sound. Although in other kinds of system the effect of such intrusions is different (e.g. in a television receiver they produce debasement of picture quality), these interferences are still termed " noise ". This wide definition includes such disturbances as MAINS HUM, and INTERFERENCE due to atmospherics, signals from unwanted stations or energy radiated by nearby electrical apparatus. However, the term noise is often qualified by an adjective denoting the origin of the disturbance, e.g. IMPULSE NOISE resulting from a sudden disturbance of short duration, or VALVE NOISE due to variations of anode current such as the SHOT and PARTITION effects. See also BACKGROUND NOISE, GALACTIC NOISE, JOHNSON NOISE, THERMAL NOISE. The extent to which it is useful to increase the sensitivity of a receiver is limited to that at which the noise content of the output so debases the quality that the output is no longer intelligible or enjoyable. At the lower radio frequencies this limit is usually set by the noise in the form of unwanted signals picked up by the aerial, but at very high frequencies it is the noise generated in the apparatus itself and in the signal source (e.g. the aerial) which limits the useful sensitivity. While, therefore, in the low-frequency case the limiting factor is the SIGNAL-TO-NOISE RATIO, for the higher frequencies the limiting factor is the NOISE FACTOR or noise figure which takes into consideration the effect of valve and thermal noise.

Noise Diode. See NOISE GENERATOR.

Noise Factor (Noise Figure). A measure of the extent to which the noise content of the output is increased by noise generated in the circuit. It may be roughly defined as the relation between the SIGNAL-TO-NOISE RATIOS at the output and input. Since, however, the internally-generated noise is a function of the temperature, and its effect is of importance only in so far as it is manifest over the frequency range of the apparatus, the noise factor is more strictly defined as the ratio of the total mean square noise output electromotive force to that part of it which is due to the thermal noise of the source circuit treated as a passive network at 290° K, over the frequency range which can be considered to limit the signal channel of the receiver.

Noise Generator. A device for generating a constant or adjustable noise signal which can be used as a standard in measurements of NOISE FACTOR. Typical devices which can be used as noise generators are temperature-limited (i.e. saturated) diodes, thyratrons, fluorescent tubes, klystrons and crystals.

Noise Limiter. Circuit device intended to limit the extent to which noise signals included in the input to a radio or television receiver are reproduced in the output. A basic circuit of the type frequently used in television receivers is shown in Fig. N-8. Here,

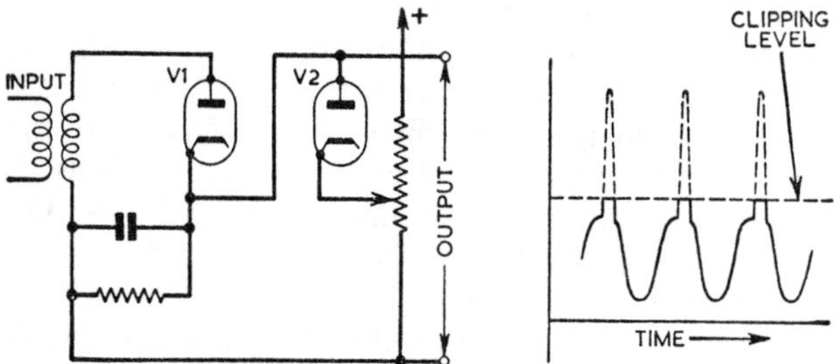

FIG. N-8.—SIMPLE NOISE LIMITER CIRCUIT.

V1 is the diode detector and V2 a second diode used as the limiter valve. The cathode of V1 is connected to the anode of V2, and the cathode of V2 is positively biased so that the valve conducts only when the potential at its anode, due to the signal passed by the detector, exceeds the bias voltage. As indicated in the figure, a signal including a large noise pulse is clipped due to V2 conducting, so that the noise amplitude in the output is greatly reduced. This type of limiter is not ideal for audio-frequency applications, since it is difficult to effect a compromise between efficient noise clipping and the risk of clipping the actual audio signal also. This difficulty can be surmounted by circuits of the type shown in Fig. N-9. In this arrangement the cathode of the detector diode is coupled to the cathode of the limiter diode. This valve is included in a voltage divider chain comprising R1, V2 and R2, the values of the two resistors being so chosen that V2 is just conductive, while the value of the capacitor C is such that the valve will continue to conduct over the complete audio-frequency range. The arrival of a noise pulse causes V2 to be cut off, allowing C to charge from the h.t.

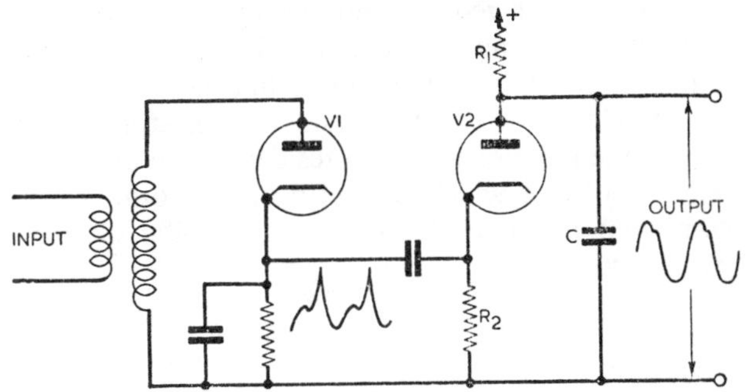

FIG. N-9.—BASIC CIRCUIT OF THE " FOLLOWER-LIMITER " SHOWING INPUT WAVEFORM WITH NOISE PULSE AND RESULTANT WAVEFORM.

supply via R1 at a rate governed by the values of R1 and C. The residual waveform then contains only a vestigial trace of the noise pulse.

Nominal Valve. A hypothetical thermionic valve, all the characteristics of which are identical with the manufacturer's published data. These data are, however, mean values calculated from measurements taken on large numbers of production valves, and in practice there is a certain " spread " of characteristics, i.e. small differences between the characteristics of one valve and another.

Non-conductor. A material in which, under normal conditions, there are very few free electrons so that no appreciable electric current can be made to flow through it.

Non-directional. Said of an aerial which radiates equally in, or absorbs energy equally from, all directions.

Non-inductive. Said of a circuit or circuit element which possess negligible inductance.

Non-linear Resistance. A device the resistance of which is not the simple ratio of the applied electromotive force and the current.

Nonode. Thermionic valve having nine electrodes—anode, cathode and seven grids.

Notation, Scales of. The decimal scale of notation, (1, 2, 3, . . . 10) requires ten different symbols or digits, (0, 1, 2, 3, . . . 9) in order to permit all numbers to be expressed. It is therefore not the most suitable for use in electronic digital computers, for which the BINARY SCALE, employing two digits only, 0 and 1, is the most convenient.

Noval Base. One of the standard forms of valve base having nine contact pins of standardized size and arranged in a specified pattern and with specified spacings. See VALVE BASE.

Nucleonics. The study of the atomic nucleus and its reactions.

Nucleus, Atomic. The central " core " of an atom, in which the greater part of the mass of the atom resides. The nucleus carries a positive electric charge which, in the normal atom, is neutralized by the combined negative charges of the orbital electrons. See ATOM, STRUCTURE OF.

O

Occlusion. Property possessed by certain solids, notably some metals, of retaining gases either within the solid or on the surface. There is no chemical combination in the accepted sense. In the process of evacuating high-vacuum electron tubes special techniques are employed to ensure the release and removal of the occluded gases before finally sealing the envelope.

Octode. Thermionic tube having eight electrodes, namely cathode, anode and six intermediate grids. It is mainly employed as a FREQUENCY CHANGER in supersonic heterodyne radio receivers. A basic circuit is given in Fig. O-1. Here the cathode and grids 1 and 2 form the local oscillator; grid 3 is an accelerator electrode; and the remaining three grids and the anode form, in effect, a pentode mixer, the incoming signal being introduced at grid 4.

Odd Lines. In a television transmission, if the lines of horizontal scan are numbered consecutively from the top of the picture, the first, third, fifth, . . . etc., lines are the " odd " lines and in the interlaced scanning system are transmitted in succession to produce one FRAME, after which the second, fourth, sixth, . . . etc., " even " lines are transmitted to produce the second frame. One odd frame and the following even frame produce one complete picture.

Ohm. (Symbol Ω) The practical unit of electrical resistance. A conductor has a resistance of one ohm when it is necessary to apply a potential difference of one volt in order to drive a current of one ampere through the conductor.

Oil—Applications of Electronics in the Oil Industry. A vast amount of electronic equipment is employed in plants in which oil is refined or is utilized. Many of these applications are automatic control systems common to many industries, while others are of a more specialized nature. A few typical examples are given below.

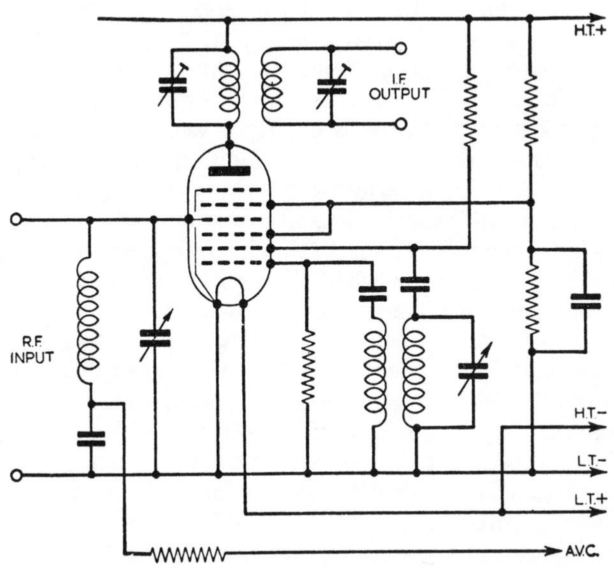

FIG. O-1.—BASIC CIRCUIT OF AN OCTODE EMPLOYED AS AN ELECTRON-COUPLED FREQUENCY CHANGER.

(1) In oil refineries recording pH meters are used to maintain a continuous check on the acidity of condensates at various stages in processing, so that prompt regulation of an alkaline reagent can be exercised in order to prevent corrosion of condensers and other equipment.

(2) The cavitation process, resulting from the application of ULTRASONIC vibrations, can be used to extract oils from animal and vegetable materials.

(3) Electronic control equipment is employed in oil-fired heating and air-conditioning installations in conjunction with thermostats, pressurestats, humidistats, etc., in order to maintain pre-determined

conditions, while devices incorporating photo-electric cells are used to shut down the plant and/or to give warning in the event of flame failure.

Omni-directional Aerial. An aerial which radiates or collects energy equally in any direction which makes the same angle with the vertical.

Omni-directional Radar Beacon. Combination of a fixed-position radar transmitter and an omni-directional aerial which radiates a characteristic signal which can be received by aircraft or ships fitted with DIRECTION-FINDING EQUIPMENT.

On–Off Control (Stop–Go Control). Automatic control system which maintains a particular condition or conditions at a substantially constant value by alternately switching on or off the apparatus which determines the condition. For example, the temperature at which a certain process is carried out can be kept reasonably constant by switching off a heating device as soon as the temperature exceeds the desired value by a pre-determined amount, and switching it on again when the temperature has fallen below the desired value by a pre-determined amount.

Open-circuit. A normally conducting circuit which has been interrupted so that a current cannot be maintained through it.

Open-circuit Voltage. The potential difference at the terminals of an electric current source when the external circuit is interrupted so that the source supplies no current. When current is drawn from the source the terminal voltage is reduced by an amount equal to the voltage drop across the internal resistance of the source. Thus, if the output current is I amps, and the internal resistance r ohms, the drop in voltage is $I \times r$ volts.

Operating Point. The electrical condition of a thermionic valve or of a transistor when the various supply voltages are applied but no input signal. In the case of a thermionic valve the operating point corresponds to a specified steady value of anode voltage and a specified steady value of anode current, the latter, of course, being determined by the grid-bias voltage. In the case of a transistor the operating point is specified by given values of collector voltage and current. The operating point is also termed the working point or the no-signal condition. The operating point is indicated at X in Figs. N-7 and O-2.

Optical System (for Projection Television). The optical system used in PROJECTION TELEVISION consists essentially of a spherical mirror and one or more "corrector" lenses for compensating spherical aberration and thus ensuring that the light emitted from the luminescent screen of the small projection type cathode-ray tube is sharply focused at the viewing screen. Usually the system also includes one or more plane mirrors which intercept the beam, and are located at an angle of 45° to the path of the beam, the object being to " fold " the beam path so that, while the optical distance between spherical mirror and viewing screen is of the correct length for sharp focus at the desired picture size, the physical distance is reduced so that the complete equipment can be accommodated in a cabinet of reasonable dimensions.

Optimum Value. The most favourable value for a certain quantity from the point of view of specific performance. For example, the " optimum " load of an amplifying valve is that which ensures the largest voltage or power gain.

Orbit. The closed path, either circular or elliptical in shape, followed by a body which revolves about another body. Originally applied mainly to the paths of the heavenly bodies as determined by gravitational forces, the term is now also used for the path followed by an electron as it revolves about the nucleus of an atom.

Orientation. The position or direction, or the change of position or direction, of a system or part of a system as a result of external influences or of changes in prevailing conditions. For example, a freely suspended magnet tends to orient itself in the direction of the prevailing magnetic field.

Orthicon. Form of television CAMERA TUBE in which the optical image to be transmitted is projected on a photo-emissive MOSAIC on the far side of a transparent signal plate, a charge pattern thus being produced on the mosaic. The mosaic is scanned by low-velocity electrons projected from an electron gun at the far end of the tube, thus progressively neutralizing the charge image. The resulting change of potential at the signal plate is the basis of the video signal.

Oscillating. A thermionic valve is said to be oscillating when it generates electrical oscillations.

Oscillation. (1) Rhythmic variation set up in or transmitted by a system possessing both elasticity and inertia or their electrical counterparts, capacitance and inductance.

(2) The process of generating alternating currents, particularly of high frequency, in a circuit possessing capacitance and inductance, usually by means of one or more thermionic valves. See DAMPED OSCILLATION, FORCED OSCILLATION, FREE OSCILLATION, NATURAL OSCILLATION and PARASITIC OSCILLATION.

Oscillation Valve. Name originally given to the thermionic diode by Sir Ambrose Fleming, its inventor, in view of its obvious application as a detector (rectifier) of electrical oscillations.

Oscillator. A device, usually incorporating one or more thermionic valves and their associated circuits, and capable of generating electrical oscillations. See AUTODYNE OSCILLATOR, BEAT OSCILLATOR, BEAT-FREQUENCY OSCILLATOR, BLOCKING OSCILLATOR, RELAXATION OSCILLATOR and SQUEGGING OSCILLATOR.

Oscillatory Circuit. A circuit possessing inductance and capacitance in series or in parallel. If the inductive and capacitive components are in series the circuit has a very low impedance at a particular frequency termed the RESONANT or NATURAL FREQUENCY of the circuit. If the inductive and capacitive components are in parallel the circuit has a very high impedance at the resonant frequency.

Oscillogram. A permanent record obtained by photographing the luminous trace or image produced by an OSCILLOSCOPE.

Oscillograph. An OSCILLOSCOPE fitted with photographic equipment to enable permanent records of the image to be made.

Oscilloscope. An instrument for giving a visual (luminous) trace or image representing the variations of electric currents or voltages, and particularly of rapid variations of an oscillatory nature. See also CATHODE-RAY OSCILLOSCOPE.

Output. The useful voltage, current or power delivered by a piece of apparatus such as a generator, amplifier or radio receiver.

Output Capacitance. The capacitance between the output electrode (usually the anode) of a thermionic valve and the cathode, when all the other electrodes are connected to the cathode by paths of negligible impedance. In a practical circuit, however, the effective output capacitance depends also on the impedances of the associated circuits.

Output Circuit. The circuit into which a generator, amplifier, etc., delivers its useful output.

Output Impedance. The output impedance of a thermionic valve is the impedance represented by the ANODE RESISTANCE of the valve shunted by the OUTPUT CAPACITANCE. At the higher radio frequencies additional factors, such as the inductances of the lead-in wires, dielectric losses in the insulating material and the TRANSIT TIME of electrons, must be taken into consideration.

Output Transformer. Transformer, the primary winding of which is included in the anode circuit of the OUTPUT VALVE, the load (e.g. the loudspeaker in the case of a sound amplifier) being connected in the secondary circuit. It serves the dual purposes of isolating the load from the d.c. component of the anode current (and also from the high voltages in the anode circuit) and, when the turns ratio of the transformer is correctly chosen, of matching the impedance of the load to that of the output stage.

Output Valve. A valve used in the final or output stage of an amplifier, and capable of delivering a substantial amount of alternating power. Such valves are often termed POWER VALVES or power-amplifying valves, to distinguish them from the voltage-amplifying valves used in the earlier stages of an amplifier.

Outside Broadcast. (Abbreviation O.B.) Radio or television transmission of a programme derived from a source other than a regular studio—e.g. from a theatre, sports arena, etc. The necessary microphones, cameras and control equipment are installed on the site, either temporarily for a special occasion or permanently in the case of a building frequently used for outside broadcasts. The programme material is passed to the regular transmitting station

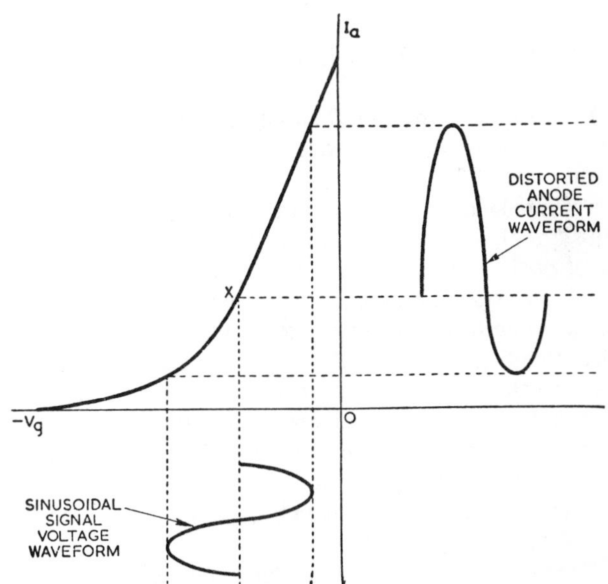

FIG. O-2.—DISTORTED WAVEFORM OF OUTPUT OF A THERMIONIC AMPLIFIER DUE TO OVERLOADING.

either by land line or by a shortwave radio link, for which purpose a mobile transmitter of comparatively low power is employed.

Overloading. The application of an excessive input, resulting either in distorted output or, in some cases, damage to the equipment. A familiar case is when the amplitude of the input signal to an amplifying valve is so great that it encroaches on the non-linear part of the anode current/grid volts characteristic of the valve, as indicated in Fig. O-2.

Overtones. Those components of a complex note or tone having frequencies greater than the fundamental frequency of the tone.

Oxide-coated Cathode. THERMIONIC CATHODE the emissive material of which is a mixture of oxides (usually barium and strontium oxides) applied as a thin layer either to an indirectly-heated metallic tubular cathode or to a directly-heated filamentary cathode.

Oxide-coated Filament. A directly-heated thermionic cathode, the surface of which is coated with emissive oxides.

P

P Band. Frequency band from 225 to 390 Mc/s employed in RADAR.

pnp Transistor. Junction TRANSISTOR consisting of a region of n-TYPE semiconductor between two regions of p-TYPE semiconductor.

p-type Semiconductor. Semiconductor material in which, due to the inclusion of a suitable additive, the crystal lattice contains a number of positive charge carriers or " holes ".

Pad. A constant-impedance resistive network inserted in a transmission line to introduce a fixed loss.

Padder (Padding Capacitor). An adjustable capacitor connected in series with the tuning capacitor of the local oscillator in a supersonic heterodyne receiver, and pre-set to the value which ensures the desired difference between the oscillator frequency and the frequency of the incoming signal.

Page Effect. Audible click which occurs when a piece of iron is magnetized or demagnetized.

Pair Production. Strictly, the conversion of a PHOTON (i.e. a quantum of radiation) into an electron and a positron. The term is, however, often employed to describe any process whereby both positive and negative charge carriers are simultaneously produced in equal numbers.

Pairing. Faulty interlacing between the lines of the odd and even frames in television reception, thereby allowing adjacent lines to overlap to a greater or less extent, thus producing dark horizontal lines between successive pairs.

Pancake Coil. Inductor having many layers of windings, each layer consisting of only a comparatively small number of turns, so that the complete coil is in the form of a flat disk.

Panel. A flat sheet, either of insulating material or of metal, upon which are mounted such circuit components as switches, variable capacitors and resistors, potentiometers, etc., thus grouping all the circuit controls for convenience of operation.

Panel Mounting. Said of a circuit component, the fixing arrangements of which are such that it may be mounted on a panel.

Panotrope. Term employed, chiefly in America, for an electrically operated gramophone, i.e. one employing an electric pick-up, thermionic amplifier and one or more loudspeakers.

Paper Capacitor. Fixed-value capacitor in which the dielectric consists of thin paper and the plates consist of metal foil.

Parabolic Mirror. Mirror, the reflecting surface of which is a paraboloid of revolution. Incident light parallel to the axis is brought to a point focus free from aberration, or light from a point source situated at the focus of the mirror is projected as a parallel beam.

Parabolic Reflector. System of parabolic form, made from metallic sheet or of wires, having a similar effect upon radio waves to that of a parabolic mirror upon light. It is used in both the transmission and the reception of highly-directional signals.

Parafeed Coupling. Form of INTERVALVE COUPLING combining the resistance–capacitance and the transformer coupling systems.

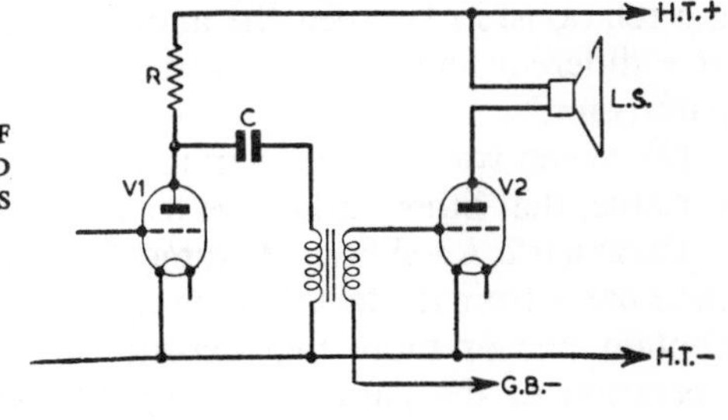

FIG. P-1.—BASIC CIRCUIT OF AMPLIFIER WITH PARAFEED COUPLING BETWEEN VALVES V1 AND V2.

Parallel

A basic circuit is shown in Fig. P-1. The anode of the valve V1 is fed from the h.t. supply via the resistor R, but the alternating component of the anode current is diverted via capacitor C to the primary winding of the transformer T. As the transformer does not have to carry the d.c. component it can be made much smaller and at lower cost.

Parallel. Two or more circuits or circuit elements are said to be connected in parallel when the total current flow is divided between them.

Parallel Feed. Method of connecting the anode of a thermionic valve to the h.t. supply through a resistor or inductor, the alternating component of the anode current being diverted via a capacitor. Also termed shunt feed. The parafeed coupling described above is an example of parallel feed.

Paralysis. Effect of applying such an excess signal to a thermionic valve that the circuit capacitances are charged during the positive-going part of the cycle to such an extent that they cannot discharge completely during the negative-going part of the cycle. Part of the signal is thus not amplified. In the case of radar installations, and particularly when the target is at short range, overloading in this way does not provide time for discharge between the transmission of the pulse and the reception of the echo.

Paramagnetic. Said of a substance which can be magnetized in the direction of the magnetizing field.

Parameter. A variable quantity, the value of which determines or affects the values of two or more other quantities or the relationship between them. The term is used in a variety of senses, the following being the more usual:

(1) A variable quantity which may be kept constant while the effect of other variables is being investigated. Thus, the " family " of anode current/anode volts characteristics of a thermionic valve shown in Fig. V-1 consists of a number of curves, each showing the relationship between the anode current and the anode voltage at a different value of grid voltage. The grid voltage is here the parameter.

(2) When two or more variables are all functions of some other variable, that other variable is termed a parameter.

Parametric Amplifier. Parametric or reactance amplifiers derive their name from the fact that the equations governing their operation contain one or more time-dependent reactance parameters. The operation of the parametric amplifier depends on the fact that a time-varying reactance can exhibit negative-resistance characteristics under certain conditions, or can act as a frequency converter under other conditions. A feature is the low noise and reasonable bandwidth possible, e.g. with the gain adjusted to about 20 dB a bandwidth of about 5 Mc/s is possible with a noise figure of 5 dB. Noise figures as low as 1 dB have been obtained.

Paraphase. Term descriptive of the production or application of two alternating voltages of identical waveform frequency and amplitude, but of opposite phase, obtained by applying a fraction of the output voltage of one amplifier to the input of a similar amplifier, the second amplifier being so adjusted that the two outputs are equal but in anti-phase. The paraphase output is suitable for application to the two grid circuits of a pair of amplifying valves operated in PUSH–PULL.

Paraphase Amplifier. Amplifier preceding a push–pull stage, and employing the paraphase principle.

Parasitic Aerial. That part of a directional aerial which is not connected directly to the transmitter or receiver. See also PASSIVE AERIAL.

Parasitic Oscillation. Undesired oscillation occurring in the circuit of a thermionic valve, generally due to unwanted coupling in the anode, screen or grid circuit of the valve.

Parasitic Stopper. Device, such as a resistor or inductor, included in the grid, screen or anode circuit of a valve in order to damp out parasitic oscillations. Sometimes called a grid stopper, screen stopper or anode stopper.

Paraxial. Said of the path of a beam which is parallel to the axis of the optical (or electron-optical) system.

Particle Accelerator. Device for accelerating charged particles of atomic magnitude to very high velocities corresponding to energies in the order of millions of electron-volts. See also BETATRON, CYCLOTRON and LINEAR ACCELERATOR.

Particle Counters and Detectors. Devices for detecting or counting particles of atomic magnitude. Charged particles, i.e. alpha particles, beta particles, protons and mesons can be detected by reason of the IONIZATION or of the EXCITATION which they produce when passing through matter (e.g. gas in an IONIZATION CHAMBER). In the case of uncharged particles, such as neutrons and neutral mesons, it is first necessary to cause them to produce secondary charged particles. For example, high-energy neutrons can produce positively-charged particles (protons) by collision with hydrogen atoms, while low-energy neutrons can be made to bombard boron-10, one of the stable isotopes of boron, when helium and lithium nuclei are ejected from the boron.

Partition Noise. NOISE occurring in a circuit due to random variations in the distribution of electron flow to the screen and anode of a multi-grid thermionic valve.

Passive Aerial. Also termed parasitic aerial. That part of a directional aerial which is not connected to the transmitter or receiver. If located behind the aerial proper or " active aerial ", the passive aerial is called a REFLECTOR; if in front of the active aerial it is termed a DIRECTOR.

Passive Network. Electrical network which contains no source of electromotive force or gain.

Pattern. The luminous trace produced on the screen of a cathode-ray tube due to the movement of the electron beam.

Pattern Generator. Generator for producing a signal which, when applied to the input terminals of a television receiver, will produce a PATTERN on the screen of the picture tube. It is, in effect, a low-power television transmitter which is connected directly to the receiver for checking its performance during testing or servicing.

Peak. The maximum positive or negative instantaneous value of a variable quantity, and particularly of a periodic quantity such as an alternating voltage or current. See Fig. P-2.

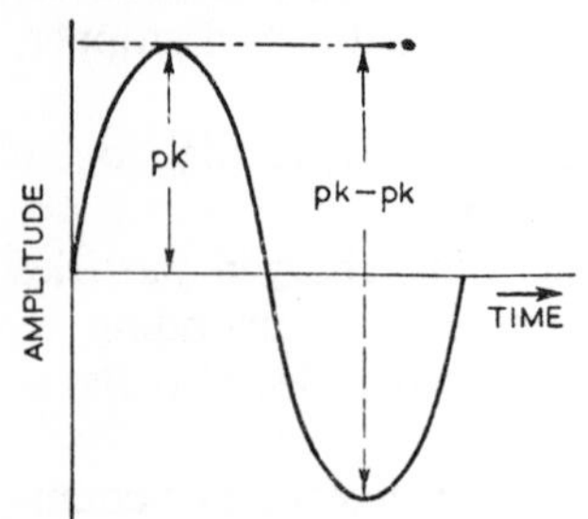

FIG. P-2.—GRAPHICAL REPRESENTATION OF A SINE WAVE ILLUSTRATING THE PEAK (pk) AND PEAK-TO-PEAK (pk–pk) VALUES OF THE AMPLITUDE.

Peak Clipping. Process of suppressing the peaks of a speech-frequency waveform, thus making possible a greater modulation level at the expense of some slight increase in distortion. Fig. P-3 shows the envelope of a modulated carrier without and with peak clipping.

Peak Inverse Voltage. (Abbreviated to p.i.v.) The peak value of the voltage applied between the anode and cathode of a thermionic valve in the reverse direction to that which produces the normal flow of anode current.

Peak Power. The maximum instantaneous value of the electrical power in watts delivered by a transmitter, and particularly the power delivered during a pulse. Since a pulse is of very short duration, and is separated from the previous and following pulses by an appreciable period of time, so that adequate cooling can take place between successive peaks, a valve may be rated for a higher peak output power for pulse operation than the average power over a period of time.

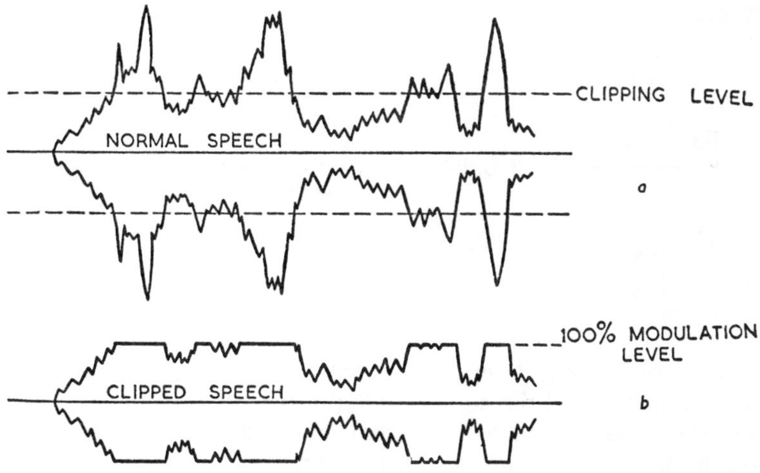

FIG. P-3.—SPEECH-FREQUENCY WAVEFORMS SHOWING AT (b) THE EFFECT OF PEAK CLIPPING.

Peak-to-peak Value. The arithmetical (*not* algebraic) sum of the positive and negative peak values of an alternating quantity. See Fig. P-2.

Peak White. The amplitude of the direct voltage corresponding to the pure white portions of a television image.

Penetration. A high-frequency current in a solid conductor tends to flow near the surface. This is known as the skin effect, and as a result the effective resistance of the conductor to high-frequency currents is greater than to direct currents. The depth of penetration is defined as the wall thickness of a hollow conductor of the same overall dimensions, which, if the high-frequency current were distributed uniformly over its cross-section, would have the same resistance to high-frequency currents as the solid conductor.

Pentagrid. Alternative name for the HEPTODE or seven-electrode thermionic valve.

Pentavalent. Said of an atom which can combine with five hydrogen atoms or their equivalent.

Pentode. Electron tube having five electrodes. Although originally, and still mainly, applied to five-electrode thermionic valves, the term can properly be applied also to those forms of cathode-ray tube having five electrodes. In the pentode valve, the conventional symbol for which, with an indirectly-heated cathode is illustrated in Fig. P-4, the electrodes comprise a cathode, an anode and

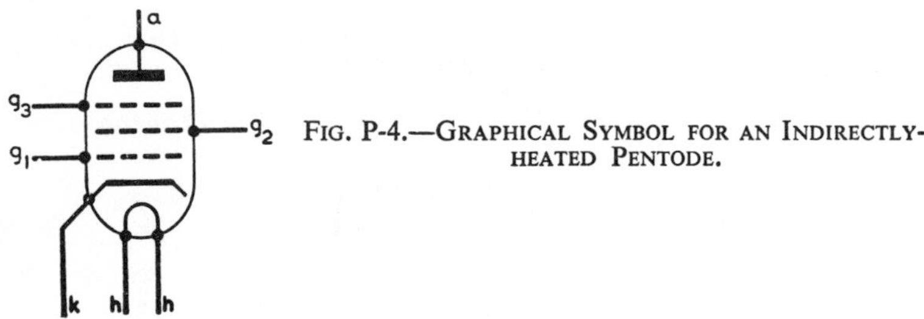

FIG. P-4.—GRAPHICAL SYMBOL FOR AN INDIRECTLY-HEATED PENTODE.

three intermediate grids termed the control grid (nearest the cathode), the screen grid and the suppressor grid (nearest the anode). The pentode is thus a development from the TETRODE, which has only two grids: control grid and screen grid. The function of the additional (suppressor) grid in the pentode is to prevent secondary electrons, emitted from the anode, from reaching the screen grid. This is achieved by maintaining the suppressor grid at a negative potential with respect to the anode, usually by connecting the suppressor grid to the cathode, either by a permanent connexion within the envelope or by external wiring. The latter arrangement has the advantage that it permits potentials other than that of the cathode to be applied to the suppressor for special applications. The negative potential at the suppressor grid repels the secondary electrons ejected from the anode, and they therefore return to the anode instead of travelling to the screen. The negative resistance "kink" in the anode current/anode volts characteristic of the tetrode does not therefore appear in the pentode characteristic.

Fig. P-5 shows a family of anode current/anode volts characteristic curves of a typical pentode, measured at a constant value of screen-grid voltage and for a number of different values of control-grid voltage. It will be clear that, owing to the absence of the negative resistance kink, a pentode will give stable operation over a very much greater anode voltage swing than a comparable tetrode. It will also be noticed that over that part of the characteristic beyond the "knee" of the curve the value of the anode current does not greatly change with variation of anode voltage. This means that

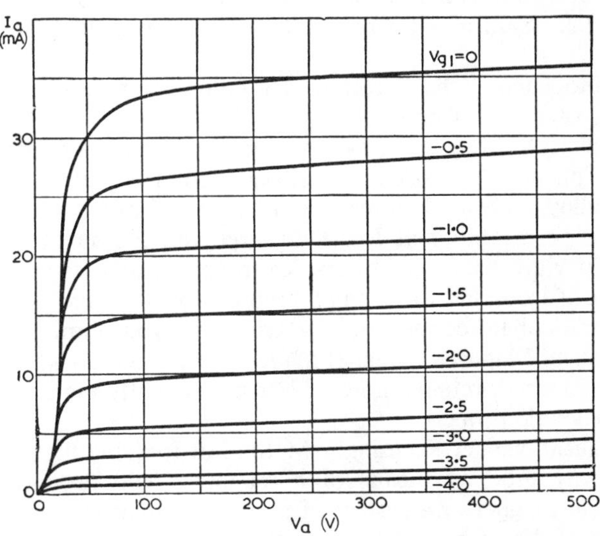

FIG. P-5.—FAMILY OF ANODE VOLTS/ANODE CURRENT CHARACTERISTIC CURVES OF A TYPICAL HIGH-SLOPE PENTODE.

the DYNAMIC CHARACTERISTICS of the valve are a much closer approximation to the STATIC CHARACTERISTICS than in a triode. Pentodes are available in two main forms—power pentodes, intended for use as output valves, and voltage-amplifying pentodes. The latter may again be subdivided into types suitable for low-frequency applications and those especially designed for use in a high-frequency circuit, that is to say as radio-frequency or intermediate-frequency amplifiers, mixers, etc. High-frequency pentodes are available in several types, for example the "straight" or high-slope pentodes and those with variable-mu characteristics for use in stages embodying automatic volume control.

Percentage Modulation. See MODULATION DEPTH.

Perikon Detector. Form of crystal detector employed in the early days of radio broadcasting. It consists of a crystal of zincite (a naturally-occurring oxide of zinc) and a crystal of bornite (a mixed sulphide of copper and iron) so mounted that there is a point contact between them.

Period. One complete cycle of an oscillating or other cyclic phenomenon, or the time occupied by one cycle.

Period of Decay. The HALF-LIFE or period of time taken for the activity of a radioactive substance to fall to half its original value.

Periodic. Said of a phenomenon which repeats itself in regular cycles.

Periodic Time. The duration of a complete cycle of a periodic quantity or phenomenon.

Periodicity. Frequency, i.e. the number of complete cycles of a periodic phenomenon occurring in one second.

Permalloy. General name for a group of alloys having high magnetic permeability at low field strength, and small hysteresis loss. They are composed of approximately four parts of nickel to one part of iron, and often small amounts of other metals, such as chromium, cobalt, copper, manganese or molybdenum.

Permanent Magnet. Magnet made from a material which, when once magnetized, retains more or less permanently the greater part of its magnetic properties.

Permanent-magnet Focusing. Method of focusing the beam in a cathode-ray tube by means of a magnetic field produced by a permanent magnet or a system of permanent magnets mounted on the neck of the tube. See MAGNETIC FOCUSING.

Permeability. (Symbol μ) The ratio of the magnetic induction B, in a magnetized material to the magnetizing force H.

Permeability Tuning. Method of tuning an oscillatory circuit by adjusting the position of a piece of ferromagnetic material, e.g. an iron-dust core or a ferrite slug, with respect to the winding of an inductor, thus altering the inductance of the circuit.

Permittivity. (1) The absolute permittivity of a dielectric is the ratio of the electric displacement to the electric force producing it. It is measured in terms of the capacitance of a unit cube of the dielectric.

(2) The relative permittivity of a dielectric (also known as the dielectric constant or specific inductive capacity) is the ratio of the electric flux density produced in the dielectric to that which would be produced in a vacuum by the same electric force.

Persistence. The property possessed by PHOSPHORS (phosphorescent materials) of emitting light after the exciting influence has ceased. The materials suitable for coating the screens of cathode-ray tubes have different degrees of persistence, as measured by the time taken for the illumination to decay to a specified percentage of its maximum value. This may range from a few tens of milliseconds to over a minute.

Persistence of Vision. The ability of the eye to retain perception for a short time after the original stimulus has ceased. As a result, the eye cannot respond to changes of image occurring more rapidly than about 25 per second. It is this property which permits the eye to interpret as a continuously moving picture the rapidly changing picture elements presented in rapid succession in a television screen.

pH Meter. Instrument for determining the pH value of solutions. The instrument actually measures the electro-motive force generated in an electrolytic cell having specially designed electrodes and with the solution under test as the electrolyte. As this electro-motive force is in the order of tens of millivolts only, some form of VALVE-VOLTMETER must be employed. The instrument can be arranged to indicate or to record its readings, or may be adapted for the automatic control of acidity or alkalinity in chemical processing. In this application the " signal " obtained from the measuring unit can be compared with a reference voltage corresponding to the degree of acidity or alkalinity it is desired to maintain, and the difference or error signal, suitably amplified, can be made to operate a valve or other device for controlling the supply of suitable reagents.

pH Value. A number applied to a solution to indicate its degree of acidity or alkalinity in terms of its hydrogen-ion content. It is, in fact, the logarithm to base 10 of the reciprocal of the hydrogen-ion concentration, the hydrogen-ion concentration in a neutral solution being 10^{-7}. The pH scale ranges from zero for a solution of extreme acidity containing one gram-ion of hydrogen (positive) ions per litre, to 14 for a solution of extreme alkalinity containing one gram-ion of hydroxyl (negative) ions per litre.

Phantom Aerial. See DUMMY AERIAL.

Phase Angle. When two alternating quantities have the same frequency but their maximum values do not occur at the same instant of time they are said to have a phase difference. The phase displacement is usually indicated by the angle between the vectors representing the two quantities, and may be expressed in degrees of arc or in radians. If the two quantities are represented graphically on a time scale the phase angle can be indicated by dividing the period of one cycle into 360° or 2π radians (see Fig. P-6).

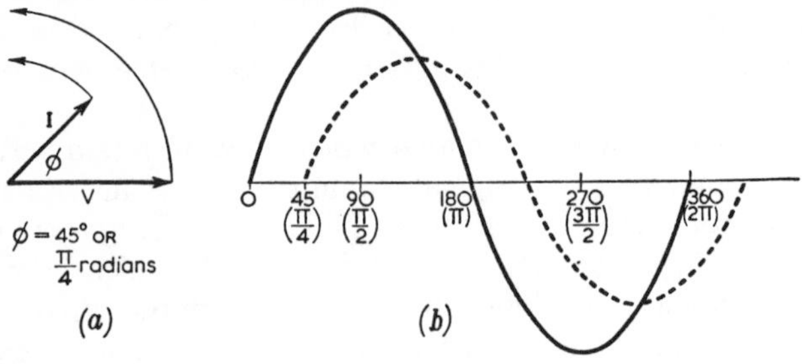

FIG. P-6.

(a) Current and voltage vectors indicating phase angle (ϕ).
(b) Corresponding current and voltage waveforms indicating phase angle in terms of degrees (45°) and radians ($\pi/4$).

Phase Difference (Phase Displacement). See PHASE ANGLE.

Phase Distortion. Distortion of a signal due to the velocity at which the energy associated with a wave is propagated varying with the frequency.

Phase Inverter. Circuit which provides an output in anti-phase (180° phase difference) with the input.

Phase Modulation. A modulation system in which the phase of the carrier is advanced and retarded at a rate equal to the frequency of the modulating signal, the phase shift being proportional to the amplitude of the modulating signal. A phase-modulated signal can be converted to a frequency-modulated signal by inserting a simple network.

Phase Reversal. General term for the process of obtaining a signal of identical waveform but of opposite phase to an original signal, the two signals being then applied to the input of a PUSH–PULL amplifier.

Phase Shift. Change of phase relation (phase angle) between two alternating quantities of equal frequency, either deliberately introduced or as the result of some undesirable circuit condition. An example of intentional phase-shift is the adjustment of the phase angle between the control voltage applied to the grid of a THYRATRON and the alternating voltage applied to the anode in order to control the time during which the tube conducts in each cycle, and thus to control the mean value of the anode current. An example of unwanted phase shift is the effect sometimes observed in a television receiver when, owing to the effects of stray capacitances, components of different frequencies in the video waveform are thrown out of step, and arrive at slightly different times, thus causing distortion of the picture.

Phase Splitter. See PARAPHASE AMPLIFIER.

Phon. Unit of loudness. The intensity of a sound is expressed in phons as the number of decibels above the threshold of hearing for a sound of the same frequency.

Phonic Wheel. A simple form of synchronous motor requiring very small input power. It may, for example, be driven from a thermionic oscillator, and used to measure the frequency of the oscillations.

Phosphorescence. Emission of luminous glow by a substance after having been excited by electron bombardment or by irradiation with electromagnetic radiation.

Phosphors. Name given to a class of material used for forming the luminous screens of cathode-ray tubes, and for converting ultra-violet radiation into visible light in fluorescent lamps. They possess the property of emitting visible light when bombarded with swiftly-moving electrons, as in the cathode-ray tube, or when irradiated with certain forms of electromagnetic radiation, as in fluorescent lamps. In the case of the phosphors employed in cathode-ray tubes, the luminescence is a combination of two main effects, fluorescence, or the emission of light during the period of stimulus, and phosphorescence, or the continuation of luminescence for a shorter or longer period after the stimulus has ceased. The latter effect is also known as PERSISTENCE. The various available materials differ in respect of the colour of the emitted light, their persistence or period of afterglow, and their luminous efficiency. A phosphor giving a greenish illumination is normally used in oscilloscope tubes when the image has to be viewed by direct vision, but a phosphor giving a blue luminescence is more suitable when the trace is to be recorded photographically. The screens of television picture tubes consist of a combination of materials giving a substantially white light, with a slight admixture of other colours. The duration of after-glow may range from some milliseconds to several minutes. Phosphors of short persistence are chosen for television and for oscilloscopy where photographic records of rapidly changing patterns have to be made; tubes of medium to long persistence are used in oscilloscopes for applications involving visual examination of the trace; and long-persistence tubes for low-speed applications, the observation of transients and for radar. The chief substances employed in phosphors for cathode-ray tubes are zinc orthosilicate (green luminescence), calcium tungstate (blue-violet), zinc sulphide (blue or green) and cadmium sulphide (blue or green), these substances being used either singly or in combination. Frequently a small proportion of some other material, usually metallic, e.g. copper, manganese or silver, is added as an actuator and for colour determination.

Phot. Unit of luminous flux equal to the illumination produced by one lumen on a surface of one square centimetre.

Photicon. Proprietary name for a miniature CAMERA TUBE of the image iconoscope type.

Photo Cathode. Cathode which emits electrons when irradiated by light. See PHOTO-EMISSIVE CELL.

Photo Cell (Photo-electric Cell). Device the current through which is governed by the intensity of the incident illumination. Photo cells are of three main types—photo-conductive, photo-voltaic and photo-emissive cells, of which the last named is a true electron tube.

Photo-chemical Cell. Light-sensitive cell consisting of two similar electrodes immersed in an electrolyte. When one electrode is illuminated a potential difference is set up between the two electrodes. Also termed a photo-electrolytic or photo-voltaic cell.

Photo Conduction. Property possessed by certain substances, notably selenium, whereby their conductivity increases with the intensity of the light falling upon them.

Photo-conductive Camera Tube. A form of CAMERA TUBE of the type represented by the VIDICON, in which an image of the scene to be televised is projected optically through a transparent metal signal plate on to a target which consists of a layer of photo-conductive material backing the signal plate. The rear surface of the photo-conductive layer, i.e. that farthest from the signal plate, is scanned by a low-velocity electron beam projected from an electron gun. The scanned surface is substantially at cathode potential, and the signal plate is held a few volts positive thereto. In the absence of illumination the transverse resistance of the photo-conductive layer is high, and therefore no significant electron current flows from the target to the signal plate. When, however, the front surface of the target, i.e. the surface in contact with the signal plate, is illuminated by the picture, the conductivity of each elemental area of the target increases in proportion to the amount of light falling upon it, and a positive charge leaks through to the scanned side, thus building up a charge image which is progressively discharged by the scanning beam. See Fig. P-7.

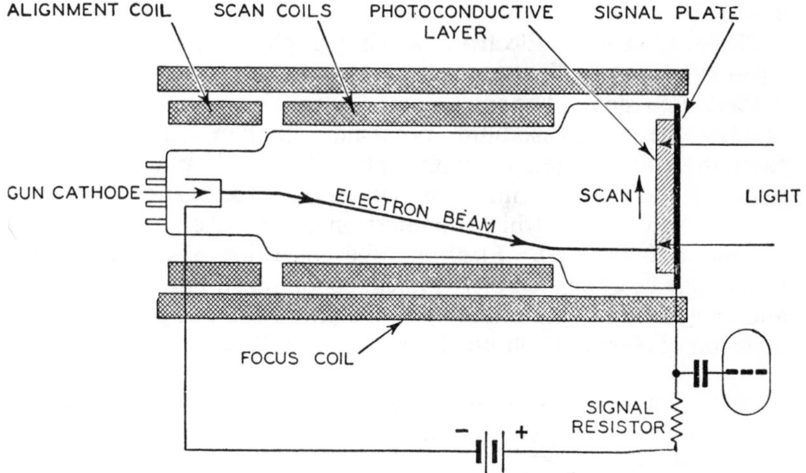

FIG. P-7.—BASIC PRINCIPLE OF THE PHOTO-CONDUCTIVE CAMERA TUBE.

Photo-conductive Cell. Photo-electric cell containing one of a number of materials, e.g. selenium, the conductivity of which changes when the material is irradiated by light.

Photo Current. Current represented by the flow of electrons, emitted by a photo-cathode when illuminated, and collected by an anode maintained at a positive potential with respect to the photo-cathode.

Photo Diode. Semiconductor diode which exploits the fact that an increase in reverse current occurs when the junction is exposed to visible or infra-red radiation.

Photo-electric Cell. See PHOTO CELL.

Photo-electric Effects. The changes in the electrical state of an insulated conductor when irradiated by light, and particularly the loss of negative charge or gain of positive charge resulting from PHOTO-EMISSION.

Photo-electric Exposure Meter. Instrument comprising a milli-ammeter, a photo-electric cell and a battery. It measures the intensity of the illumination falling upon the light-sensitive element of the cell, and from the readings the appropriate exposure for photographic purposes can be determined.

Photo-electric Pick-up. A device in which changes of illumination produce corresponding changes in an electric circuit. Photo-electric cells, and also such devices as television cameras, are photo-electric pick-ups.

Photo Electrons. Electrons leaving a photo-emissive cathode when irradiated by light.

Photo Emission. The emission of electrons by certain substances, notably the metals sodium, potassium, lithium, rubidium and caesium, when irradiated with light. For each photo-emissive material there is a minimum THRESHOLD FREQUENCY for the incident light, below which no emission takes place.

Photo-emissive Cell. Electron tube consisting of an envelope, which may be evacuated or gas-filled, containing a PHOTO CATHODE and an anode. Light falling upon the photo cathode produces the emission of electrons (photo electrons) which flow through the tube

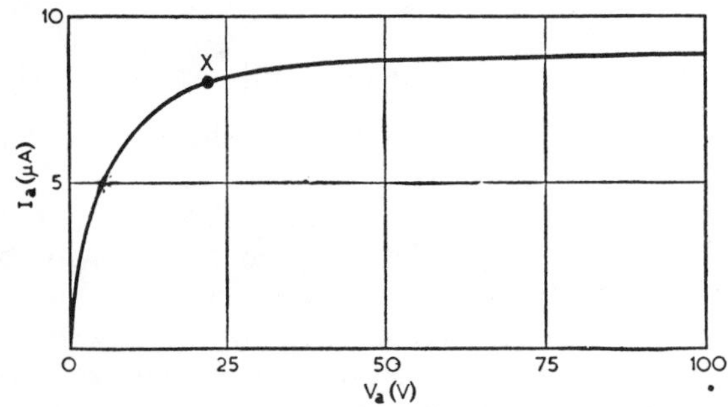

FIG. P-8.—GENERAL FORM OF ANODE VOLTS/ANODE CURRENT CHARACTERISTIC OF A HIGH-VACUUM PHOTO-EMISSIVE CELL FOR A GIVEN ANODE LOAD AND CONSTANT ILLUMINATION.

X is the saturation point.

to the anode, which is maintained at a positive potential with respect to the cathode. An electric current, the ANODE CURRENT, is thus maintained in the external anode circuit, the strength of this current, within certain limits, being governed by the intensity of the illumination and by the anode voltage. In a typical construction the cathode is a semi-cylinder, coated on the concave side with photo-emissive material, and the anode is a metal rod situated at the axis of the semi-cylindrical cathode.

The two most commonly used photo cathodes are: (1) a monatomic layer of caesium on silver oxide, and (2) a thin layer of caesium on antimony. The former has maximum sensitivity to incandescent light and NEAR INFRA-RED radiation; the latter is most sensitive to daylight and to light with a blue predominance.

The anode volts/anode current characteristic of a high-vacuum photo cell, for a given amount of illumination, is of the form shown in Fig. P-8, from which it is seen that a condition of saturation is reached at X, that is to say, any increase of anode voltage produces negligible increase of anode current. At anode voltages above the saturation value, therefore, the value of the anode current is determined entirely by the incident illumination.

The general form of the anode volts/anode current characteristic of a gas-filled photo-emissive cell is shown in Fig. P-9. In this

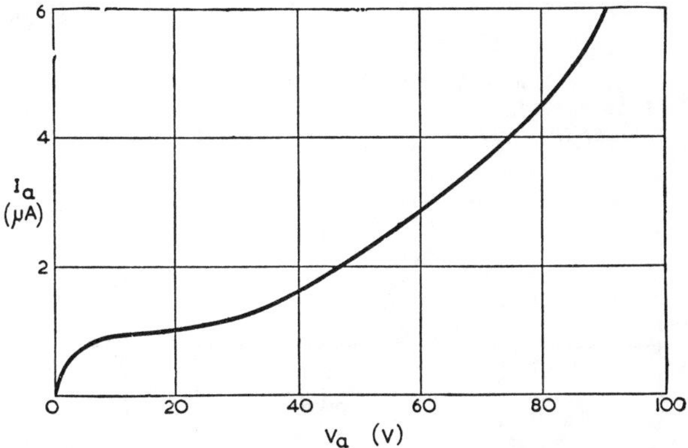

FIG. P-9.—GENERAL FORM OF ANODE VOLTS/ANODE CURRENT CHARACTERISTIC OF A GAS-FILLED PHOTO-EMISSIVE CELL UNDER CONSTANT ILLUMINATION.

type of cell the anode current is greater than that represented by the actual emission, by reason of the GAS AMPLIFICATION, i.e. the release of electrons from gas atoms due to collisions between electrons and gas atoms. The degree of gas amplification is largely governed by the anode voltage, so that the anode current increases progressively with increasing anode voltage. Due to the gas amplification, a gas-filled photo cell is more sensitive than a vacuum cell of exactly similar design. This is indicated in Fig. P-10, which shows the characteristics of a vacuum cell and a gas-filled cell of identical dimensions. Provided that the anode voltage is kept above the saturation value, the anode current of a vacuum-type photo cell is proportional to the amount of light falling upon the cathode, and such cells are particularly suitable for applications in

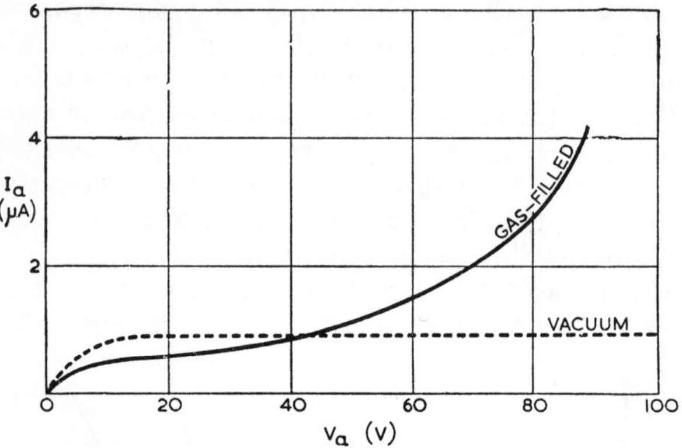

FIG. P-10.—ANODE VOLTS/ANODE CURRENT CHARACTERISTICS OF A HIGH-VACUUM (BROKEN LINE) AND A GAS-FILLED (HEAVY LINE) PHOTO-EMISSIVE CELL OF IDENTICAL DIMENSIONS AND UNDER EQUAL ILLUMINATION.

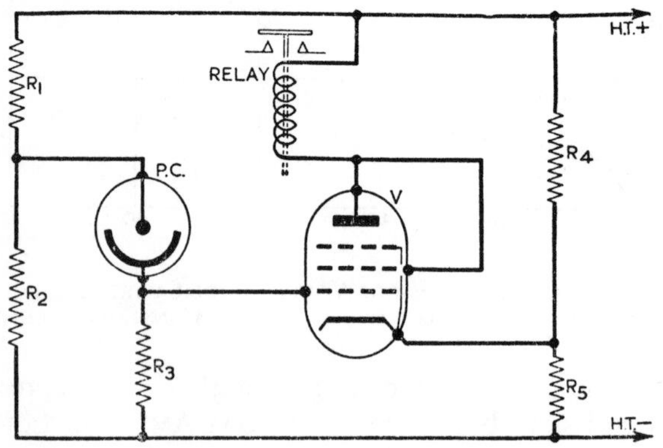

FIG. P-11.—BASIC CIRCUIT IN WHICH THE VARIATIONS OF ANODE CURRENT OF PHOTO CELL PC ARE AMPLIFIED BY THE PENTODE V, THE PENTODE IN THIS EXAMPLE BEING CONNECTED AS A TRIODE.

which accurate measurements or proportional control are required. In gas-filled cells the anode current varies with the anode voltage over the whole working range. Such cells are therefore not suitable for quantitative work, but have a wide field of application in

" on–off " or " stop–go " devices operated by small but sudden changes in illumination.

A basic photo-cell circuit is shown in Fig. P-11. The positive potential at the anode of the cell is derived from the potentiometer R1, R2. R3 is the load resistor of the photo cell and also serves as the grid resistor of the amplifying valve V. The cathode bias for valve V is derived from the potentiometer R4, R5. The anode current of the photo cell, flowing in R3, produces a voltage drop which is applied as the input signal between the grid and cathode of the amplifying valve. A relay or an indicating instrument can be included in the anode circuit of the amplifying valve.

Photo Multiplier. Photo-electric cell incorporating a number of DYNODES thus obtaining a high degree of amplification. The general structure of a typical photo multiplier is shown in Fig. P-12. The photo-cathode is marked k_1 and the eleven dynodes k_2, k_3 . . . k_{12}. Current gains in the order of 3×10^7 are obtainable. See also ELECTRON MULTIPLIER.

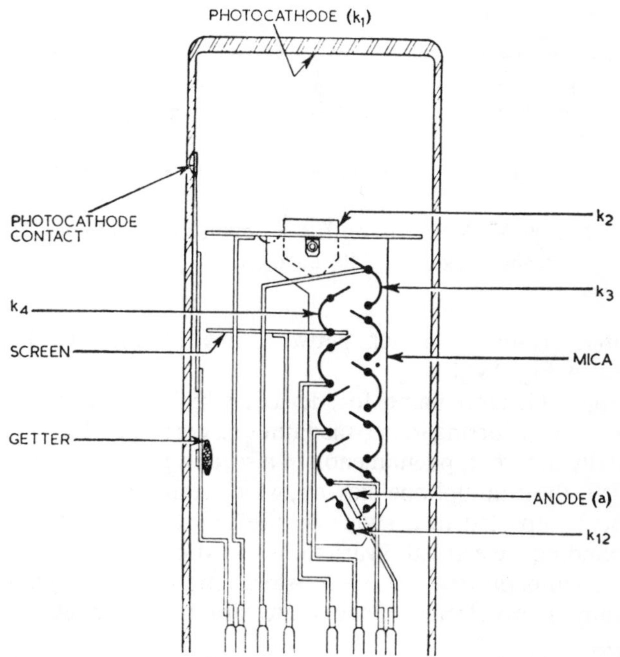

FIG. P-12.—ELECTRODE STRUCTURE OF A PHOTO MULTIPLIER TUBE.

Photo-radiogram. A still picture transmitted by radio.

Photo-sensitive. Said of a substance which exhibits change of its chemical or electrical state under the action of light.

Photo Transistor. A form of JUNCTION TRANSISTOR so constructed and connected as to exploit the fact that a current is generated at the emitter junction when exposed to light, this current being then amplified by transistor action.

Photon. A light quantum, i.e. a definite amount of radiation having a frequency within the visible spectrum. A photon is emitted from an excited atom when one of the orbital electrons, having been transferred to an orbit of higher energy level, suddenly returns to its former orbit. A photon may be considered either as a train of electromagnetic waves or as a particle having a mass equal to $h\nu/c^2$ where ν is the frequency, h is PLANCK'S CONSTANT and c the velocity of light.

Pi-attenuator. (π-attenuator) An attenuator network having one of the general forms shown in Fig. P-13.

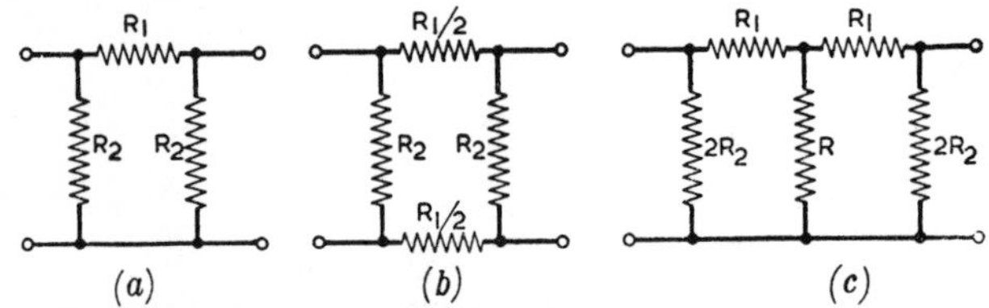

FIG. P-13.—VARIANTS OF THE π-ATTENUATOR NETWORK.
(a) Unbalanced. (b) Balanced. (c) Recurrent.

Pi-filter. (π-filter) Filter network having one of the forms depicted in Fig. P-14.

Pick-up. General name for devices which translate a varying phenomenon occurring in one medium to a correspondingly varying, but usually different, phenomenon in a second medium. A familiar example is the gramophone pick-up, which translates the mechanical movement imparted to a stylus by the grooves of the record into corresponding electrical variations. Microphones, television cameras, temperature-sensitive resistors, strain gauges, photo cells and many piezo-electric devices are among other examples of pick-ups.

Pico. Prefix denoting 10^{-12}.

Picofarad. (pF) A micro-microfarad, or one-millionth of a MICROFARAD.

Picture Element. A small area of a television picture, ideally a square having a side equal to the distance between successive lines of scan. In the British 405-line system with 25 complete pictures per second, the number of picture elements in one second is something over 4,500,000.

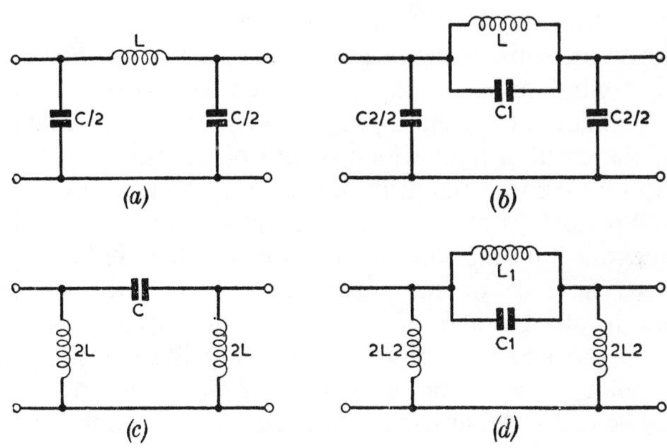

FIG. P-14.—VARIANTS OF THE π-SECTION FILTER.

(a) Basic π-section low-pass filter;
(b) Shunt-derived π-section low-pass filter;
(c) Basic π-section high-pass filter;
(d) Shunt-derived π-section high-pass filter.

Picture Frequency. Number of times the whole of the picture area is scanned in one second during television transmission. In the British system the picture frequency is 25.

Picture Information. The details, as regards the light values of successive picture elements, and the commencement and ending of successive line and frame periods in a television signal, transmitted as modulation of the vision carrier wave.

Picture Ratio. Ratio between the width and height of a television picture. In the British system it is 4 : 3. More usually termed the ASPECT RATIO.

Picture Signal. That part of a television signal which transmits the PICTURE INFORMATION as opposed to the sound accompaniment.

Picture Strip. One complete line of a television picture.

Picture Telegraphy. See FACSIMILE TELEGRAPHY.

Picture-to-sync. Ratio. The ratio between that proportion of the peak amplitude of a television waveform reserved for the transmission of details of the actual picture and that proportion occupied by the synchronizing pulses. In the British system this ratio is 7 : 3. See also TELEVISION WAVEFORM.

Picture Tube. Cathode-ray tube designed particularly for use in a television receiver. Television picture tubes are designed for magnetic deflexion of the beam, and, until recently, for magnetic focusing. However, later types have gun assemblies which permit electrostatic focusing of the beam. The screen phosphor gives substantially white luminescence, and is often backed by a thin deposit of metal, usually aluminium, for the purpose of directing forward much of the emitted light which would otherwise either be lost by absorption by the internal graphite coating of the tube or, by being reflected forward from the electrode system, would give an additional overall illumination of the screen, thus reducing picture contrast. The face of the screen upon which the phosphor is deposited is often made of tinted glass. This improves picture contrast in the presence of strong ambient illumination, at some slight sacrifice of overall brightness. The gun structure of a picture tube may be of triode, tetrode or pentode form—the last-mentioned for electrostatically-focused tubes. Picture tubes are designed for use at anode voltages in the order of some kilovolts, the present limit for tubes for domestic receivers being about 18 kV for direct-viewing tubes and 25 kV for projection tubes. The internal surface of the neck and cone of the envelope is coated with a thin layer of graphite, which forms part of the conductive path between the anode of the tube and the e.h.t. terminal which is sealed into the glass. The external surface is also coated with graphite, the internal and external graphite coatings, together with the glass between them, forming a capacitor which may be used as part of the smoothing filter for the e.h.t. supply. The gun system often embodies an ION TRAP to deflect and collect negative ions produced in the region of the cathode and which otherwise would travel to the luminescent screen, their impact being sufficient to destroy the luminescent properties of the phosphor.

Piezo. Prefix signifying pressure. See PIEZO-ELECTRIC EFFECT.

Piezo-electric Effect. Phenomenon exhibited by certain crystals, notably quartz, tourmaline and Rochelle salt, whereby the application of an electric field causes expansion along one axis of the crystal and contraction along another axis. Conversely, the application of mechanical pressure between one pair of faces of the crystal generates a potential difference between another pair of faces. The effect is exploited in CRYSTAL MICROPHONES, CRYSTAL OSCILLATORS, CRYSTAL PICK-UPS, etc.

Piezo-electric Transducer. TRANSDUCER in which the transformation of energy from electrical to mechanical or vice versa is the result of the PIEZO-ELECTRIC EFFECT.

Piezo Microphone. See CRYSTAL MICROPHONE.

Piezo Pick-up. See CRYSTAL PICK-UP.

Pillow Distortion. Form of distortion of a television picture in which the raster assumes a shape similar to a pillow, that is to say, with concave boundaries. See PIN-CUSHION DISTORTION.

Pilot Lamp. Small lamp included in an electrical circuit to indicate when the circuit is alive. In radio receivers the pilot lamp usually serves also to illuminate the tuning dial.

Pinch, Valve. Form of construction used in certain types of electron tubes (and also in incandescent electric lamps) in which the connecting leads between the electrodes and the external circuit are sealed into a re-entrant part of the envelope. Often the pumping tube is included in the pinch. Fig. P-15 shows this form of con-

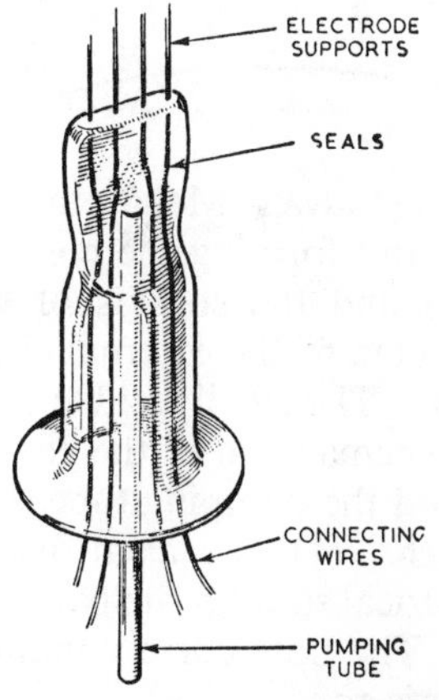

FIG. P-15.—FOOT OF A THERMIONIC VALVE SHOWING PINCH CONSTRUCTION.

struction, which commences with a flanged " foot-tube ", the pumping tube and the requisite number of lead-in wires. Each wire is a composite assembly consisting of a length of copper wire for ultimate connexion to the VALVE PIN, a short length of stouter wire to which the appropriate valve electrode is later welded and, between these two, a shorter length of special wire having the same coefficient of expansion as the glass envelope. The lead-in wires and the pumping tube are held by a jig in the correct positions in the foot-tube, the top of which is then softened by a blow-pipe flame, after which mechanical pressure is applied to seal the wires into the glass as indicated in the sketch. During this operation the pumping tube is kept open by a stream of compressed air. When the support wires have been cut and bent to shape the electrodes are welded to them, after which the bulb is fused to the foot as indicated in the dotted line, and the envelope evacuated via the pumping tube.

Pin-cushion Distortion. Distortion of the reproduced television picture due to non-uniformity of the field produced by the deflexion coils, whereby the sides, top and bottom of the picture are concave as shown in Fig. P-16. Also termed PILLOW DISTORTION.

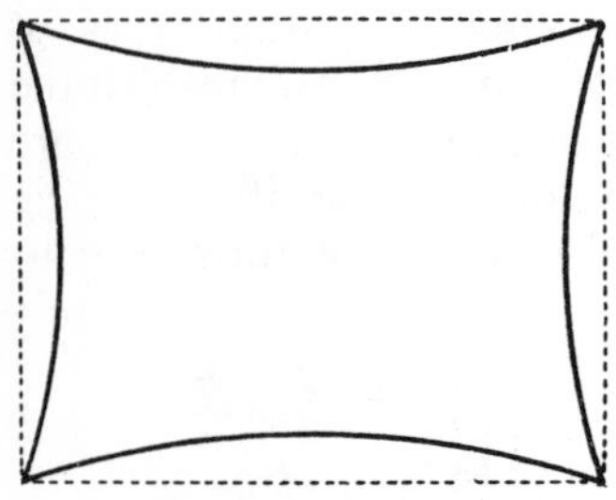

FIG. P-16.—PIN-CUSHION DISTORTION OF A RECTANGULAR PICTURE (CONSIDERABLY EXAGGERATED FOR THE SAKE OF CLARITY).

Pins, Valve. Metal pins projecting from one end of an electron tube, and forming the connexions between the different tube electrodes and the sockets of the valve-holder, whereby the tube is connected to the external circuit.

Pip. The small residue of the PUMPING TUBE of an electron tube which remains after the envelope has been evacuated or filled with gas and the pumping tube sealed off.

Pitch. (1) The axial distance between two adjacent turns of a cylindrical spiral or helix, or the number of such turns in unit length.

(2) The note corresponding to the fundamental frequency of an acoustic tone.

Plan Position Indicator. (p.p.i.) Radar display system in which the cathode-ray tube exhibits a plan or map of a circular area surrounding the radar transmitter. The transmitting aerial (scanner) is in continuous rotation, and the electromagnetic deflexion coils of the cathode-ray tube are also rotated on the neck of the tube, in synchronism with the aerial. The electron beam in the tube thus scans a circular area of the screen from the centre to the circumference in a series of successive radii. Targets within the swept area appear as bright areas upon the screen.

Planar Electrodes. Electrodes of a thermionic valve or other electron tube, formed in one plane, i.e. of flat construction instead of the cylindrical or near-cylindrical form. Planar electrodes permit the use of finer gauges of grid wires, or smaller grid mesh, and at the same time result in a more rigid construction and closer inter-electrode spacing, all of which confer special advantages by way of smaller inter-electrode capacitances and shorter transit times, important factors in obtaining large gains and stable operation at very high radio frequencies.

Planck's Constant. (Symbol h) Ratio of a quantum of energy of a given frequency and the frequency itself. The ratio is constant and is equal to $6{\cdot}624 \times 10^{-27}$ erg-seconds.

Plane-polarized Wave. Electromagnetic wave the electrical component of whose field is in one plane.

Plasma. Region in a gas-filled discharge tube where the numbers of positive and negative ions are approximately equal so that there is no appreciable residual charge.

Plasmatron. Gas-filled electron thermionic tube in which, unlike the THYRATRON, continuous control can be exercised upon the anode current. The tube has, in addition to the main cathode, an auxiliary cathode, which is used only to initiate and to maintain the ionization of the gas filling, i.e. to produce the PLASMA. The " control " or modulation of the anode current is achieved by varying the effective resistance of the path between the anode and the main cathode.

Plastic Effect. Faulty reproduction of a television picture causing loss of gradation so that, although the outline is clear, the picture has an overall grey appearance. This is usually due to poor low-frequency response in the vision channel of the receiver.

Plastics Industry. Applications of electronics in the plastics industry include electronic methods of processing, the use of electronic measuring equipment and electronic systems of automatic control. DIELECTRIC LOSS HEATING, for example, is employed for pre-heating the plastic powder before insertion in the moulding press. Electronic equipment for the control of powder level, for process timing and programme control, and automatic temperature control are a few of many other applications.

Plate. (1) One of the two conductors, separated by a DIELECTRIC, which form a CAPACITOR.

(2) Term originally used for the anode of a thermionic valve and still so used in America.

Plate Battery. Anode battery or h.t. battery.

Plate Current. Anode current.

Plate Detector. ANODE BEND detector.

Plate Voltage. Anode voltage.

Plates (Deflexion Plates). A pair of parallel metal plates mounted in a cathode-ray tube, between which passes the electron beam. A difference of potential applied between the plates causes the beam to be deflected towards the plate at the higher potential. Usually two pairs of plates are fitted, at right angles to each other, thus permitting the beam to be deflected both vertically and horizontally.

Point-contact Crystal Diode. CRYSTAL DIODE in which a finely-pointed wire (cat's whisker) just touches a crystal of p-type or n-type semiconductor material. The rectifying action can be considered to occur at the junction between the main body of the crystal and a small area of material of opposite type (n-type in the case of a p-type crystal, and vice versa) surrounding the point of the cat's whisker.

Point-contact Transistor. TRANSISTOR in which the BASE is a crystal of p-type or n-type semiconductor material and the emitter and collector are, in effect, small areas of material of opposite type formed around the points of two closely-spaced cat's whiskers. Point-contact transistors are now seldom used; the junction transistor being almost universal practice.

Polar Diagram. Graph relating to the distribution of field strength in the region surrounding a transmitting aerial, plotted in polar co-ordinates. The relative field strength at any point is represented by the radial distance, while the bearing of the point with respect to the aerial is given by the angular co-ordinate.

Polarity. The distinction between the north-seeking and south-seeking poles of a magnet, or between the positive and negative terminals of a source of electromotive force.

Polarization. The direction of the planes of the electric and magnetic components of the field of an electromagnetic wave.

Polarized Wave. Electromagnetic wave the field components of which are, to a substantial degree, limited to particular planes. The term is usually applied only to PLANE-POLARIZED WAVES.

Pole. (1) Region in a magnet, usually but not necessarily situated at one end of the magnet, at which the magnetic flux appears to leave or re-enter the magnet. Normally a magnet has two poles, respectively north-seeking and south-seeking, but magnets with a more complex arrangement of poles can occur.

(2) The point at which an electric current leaves or enters a current source, e.g. the positive and negative terminals of a battery.

Pole Face. The surface of a pole or POLE PIECE in a magnetic system.

Pole Piece. A piece of ferromagnetic material joined to the POLE of a magnet for the purpose of determining the area and shape of the external field.

Pool Cathode. Emissive cathode consisting of a liquid conductor, generally mercury. The electron emission results partly from bombardment of the surface of the mercury pool by positive ions produced by the ionization of the mercury vapour within the envelope, and partly from thermionic emission from hot spots on the surface of the mercury due to this bombardment. The ionization of the mercury vapour is initiated either by field emission resulting from the application of a positive potential to a subsidiary electrode close to the cathode or by a small arc set up between a subsidiary electrode and the surface of the pool.

Pool Cathode Tubes. Electron tubes employing a pool cathode. Typical examples are described under the entries EXCITRON and IGNITRON.

Porch. Brief portion of the television waveform during which the modulation is held steady at BLACK LEVEL. Two such periods occur in the line waveform: one, the FRONT PORCH, at the commencement, and the other, the BACK PORCH, at the completion of the line of picture. They serve to separate the synchronizing pulses from the picture modulation. See also TELEVISION WAVEFORM.

Positive. The terms " positive " and " negative " were applied somewhat arbitrarily by early scientists to distinguish between pairs of related phenomena. Thus, when it was observed that there appeared to be two kinds of electric charge, like charges repelling and unlike charges attracting each other, one type was called " positive " and the other " negative ". Since these two kinds of electrification also appeared at the two terminals of an electric battery, the terminals were also termed " positive " and " negative ". By analogy, electric current was deemed to flow from the positive terminal to the negative terminal in the external circuit, and this convention is still preserved in spite of the fact that an electric current is now considered to be a movement of ELECTRONS, which are negative charge carriers, in the opposite direction. Similarly, a point is said to be at a positive potential with respect to a second point when an electric current tends to flow from that point to the second, using the normal convention as to the direction of current flow.

Positive Charge. A body is said to carry a positive electric charge when it suffers from a deficiency of ELECTRONS.

Positive Electron. See POSITRON.

Positive Feedback. Feedback of voltage or current from the output of an amplifier to the input, in phase with the input signal. See REGENERATION.

Positive-going. Said of a change, e.g. of current or voltage, in the positive direction, that is to say from a negative value to a smaller negative value or to a positive value, or from zero or a positive value to a higher positive value. Cf. NEGATIVE-GOING.

Positive Ion. An atom or group of atoms which has been deprived of one or more electrons, and therefore exhibits a positive electric charge.

Positive Modulation. A signal, the amplitude of which increases in proportion to the increase in intensity of the information to be transmitted, and used to modulate a carrier wave. In the British television system, for example, the video signal consists of positive modulation, 30 per cent of maximum amplitude representing black level, and 100 per cent representing peak white.

Positive-ray Parabola. Trace, of parabolic form, produced on a photographic plate by allowing POSITIVE RAYS from a gas discharge tube to emerge through a perforated cathode and then to pass through mutually perpendicular electric and magnetic fields before reaching the photographic plate.

Positive Rays. Stream of positive ions forming part of the electric discharge in a gas-filled discharge tube, and travelling towards the cathode.

Positive Transmission. More correctly " positively modulated transmission "; radio transmission in which increase of signal intensity, e.g. of the sound or of the illumination at the signal source, is represented by corresponding increase in amplitude of the modulation applied to the carrier wave.

Positron. A positively-charged particle of the same mass as the electron and with a charge equivalent but opposite in sign to that of the electron. A positive electron.

Post-deflexion Acceleration. Acceleration of the electron beam in a cathode-ray tube after it has traversed the deflecting system, by means of a high positive potential, greater than that of the pre-deflexion accelerating electrode, applied to auxiliary electrodes, usually formed by graphite bands deposited on the inner surface of the envelope as indicated diagrammatically in Fig. P-17. This device

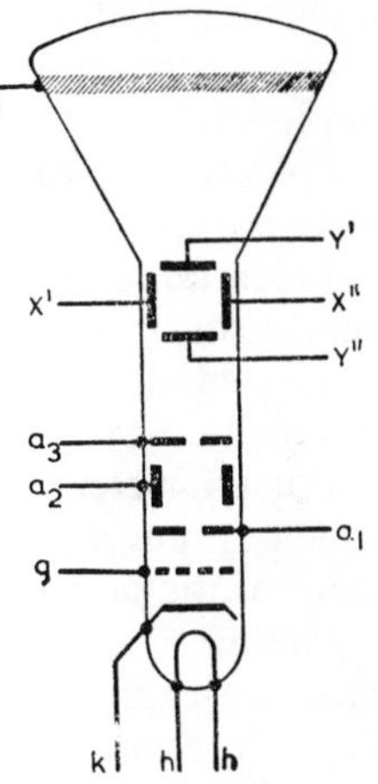

FIG. P-17.—GRAPHICAL REPRESENTATION OF A CATHODE-RAY TUBE FOR ELECTROSTATIC DEFLEXION, WITH POST-DEFLEXION ACCELERATOR ELECTRODE a_4.

gives increased brightness of the trace without the serious decrease of deflexion sensitivity which would occur if the increased accelerating potential were applied before deflexion.

Potential. According to the concept of electrical potential, if an electron tends to move from one point to another, the point towards which it moves is said to be at a higher potential than the first point, or to be at a positive potential with respect to the first point.

Potential Attenuator. A potentiometer or other potential-dividing network whereby a known voltage or a known proportion of the voltage applied to its input can be obtained at the output terminals.

Potential Difference. (p.d.) If two points are at different electrical potentials a potential difference is said to exist between them. If a conductive path is provided between two points having a potential difference an electric current will flow. Potential difference is also referred to as ELECTRO-MOTIVE FORCE (e.m.f.). The practical unit is the VOLT.

Potential Divider. A network, usually but not necessarily resistive, between the terminals of which exists a potential difference, connexions to different points in the network being provided so that potentials of intermediate value can be obtained.

Potential Drop. The difference of electric potential occurring between two points when an electric current is flowing, and representing the voltage required to drive the current through the resistance existing between the two points. The potential drop (in volts) is equal to the current in amperes multiplied by the resistance in ohms.

Potential Energy. Energy possessed by a body by virtue of its position.

Potential Gradient. The rate of change of potential along a conductor or between two points in an electric field. If the potential is plotted against distance the potential gradient at any point is represented by the slope of the curve.

Potentiometer. A potential divider. More particularly one in which an intermediate potential is continuously variable by adjustment of the position of a sliding contact.

Powder Core. Ferromagnetic core for an inductor, transformer, etc., consisting of finely-divided magnetic material, the particles of which are held together by a resin binder. By insulating the particles from each other in this way eddy-current losses are considerably decreased at some sacrifice of permeability. Over a range of radio frequencies up to about 1 Mc/s, however, the use of powder cores has definite advantages in the production of high-Q coils.

Power Amplifier. Amplifier stage incorporating one or more thermionic valves and designed to give a substantial power output as distinct from providing voltage gain.

Power Factor. Ratio of the true power (in-phase current × in-phase voltage) in an a.c. circuit to the volt-amperes in the same circuit. In a conventional single-phase circuit the power factor is equal to the cosine of the phase angle between the current and voltage vectors. The power factor is therefore represented by the symbol $\cos \phi$. In a dielectric the power factor is equal to $G/\sqrt{G^2 + \omega^2 C^2}$, where G is the conductance, i.e. the ratio between the conduction current and the applied voltage, and C is the capacitance.

Power Grid Detector. A form of LEAKY-GRID DETECTOR in which the valve is operated at a fairly high anode voltage and with low values of grid capacitor and grid leak, e.g. 50–100 pF and 100–250 kΩ respectively.

Power Pack. Equipment for obtaining, from the electricity mains, the various electrical supplies at the appropriate voltages, for operating electronic apparatus such as radio or television receivers, oscilloscopes and the like. In the case of apparatus taking a supply from a.c. mains, the power pack will include a POWER TRANSFORMER, and one or more rectifiers with their associated smoothing filters. The power transformer will also have the necessary low-voltage secondary windings for supplying the heater circuits of the valves.

Power Transformer. Static transformer taking its primary supply from the a.c. mains and providing outputs at suitable voltages for use in electronic equipment.

Pre-amplifier. (1) An additional thermionic amplifier connected between the signal source and a main amplifier.

(2) The radio-frequency amplifier in a superheterodyne receiver.

Pre-emphasis. Process whereby the depth of modulation in high-frequency or frequency-modulated or phase-modulated systems is automatically increased at the transmitter in order to improve the signal-to-noise ratio. At the receiver suitable correcting circuits (de-emphasis) are employed.

Pre-set. Said of a variable control component, e.g. a resistor, potentiometer or capacitor, the value of which is adjusted to suit normal working conditions and which normally does not require further adjustment unless conditions change.

Pressure. Term often employed for " voltage " or " potential difference ". The term " tension " probably better expresses the physical conception. Cf. HIGH TENSION, LOW TENSION, etc.

Primary Battery. A device for generating an electromotive force and thus for supplying electrical energy to a circuit by chemical action.

Primary Coil. That winding of a transformer which is connected to the source of alternating current, as distinct from the secondary coil or coils in which voltages are induced by the varying current in the primary coil.

Primary Electron. A free electron existing in a given space and which, when accelerated, can transfer some of its kinetic energy to a gas or solid atom with the result that the atom is either EXCITED or is deprived of one or more electrons, which are then termed SECONDARY ELECTRONS. Examples of primary electrons are those emitted from a thermionic or from a photo-emissive cathode, or as the result of a high potential gradient at the surface of a cold cathode.

Primary Winding. Primary coil of a transformer.

Printed Circuit. Method of constructing electronic equipment, especially receivers and amplifiers, in which the wiring, and perhaps some of the circuit elements, such as fixed-value capacitors and inductors, are produced from conductive material, stencilled, printed or otherwise deposited on an insulating base. This construction facilitates a high degree of accuracy and uniformity in wiring and component values, and permits very compact assemblies to be produced.

Probe. (1) The termination of a WAVEGUIDE which projects into a resonant cavity and thus forms the coupling between the resonant cavity (oscillator) and the transmission line.

(2) In a VALVE-VOLTMETER or other measuring instrument, such as a cathode-ray oscilloscope, an input stage incorporating a rectifying diode and associated circuits connected to the main instrument by a multi-core flexible cable. Its purpose is to reduce the self-capacitance losses which would occur if a high-frequency signal were connected to the instrument via long leads. See Fig. P-18.

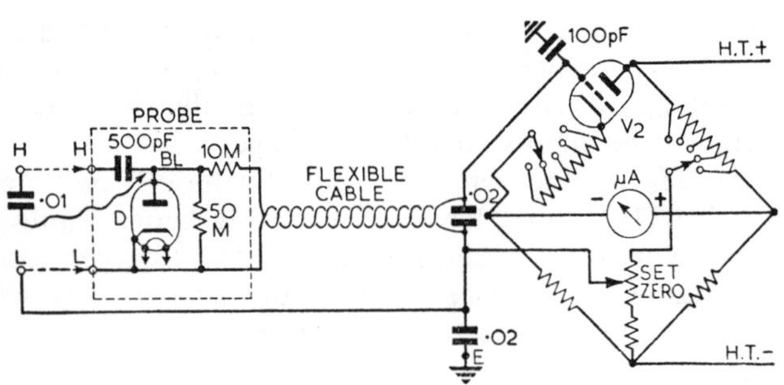

FIG. P-18.—CIRCUIT DIAGRAM OF A TYPICAL VALVE VOLTMETER AND PROBE UNIT.

Programming. Technique for automatically controlling the sequence and duration of industrial processes or operations, or of a series of operations in computer equipment.

Projection Television. Method of reproducing a television picture wherein the intensely bright image formed on the luminescent screen of a small cathode-ray tube operated at a very high anode voltage is projected through a magnifying optical system on a separate viewing screen. For domestic projection television the cathode-ray tube has a screen diameter of $2\frac{1}{2}$ in. and is operated at an anode voltage of 25 kV. Pictures up to about 4 ft by 3 ft are obtainable. For larger pictures, e.g. for theatre installations, picture tubes of 9 in. screen diameter and operated at from 50 to 80 kV may be employed. Enlargement and projection is achieved by means of a variant of the SCHMIDT OPTICAL SYSTEM, the picture being directed either on the rear of a transluscent viewing screen (back projection) or on the front surface of a reflecting screen (front projection).

Proton. Charged particle, one of the fundamental constituents of the nucleus of an atom. It carries a positive charge equal to the negative charge of an ELECTRON and has a mass about 1840 times that of an electron. See also ATOM, STRUCTURE OF.

Public Address System. Installation comprising a system of audio-frequency amplifiers and loudspeakers, together with a microphone or microphones and possibly also gramophone and/or tape recorder units, employed for amplifying and relaying speech and music to large audiences.

Puckle Timebase. Valve-operated device for generating a voltage of sawtooth waveform for use in such equipment as cathode-ray oscillators as a timebase. A capacitor is charged via a pentode and discharged through a MULTI-VIBRATOR.

Pulling on Whites. Defect in television reproduction, usually caused by poor high-frequency response of the video amplifier stages. The effect consists of momentary horizontal displacement to the right of one or more lines of picture following a white area of picture.

Pulse. Sudden signal of very short duration, representing a momentary increase or decrease of amplitude.

Pulse Counter Detector. A detector for frequency-modulated signals which functions by generating from each sine wave a unidirectional pulse, the d.c. component of which is directly proportional to the frequency of the f.m. signal. Two practical disadvantages are that the detector requires a low i.f. (150–200 kc/s) and that it has low conversion efficiency. An advantage is the absence of alignment problems.

Pulse e.h.t. Generator. Device for generating the e.h.t. supply for a television picture tube by rectifying the voltage pulses appearing in the anode circuit of a thermionic valve when the anode current is suddenly cut off.

Pulse-limiting Rate. The maximum practicable pulse-recurrence frequency for a radar transmitter. It is the highest frequency which gives sufficient time for the transmitted pulse to reach the target and to be reflected therefrom to the receiver before the next pulse is transmitted.

Pulse-modulated Navigational Systems. Navigational aids by which the position of the craft is ascertained by determining the time interval between the reception of radio-frequency pulses transmitted simultaneously from two or more fixed stations. Examples are described under GEE, the name of a British system, and LORAN, a system developed in America.

Pulse-modulated Waves. Wave trains in which the duration of the trains is short compared with the time interval between them.

Pulse-repetition Frequency. The number of PULSES generated or transmitted per second. In selecting the permissible pulse-repetition frequency for radar purposes, not only the distance between transmitter and target but also the persistence of the luminescent screen of the cathode-ray tube in the receiver must be taken into consideration.

Pulse Separator. See SYNCHRONIZING PULSE SEPARATOR.

Pulse–Time Modulation. System for modulating a microwave by a combination of PULSE MODULATION and FREQUENCY MODULATION with the object of obtaining a larger output from such tubes as

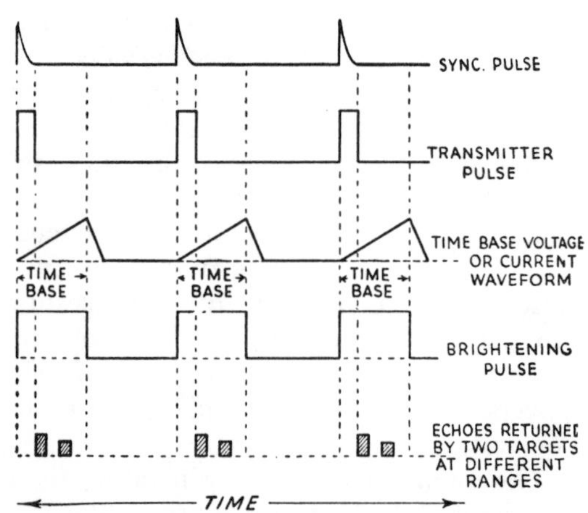

FIG. P-19.—TIME RELATION BETWEEN TRANSMITTED PULSE, TIMEBASE WAVEFORM, SYNCHRONIZING PULSES, "BRIGHTENING" PULSES AND THE RECEIVED ECHOES FROM TWO TARGETS, IN A PULSED RADAR SYSTEM.

magnetrons and klystrons than can be achieved with amplitude modulation of continuous waves in view of the comparatively low permissible anode dissipation of these tubes. The signal is modulated by a pulse having a pulse-repetition frequency much lower than the carrier frequency, the pulse signal itself being frequency-modulated at audio frequency.

Pulse Width. The time duration of a PULSE.

Pulsed Radar System. A radar system in which the transmitter sends out short pulses at regular intervals, which pulses, reflected from the target and affecting the radar receiver, are displayed on the screen of the cathode-ray tube in the receiving equipment. Fig. P-19 shows the relation between the transmitted pulse, the timebase waveform, the synchronizing pulses, the "brightening pulses" (i.e. the pulses applied to the control electrode of the cathode-ray tube to determine that part of each waveform cycle during which the beam is NOT suppressed) and the echoes from two separate targets as displayed on the cathode-ray tube.

Pumping. Factory term for the process of evacuating the envelope of an electron tube.

Pumping Tube. Glass tube of comparatively small bore, providing a through connexion between the interior of the envelope of a thermionic tube and the outside air. It is through this tube that the envelope is evacuated and/or filled with gas, after which the

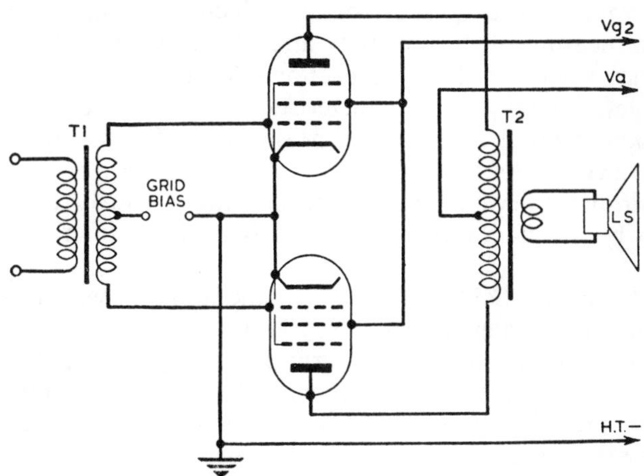

FIG. P-20.—BASIC CIRCUIT OF AN AUDIO-FREQUENCY PUSH–PULL OUTPUT STAGE.

pumping tube is sealed off by a gas flame and the excess removed, leaving the familiar " pip ". The pumping tube is sometimes called the " stem ".

Push-button Tuning. Device whereby a radio receiver can be automatically tuned to any one of a limited number of transmissions by means of a corresponding number of push buttons. The push buttons usually select appropriate pre-tuned circuits.

Push–Pull. Balanced valve operation. Method of operating two similar valves, or a double valve, to form one stage of an amplifier, such that their control grids receive signals of equal amplitude but of opposite phase, the outputs of the two valves being combined. In the basic circuit of Fig. P-20 the two signals in antiphase are derived from the two halves of the centre-tapped secondary winding of the input transformer T1, and the combined outputs are taken from the secondary winding of the output transformer T2.

Push–Pull Amplifier. An amplifier consisting of two similar valves, or two groups of similar valves, connected in PUSH–PULL.

Q

Q-band. Frequency band from 36,000 to 46,000 Mc/s (wavelengths in the order of 8 mm) employed in radar.

Q-factor. Ratio of the reactance of a capacitor or inductor to its resistance. The Q-factor of an inductor is a figure of merit, being a measure of its selectivity and voltage gain at the resonant frequency when tuned by a capacitor having no losses.

Q-point. Point on the characteristic curves of a thermionic valve corresponding to the quiescent or no-signal condition. Also termed the OPERATING POINT.

Quadrature. Two alternating phenomena of equal frequency are said to be in quadrature when there is a phase difference of 90° between them.

Quadrivalent. Said of an element the atom of which has four electrons in the valency shell. See TETRAVALENT.

Quality, Sound. An inexact term indicating the extent to which reproduced sound is a faithful replica of the original. Equipment which will reproduce sound with very good quality is termed HIGH-FIDELITY (Hi-Fi) equipment.

Quantity of Electricity. Amount of electric charge. Symbol Q, unit the COULOMB.

Quantum. A definite amount of radiant energy, such as light, X-rays, etc., which is related quantitatively to the frequency of the radiation. For radiation of frequency ν, the quantum is $\nu \cdot h$ ergs, where h is PLANCK'S CONSTANT.

Quantum Theory. Conception that energy is produced and radiated only in multiples of minimum quantities called quanta, the quantum being related to the frequency of the radiation. The theory is now to a great extent replaced by the concepts of wave mechanics.

Quarter-wave Aerial. Aerial the length of which is approximately one-quarter of the wavelength of the signal it is intended to radiate or to receive.

Quartz. Silica (silicon oxide) in its natural crystalline form. It has a very high melting point and is a good electrical insulator, retaining its high resistivity even at elevated temperatures. It is therefore used for the envelopes of certain types of transmitting valves which operate at high temperatures.

Quartz Crystal. Section of quartz exhibiting PIEZO-ELECTRIC properties, and so cut and ground that it resonates at some specified frequency.

Quartz-crystal Oscillator. Constant frequency oscillator consisting of a thermionic valve and a quartz crystal. See CRYSTAL OSCILLATOR.

Quartz-crystal Resonator. Device in which the natural resonant frequency of a quartz crystal is used as a comparison standard.

Quasi-optical Waves. Radio waves of very short wavelength, the propagation of which obeys laws similar to those for visible light.

Quenched Spark. Oscillatory spark discharge which is suppressed by mechanical or thermal means after a very short interval of time.

Quenched-spark Gap. Spark gap the electrodes of which are either cooled or made to move rapidly in order to quench the spark.

Quenched-spark System. System of radio transmission in which energy is radiated by means of oscillatory discharges across a spark gap, each spark being rapidly quenched.

Quiescent Aerial. A dummy aerial or ARTIFICIAL AERIAL.

Quiescent Carrier Modulation. System of modulation in which the carrier is suppressed during intervals when no modulation is applied.

Quiescent Push–Pull. (Abbreviation q.p.p.) Method of operating two similar thermionic valves in push–pull connexion, the circuit conditions being so adjusted that their no-signal currents are very small. Equivalent to operation under Class AB_1 conditions.

Quiet Automatic Gain Control. System of automatic gain control in which signals which are too weak to operate the gain-control feature are suppressed. A combination of automatic gain control and Noise Suppression.

Quinquivalent. Said of a chemical the atoms of which have five electrons in the valency shell, Pentavalent.

R

Rack. Iron frame of standard dimensions on which can be mounted such apparatus as amplifiers, filters and other units of communication equipment.

Radar. Term derived from the initials of the words **RA**dio, **D**etection **A**nd **R**anging, applied to the process of employing radio waves for the detection of objects (targets) and determining their position in terms of angular bearing, elevation and distance from a reference point. The process uses radio waves of very short wavelengths, propagated as a narrow beam by means of a highly directional aerial. By a combination of rotation and tilting of the aerial, the beam is made to scan a given area. If the beam strikes an object it is reflected, and part of the reflected energy returns directly towards the transmitter, where it is detected by a sensitive receiver situated near the transmitter. Since the speed of propagation of the beam, namely approximately 3×10^{10} cm/sec, is known, by measuring the time interval between the transmission of a signal and the reception of the echo the range of the target can be determined. The bearing and (in the case of an airborne target) the elevation, are indicated by the angles through which the aerial has been turned and tilted at the instant at which the target was detected. All this information is displayed on the screen of a cathode-ray tube. Extensively used during the Second World War for the detection of enemy aircraft, and later for the identification of other targets and as a navigational aid, radar has a wide field of peace-time activities in both aerial and marine navigation.

Radar Beacon. Fixed ground station comprising a receiver and a transmitter, whereby both bearing and range are indicated to the pilot of an aircraft or ship. The aircraft " interrogates " the radar beacon by sending out radar pulses which are picked up by the receiver in the beacon. The output of this receiver triggers the beacon transmitter, which sends out a characteristic signal which is picked up by the radar system of the interrogating aircraft and displayed on the screen of a cathode-ray tube.

Radar Sonde. Method of measuring and transmitting to a fixed ground station the meteorological conditions in the upper atmosphere (wind speed and direction, temperature, air pressure and humidity) from equipment carried in drifting balloons. The ground station comprises an automatic pulse transmitter which continuously " interrogates " the airborne apparatus, and a receiver and computer which receives, interprets and records the signals transmitted by the balloon. An interrogating signal pulse received by the airborne equipment is fed to a modulator stage both directly and through a delay circuit, the delay time of which is determined by the temperature-, pressure- and humidity-sensitive elements carried by the balloon, thus providing coded signals for telemetering purposes. From these signals the ground station computer automatically calculates the direction and distance of the balloon and its direction of travel and rate of travel, thus giving its position and also the direction and speed of the wind; also the pressure, temperature and humidity. These quantities are continuously recorded by pen recorders, which also indicate wind speed and altitude.

Radial Deflexion. Deflexion of the electron beam, and hence of the light spot in a cathode-ray tube, in such a way that a linear trace rotates about one of its ends, thus sweeping out a circular raster. It can be achieved either by rotating the deflexion coils around the neck of the tube, or by energizing the deflexion system from a small two-phase a.c. generator the field of which is supplied with a saw-tooth current.

Radian Frequency. Frequency of a periodic phenomenon expressed in radians per second. Equal to the frequency in cycles per second multiplied by 2π. See ANGULAR FREQUENCY.

Radiating Circuit. Circuit from which electromagnetic waves are, or can be, sent out into space.

Radiation. Emission of energy in the form of electromagnetic waves, and covering all forms of radiant energy from radio waves at the lower end of the spectrum to gamma waves at the upper end. Also applied to the energy thus emitted.

Radiation Counter. Device for detecting and measuring radiation by means of the ionization or excitation it produces. The term is used to cover the detection of both very-short-wave electromagnetic energy, such as X-rays and gamma rays, and also charged particles (e.g. alpha and beta particles, etc.) and uncharged particles (e.g. neutrons).

Radiation Counter Tube. Gas containing a cathode and anode, and means for exposing the gas filling to the radiation it is desired to detect or measure. The indication is obtained by measuring the total ionization produced by the radiation over a period of time, by measuring the mean current through the tube or by counting the individual discharge pulses, one of which is produced for each quantum of radiation or for each particle received by the tube. See also GEIGER–MULLER TUBE.

Radiation Detectors. Strictly speaking, a radiation detector is any device which reacts to, and gives an intelligible indication of, electromagnetic radiation. This wide definition would include such detectors as radio receivers, the many types of thermometer and such light-sensitive devices as the eye and the photocell. However, the term radiation detector is generally reserved for devices for detecting radiations of much shorter wavelengths, such as X-rays, gamma rays and also streams of swiftly-moving nuclear and cosmic particles, e.g. alpha and beta particles, neutrons, protons and mesons. In the case of X- and gamma rays, detection is based on one or other of the following effects: the emission of electrons from a so-called photo-emissive material when irradiated by the radiation to be detected; the COMPTON effect, i.e. the small increase in their wavelength when the rays are scattered by impact with light elements; and pair-production or the formation of a negative electron and a positron through interaction between a gamma-ray quantum and an atomic nucleus.

Non-charged particles (neutrons and neutral mesons) may be detected either by the ionization they produce when these high-energy neutral particles collide with atoms or by nuclear disintegration resulting from the bombardment of a suitable material with neutral particles of lower energy. Charged particles, alpha and beta particles, protons and charged mesons, are detected by the ionization they produce in a gas ionization chamber, or by their excitation effect on a suitable phosphor as a result of which light quanta are produced.

Radiation Efficiency (of an Aerial). Ratio of the power at a specified frequency radiated from an aerial to the total power at that frequency delivered to the aerial.

Radiation Potential. Energy, expressed in electron-volts, required to displace an electron from its normal position in an atom to an ENERGY LEVEL of greater energy. See also ATOM, STRUCTURE OF.

Radiation Resistance. That part of the AERIAL RESISTANCE which is due to the radiation properties of the aerial. Numerically (in ohms) equal to the power radiated (watts) divided by the square of the r.m.s. value of the aerial current (amperes) measured at the point where the current is a maximum.

Radio Altimeter. Instrument mounted in an aircraft to measure its altitude above ground level by observing the time taken for a radio wave, transmitted from the aircraft, to travel to the ground and return to the aircraft after reflexion from the surface.

Radio Astronomy. Man's knowledge of extra-terrestrial space and of the bodies existing therein was, until about a quarter of a century ago, limited to what had been discovered and was being discovered by observations and measurements of electromagnetic radiations whose wavelengths fell within the visible spectrum and, to a lesser extent, of radiations in the ultra-violet and infra-red regions. However, it is now known that waves of other frequencies originate in outer space and that of these, radio-frequency waves of wavelengths between a few centimetres and a few tens of metres reach the earth without, on the one hand, being absorbed by the atmosphere or, on the other hand, being reflected by the ionosphere. These waves can be received and detected by means of suitable aerial systems and sensitive receivers. By this means it has been possible to receive radio waves originating at definite sources in outer space—sources which are now termed " radio stars ". Investigation of these radio stars is one important branch of radio astronomy, termed extra-solar radio astronomy.

Radio astronomy also includes investigation of phenomena occurring within the solar system. Just as short radio waves of the waveband mentioned above can reach the earth from outer space, so can waves of similar wavelengths, generated in a terrestrial station, pass through the atmosphere and the ionosphere into space, and can be reflected back to earth if they strike an object. This makes possible a kind of celestial radar whereby, for example, the velocity and direction of meteors can be measured and their orbits determined. The giant radio telescope at Jodrell Bank, Cheshire, can be directed to any point in the visible heavens and made to follow the transit of objects. It has, for example, been successful in tracing the orbits of artificial earth satellites.

Radio-autograph. Image of a thin specimen containing a RADIOACTIVE ISOTOPE and obtained by placing the specimen in contact with a photographic plate. The image shows the distribution of the radioactive material.

Radio Beacon. A radio-transmitter which radiates a steady beam of given wavelength as a navigational aid. The beam may be transmitted in only one, or in a number of specified directions, or it may be omni-directional, when it can be used for taking bearings.

Radio Beam. Radio waves, concentrated within a limited angle by means of a specially designed directional aerial.

Radio Communication. Transmission of information in the form of suitably interrupted or modulated electromagnetic waves of radio frequency.

Radio Compass. Combination of a radio receiver and a frame aerial, in which the aerial is driven by a servo-mechanism so that it is always aligned with the bearing of the station to which the receiver is tuned. The orientation of the aerial is fed back to an indicating instrument with a 360° angular scale, so that the bearing of the station with respect to the line of travel of the aircraft can be read directly.

Radio Direction-finding. Determination of the bearings, e.g. of a ship or aircraft, either by observing the directions from which signals from two or more fixed transmitters reach the station whose bearings are required or by observing at two fixed receiving stations the directions from which a signal transmitted by the mobile station are received. See also DIRECTION FINDING.

Radio Frequency. (Abbreviation r.f.) Applied to electromagnetic frequencies which are suitable for radio communication.

Radio-frequency Amplifier. Thermionic amplifier which will operate on signals of radio frequency, and more particularly of the station frequency to which a receiver is tuned.

Radio-frequency Cooking. Cooking of food by the application of radio-frequency energy which is converted into heat energy.

Radio-frequency Heating. Industrial heating processes in which radio-frequency electrical energy is converted into heat energy. There are two forms of radio-frequency heating, INDUCTIVE HEATING or EDDY-CURRENT HEATING, in which metal objects are heated by eddy currents induced by high-frequency currents flowing in a solenoid; and DIELECTRIC-LOSS HEATING in which non-conductive material is heated by the energy dissipated in it when situated in a radio-frequency electric field. See also HIGH-FREQUENCY HEATING.

Radio-frequency Resistance. The resistance of a conductor to current of radio frequency. The resistance is then greater than that to direct currents due to the circulation of eddy currents, to the SKIN EFFECT and to dielectric losses in surrounding insulating material. See also HIGH-FREQUENCY RESISTANCE.

Radio-frequency Transformer. Static transformer for operation at radio frequency. Radio-frequency transformers may have an air core, or the core may be of iron dust or one of the ferromagnetic FERRITES which, being non-conductive, involves no eddy-current losses. Usually either the primary or the secondary winding, or both, are tuned.

Radio Link. That part of a telecommunication system or circuit in which information is transmitted by radio, the remainder of the route being by land line, submarine cable, etc.

Radio Sounding (Radiosonde). The gathering of meteorological information by sending up balloons equipped with meteorological instruments the readings of which are transmitted to a ground station by radio. See also RADAR SONDE.

Radio Station. Installation for transmitting and/or receiving radio signals.

Radiotelegraphy. Form of telecommunication in which information is transmitted by radio waves as a series of impulses according to a pre-arranged code.

Radio Telephony. Form of telecommunication in which information is transmitted by a radio CARRIER WAVE modulated at audio frequency.

Radiotherapy. Treatment of disease by exposure to X-rays.

Radio Telescope. Combination of a highly directional aerial system and a very sensitive transmitting and receiving equipment employed in studying the radiation emitted or reflected from bodies situated in outer space. See RADIO ASTRONOMY. The largest steerable radio telescope at the present time is at the Jodrell Bank experimental station of Manchester University. Its design includes a sheet-steel paraboloid reflector 250 ft in diameter and weighing some 500 tons.

Radio Transmitter. Equipment capable of generating and of emitting radio-frequency waves.

Radioactivity. Spontaneous disintegration of an atomic nucleus to produce a more stable nucleus and accompanied by the emission of charged particles and possibly also gamma rays.

Radioactive Isotope. ISOTOPE the nuclei of which disintegrate over a period of time, the disintegration resulting in the emission of alpha, beta or gamma rays and the ultimate formation of a stable isotope. See HALF-LIFE. These radiations produce IONIZATION and can therefore be detected by various forms of RADIATION DETECTORS and RADIATION COUNTERS. Extremely minute quantities of suitable radioactive isotopes mixed with normal substances can be used to trace the movement of the material—for example during its passage through the human body. It is then called a " tracer ". On the other hand, since the ionizing action of the radiation has the power of destroying living cells, dosage, either deliberate or accidental, must be severely limited; the maximum total dosage over the life-time of a human being is about 25 RÖNTGENS.

Radiogoniometer. Device for measuring the angular bearing in radio direction-finding. Used in conjunction with two large frame-aerials mounted at right angles to each other, it comprises two small coils, also mounted at right angles and connected to the frame aerials, and a small search coil which can rotate around the fixed coils. The search coil permits the direction of the resultant flux through the fixed coils to be determined. See Fig. R-1.

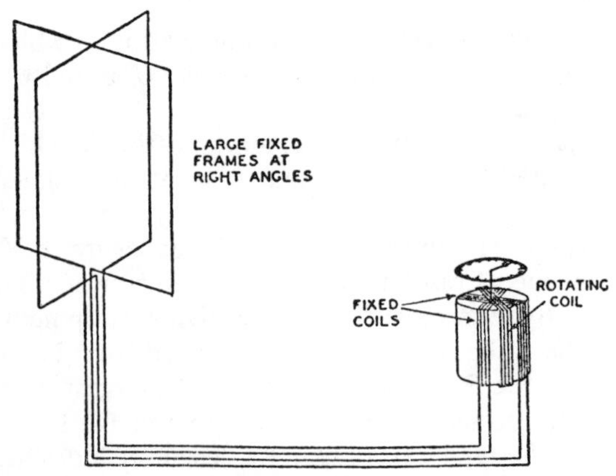

FIG. R-1.—RADIOGONIOMETER CONNECTED TO A BELLINI–TOSI SYSTEM OF FRAME AERIALS FOR GROUND STATION DIRECTION-FINDING.

Radiogram. A telegraphic message transmitted by radio.

Radio-gram (Radio-gramophone). An instrument combining a radio broadcast receiver and a gramophone reproducer.

Radiography. Production of images on a fluorescent screen or photographic plate by means of X-rays.

Radiolocation. The technique of determining the position of a distant object or surface (the target) by observation of radio waves reflected therefrom. See also RADAR.

Radiology. Branch of medical science covering the examination of the body by X-rays, the interpretation of X-ray photographs and the treatment of disease with X-rays.

Radiophare. A RADIO BEACON.

Radiophone. Telephone system in which the information is transmitted by radio.

Radiophotogram. A still picture transmitted by radio. A PHOTORADIOGRAM.

Radiovision. Television system in which the picture is transmitted by radio as distinct from CLOSED CIRCUIT television in which transmitter and receiver are linked by a conductive circuit.

Radiovisor. A television receiver.

Rail. Conductor joining a number of points in a circuit which are at the same potential. A BUSBAR.

Range. (1) Limits between which a quantity may be expected to vary.

(2) Maximum distance from a transmitter at which signals are receivable at useful strength.

(3) Distance of a given location or target from a point of observation.

Rare Gases. Group of gases, the inert gases helium, neon, argon, krypton and xenon, which are chemically inert. They are used for the gas-filling of cold-cathode electron tubes.

Rare-gas Cartridge. Cold-cathode, gas-filled diode containing one of the rare (inert) gases, and designed for use as a surge arrester.

Raster. Area of screen of a television picture tube illuminated by the pattern of horizontal lines produced during a complete frame scanning period. Intensity modulation of the beam during the scanning period produces the variations of light and shade to form the picture image.

Rating. Specified operating conditions or performance of a piece of equipment by way of input, output, etc. Generally normal ratings are quoted, but in addition maximum (or minimum) limits are often also specified.

Ratio Detector. The most usual form of detector (demodulator) for FREQUENCY-MODULATED signals. A greatly simplified basic circuit is given in Fig. R-2. Its operation depends on the fact that in the final i.f. transformer of the receiver, both windings of which are tuned to the centre frequency, the voltages across the two windings at the centre frequency are in quadrature (90° phase difference) and that at other frequencies, corresponding to the frequency deviations constituting the frequency modulation, the phase difference is greater or less than 90° according to whether the

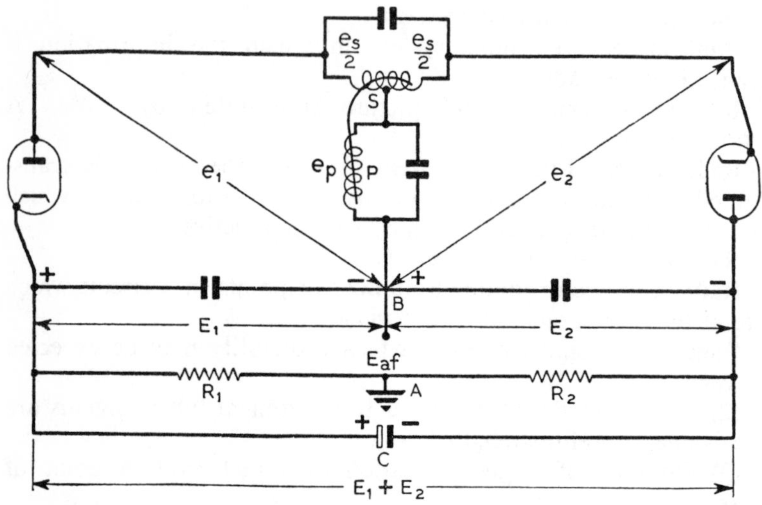

FIG. R-2.—SIMPLIFIED BASIC CIRCUIT OF THE RATIO DETECTOR.
e_s — secondary voltage; e_p — primary voltage.
Frequency-dependent voltages e_1 and e_2 are rectified by the left-hand and right-hand diodes respectively to produce the rectified voltages E1 and E2. R1 and R2 are the load resistors, which are shunted by capacitor C. The audio-frequency output voltage E_{af} appears between points A and B.

frequency deviation is positive or negative. The vector sum of the voltages across the primary winding and across one half of the secondary is rectified by one diode (V1) and the vector sum of the voltage across the primary and across the other half of the secondary is rectified by another diode (V2). The two diodes are connected BACK-TO-BACK and their outputs are combined, the a.f. component appearing between points A and B.

Ray, Direct. The shortest path of a radio wave from transmitter to receiver. See Fig. R-3.

Ray, Indirect. Path of a radio wave which is reflected from the fonosphere before reaching the receiver.

Ray, Ionospheric. Preferred term for indirect ray.

Reactance. That part of the impedance of a circuit or of a circuit element which is due to its inductance or capacitance. Symbol X. Practical unit, the ohm.

Reactance Coil. An inductor included in a circuit in order to introduce inductive reactance. See CHOKE COIL.

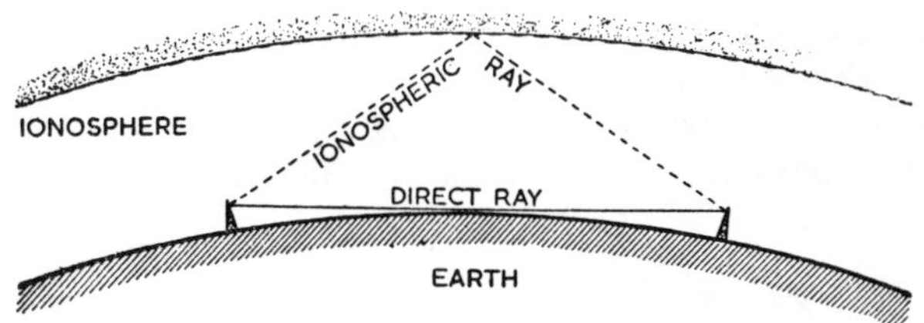

FIG. R-3.—DIRECT RAY AND INDIRECT OR IONOSPHERIC RAY.

Reactance Coupling. Coupling between two circuits due to inductive reactance common to both circuits.

Reaction. Feedback of energy from the (amplified) output of a thermionic valve to the grid circuit in phase with the original signal, thus providing an augmented signal for further amplification. The effect of resistance losses in a resonant circuit can thus be reduced, and if reaction is suitably controlled, increased gains can be obtained. The cumulative effect of uncontrolled reaction, however, is to set up free oscillations in the circuit. Preferred terms are RETROACTION, REGENERATION, and POSITIVE FEEDBACK, REGENERATIVE FEEDBACK or RETROACTIVE FEEDBACK.

Reaction Capacitor. Variable capacitor so connected in a valve circuit that it controls the degree of reaction.

Reaction Circuit. That part of the external anode circuit of a thermionic valve which is coupled to the control-grid circuit in such a way that positive feedback (regeneration) takes place.

Reaction Coil. Inductor included in the anode circuit of a thermionic valve and inductively coupled to the grid circuit in order to produce reaction.

Receiver. Device which accepts an incoming signal and converts it into an intelligible form.

Record. Registration of information, usually of sounds but also of visible phenomena, in such a way that the information can be reproduced at will. Thus the display on the screen of a cathode-ray oscilloscope may be recorded by means of a photographic negative, and sounds by photography (sound-on-film) or magnetically (tape recording) or mechanically (gramophone disk). Both the sound and the vision signals of a television programme can be recorded on tape for re-transmission. This is termed " telerecording ".

Recovery Time. The time which elapses between the cessation of anode current in a THYRATRON and the instant at which the grid regains control. During this time the positive ions remaining in the tube recombine with electrons to form neutral gas atoms. Also known as DEIONIZATION TIME.

Rectification. Process of converting an alternating current into a unidirectional current by means of a device which has a com-

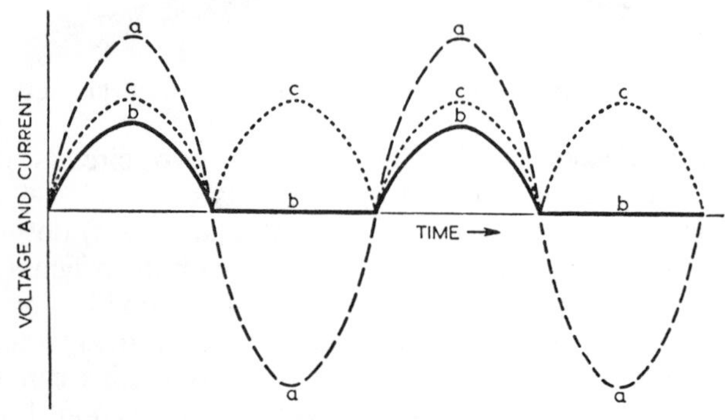

FIG. R-4.
aaaa: Waveform of an a.c. supply;
bbbb: Waveform after half-wave rectification;
cccc: Waveform after full-wave rectification.

paratively low resistance to current flow in one direction and a much higher resistance to current flow in the reverse direction. See Fig. R-4.

Rectifier. Device the conductivity of which is unidirectional or at least asymmetrical, so that it is able to rectify an alternating current by suppression of alternate half waves. See also CRYSTAL RECTIFIER, THERMIONIC RECTIFIER, MERCURY-VAPOUR RECTIFIER and METAL RECTIFIER.

Rectifier Instrument. Moving-coil instrument adapted for measuring alternating currents or voltages by incorporating a rectifier device so that the alternating quantity is first converted into a unidirectional quantity, thus permitting the more accurate moving-coil type of instrument to be applied to a.c. measurements.

Rectifying Detector. Any device for detecting radio waves by rectifying the high-frequency currents produced by them. This class of detector includes thermionic valves and crystal diodes.

Rectifying Valve. Thermionic valve in which the property of unilateral conductivity is exploited for rectifying an a.c. input, as distinct from a valve employed primarily as an amplifier or as an oscillator.

Reference Level. A value of a particular quantity (e.g. a voltage) which is taken as the datum point for other measurements.

Reference Voltage. Potential at one point in a circuit which is maintained very accurately at a constant value in order to serve as a datum or as a standard for comparison.

Reference Voltage Tube. Cold-cathode tube used for maintaining a constant reference voltage. See VOLTAGE REFERENCE TUBE and VOLTAGE STABILIZER.

Reflector. Conductor located behind an aerial but not connected thereto, for the purpose of producing directional effects. A similar conductor placed in front of an aerial is called a DIRECTOR, and also improves the directional properties and increases the amount of energy picked up by the aerial.

Reflex Amplification. Process whereby one valve amplifies a signal twice (first at one frequency and then at another frequency), for example at both station and intermediate frequency, or at both station or intermediate frequency and audio frequency.

Reflex Klystron. Form of KLYSTRON in which the normal anode or collector electrode is replaced by an electrode maintained at a negative potential so that it repels the velocity-modulated electron stream, which therefore passes a second time through the resonant system, but in the reverse direction, imparting energy to the system and resulting in the generation of oscillations. See Fig. R-5.

Reflexion, Radio. Change of direction of a radio wave when it encounters an obstacle. Thus, radio waves are reflected from the ionosphere, and the radio beam transmitted by RADAR equipment is reflected from the target.

Refraction. Deviation of the path of a radio wave when it enters a region of different permittivity.

Regeneration. Alternative term for REACTION or retroaction.

Regulation. (1) Adjustment, either automatic or manually controlled, for the purpose of maintaining output, or some other operational function or condition at the desired value.

(2) The extent to which some aspect of the performance of a device is affected by a change in some specified working condition. In particular, the extent to which the output voltage of a source of electric power varies with change of output current.

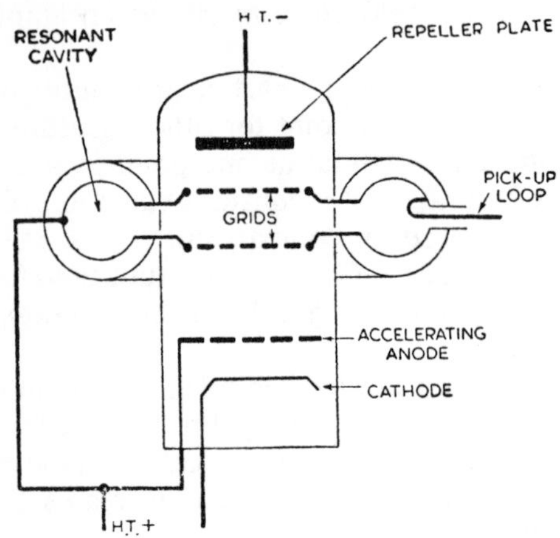

FIG. R-5.—DIAGRAMMATIC SECTION OF A REFLEX KLYSTRON.

Regulation Curve (of Power Supply Source). Graph relating output voltage to output current. See Fig. R-6.

Rejector Circuit. Combination of an inductor and a capacitor connected in parallel and thus offering a high impedance to signals of the frequency to which the combination is tuned but a lower impedance to all other frequencies. Such a circuit may be connected in series with a signal source, such as an aerial, and tuned to the frequency of an interfering signal, which is thus eliminated.

Relaxation Oscillator. Circuit for generating electrical oscillations, the operation cycle of which comprises a period during which energy is stored, e.g. by charging a capacitor, the voltage across which therefore rises, followed by a shorter period during which the stored energy is discharged. A simple form of relaxation oscillator is described and illustrated under the entry TIMEBASE GENERATOR.

Relay. Device in which a small amount of electrical energy expended in one circuit controls or releases a much larger amount of energy in a second circuit, through the intermediary of a magnetically-operated switch or of an electron tube and its associated circuits.

Relay, Gas-filled. Gas-filled thermionic tube which becomes conductive when the control-grid potential is raised to a critical value, the grid thereafter having no further control on the anode current. A THYRATRON.

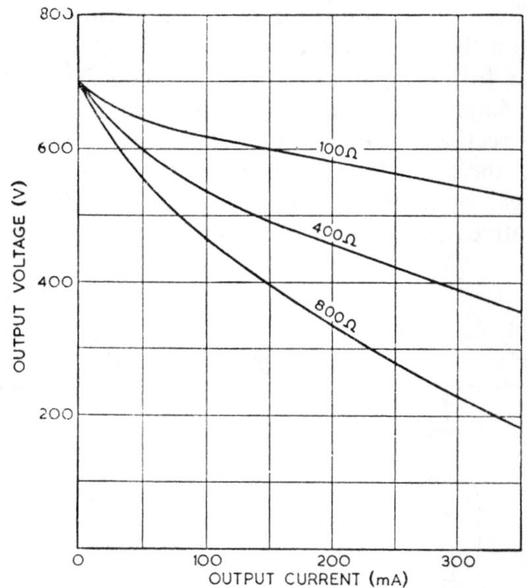

FIG. R-6.—TYPICAL REGULATION CURVE OF A HIGH-TENSION SUPPLY UNIT CONSISTING OF A FULL-WAVE THERMIONIC RECTIFIER AND CAPACITOR INPUT TO THE LOAD CIRCUIT.

The three curves are for three different values of internal resistance.

Reliable Valves. Thermionic valves the mechanical or electrical design and construction of which permit them to withstand successfully operating conditions more severe than those encountered in normal domestic or industrial applications. Also termed SPECIAL-QUALITY or special-service valves and rugged valves (American).

Repeater. Apparatus in which incoming currents or signals are transferred to another circuit, usually in amplified form.

Repeating Timebase. Periodic voltage or current of constant frequency and usually of sawtooth waveform, used to produce the continual deflexion of the beam in a cathode-ray tube.

Repetition Frequency. Number of times a cyclic phenomenon occurs in a given period of time, usually in one second.

Replay Head. That component of a TAPE RECORDER in which the variations of magnetization along the tape, and corresponding to the recorded sound, induce corresponding electrical variations in a pick-up circuit; these variations, after amplification, are used to operate a loudspeaker, thus reproducing the original sound.

Re-radiation. Re-transmission of a signal from a receiving aerial resulting from the generation of radio-frequency oscillations in the receiver, due, for example, to excessive use of REACTION.

Reservoir Capacitor. Capacitor connected in parallel with the output of a rectifier. During the positive half cycles of the alternating input the capacitor charges while the input voltage is rising, and discharges while the input voltage is falling. It also discharges during negative half cycles. The unidirectional output current,

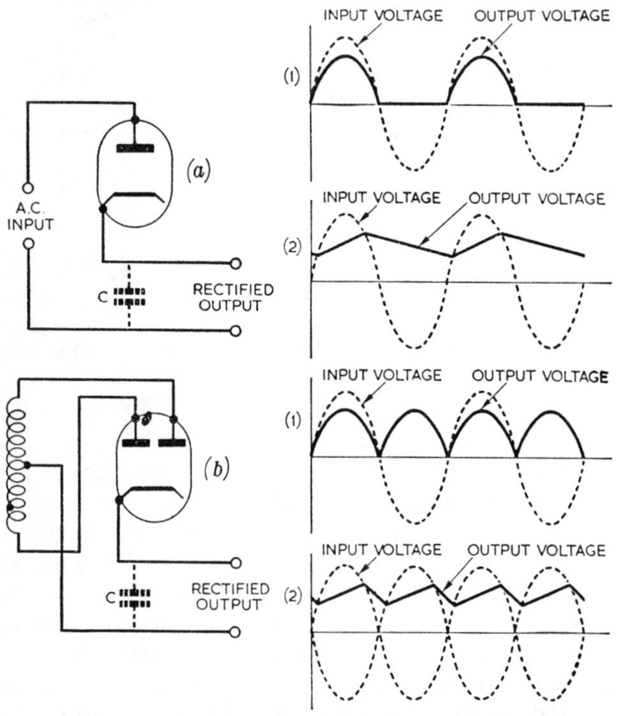

FIG. R-7.—EFFECT OF RESERVOIR CAPACITOR (C).
(a) HALF-WAVE RECTIFIER. (b) FULL-WAVE RECTIFIER.
(1) Input and output voltages without reservoir capacitor.
(2) Input and output voltages with reservoir capacitor.

which would otherwise be intermittent, becomes continuous, but carries a ripple which is usually reduced by the application of a SMOOTHING CIRCUIT. Fig. R-7 shows the effect of the reservoir capacitor on the output current.

Resistance. Opposition to the flow of electric current exhibited by matter. In a solid CONDUCTOR resistance may be envisaged as the effect of collisions between charge carriers (electrons) and the more massive positive ions. The fact that in most conductors resistance increases with temperature is attributable to increased thermal agitation with corresponding increase in the number of collisions. In conductors whose resistance decreases with rise of temperature this is due to increased ionization (release of electrons) at the higher temperature.

Resistance–Capacitance Amplifier. Thermionic amplifier in which the amplified signal voltage appearing across a resistive load in the

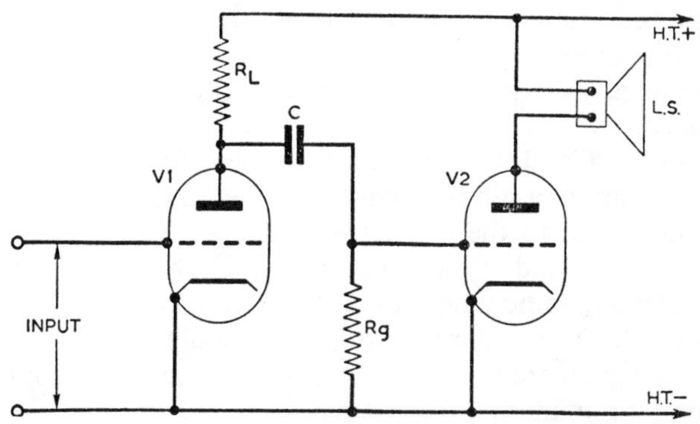

FIG. R-8.—BASIC CIRCUIT OF A RESISTANCE–CAPACITANCE AMPLIFIER.
R_L is the resistive anode load of V1, C is the coupling capacitor and Rg is the grid resistor of V2.

anode circuit of one valve is transferred to the grid circuit of the following valve via a capacitor. A basic circuit is given in Fig. R-8.

Resistance–Capacitance Coupling. Coupling between the resistive load of one valve and the grid of a second valve by means of a capacitor.

Resistance Pick-up. A device in which variations of some quantity, e.g. temperature or pressure, causes proportional variations of electrical resistance. Thus, a carbon microphone is a resistance pick-up, as is also the temperature-sensitive element of a resistance pyrometer.

Resistance Welding. Method of welding metals by passing an electric current through their point or area of contact, the contact resistance causing the metal to become heated and plastic, after which the current is interrupted and mechanical pressure applied to produce a strong joint. According to the type of joint and the method adopted, resistance welding is described as butt-, flash-, percussive-, seam- or spot-welding. Resistance welding is particularly suitable for automatic control by electronic means. See WELDING, ELECTRONIC, CONTROL OF.

Resistivity. Figure of merit for a conducting material. See SPECIFIC RESISTANCE and VOLUME RESISTIVITY.

Resistor. Device composed of a substance having a specified resistance, and included in a circuit for the deliberate introduction of resistance. May be employed to produce a voltage drop or to determine the amount of current which can flow in the circuit.

Resolving Power. Ability of an optical system or a quasi-optical system, such as a television receiver, to reproduce fine detail in an image.

Resonance. Condition in a circuit when, for an applied alternating voltage of a given frequency, the inductive reactance is numerically equal to the capacitive reactance. In a resonant circuit the inductive and capacitive elements of which are in series, the impedance is a minimum and the current a maximum at the resonant frequency. In a resonant circuit the inductive and capacitive elements of which are in parallel, the impedance is a maximum and the current a minimum at resonance.

Resonance Curve. Graph showing the variation of current in a resonant circuit when the frequency of an applied voltage of constant amplitude is varied. A RESPONSE CURVE.

Resonant Cavity. Resonant circuit forming part of certain forms of MICROWAVE TUBES and consisting of a space almost entirely bounded by a conductor. Also known as a RHUMBATRON. See KLYSTRON and MAGNETRON.

Resonant Circuit. Circuit consisting essentially of an inductor and a capacitor connected either in series or in parallel, and which exhibits the condition of RESONANCE at a particular frequency known as its NATURAL FREQUENCY or RESONANT FREQUENCY.

Resonant Frequency. The frequency at which a particular circuit is in resonance. Its value is $1/(2\pi\sqrt{LC})$ cycles per second where L is the inductance in henrys and C the capacitance in farads.

Resonator. A device which can be brought into the condition of resonance. The term is not confined to resonant circuits, but also to such devices as PIEZO-ELECTRIC crystals.

Response. Relative output of a device, and particularly of a resonant circuit, to an input of a given frequency.

Response Curve. (Frequency response curve) A graph in which the relative impedance of, and hence the voltage developed across, an electrical circuit or network is plotted against the frequency of the applied alternating voltage or SIGNAL.

In the case of an oscillatory circuit, such as the tuning circuit of a radio receiver or a high-frequency inter-valve coupling circuit, the curve usually covers a limited frequency range on either side of the RESONANT FREQUENCY. A sharply tuned circuit has a frequency-response curve of the form shown in Fig. R-9(a). Such a circuit

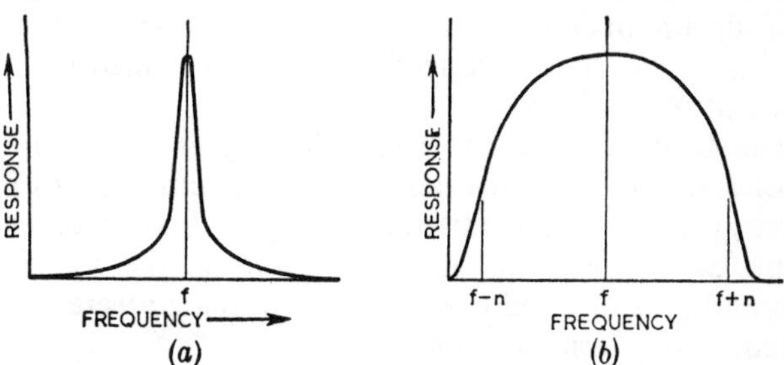

FIG. R-9.—RESPONSE CURVES OF (a) A SHARPLY TUNED CIRCUIT AND (b) A FLATLY TUNED CIRCUIT.

has a high degree of SELECTIVITY, that is to say it has a poor response to signals of frequencies only slightly different from that to which the circuit is tuned, e.g. to signals on adjacent CHANNELS to the "wanted" signal. It may, however, introduce FREQUENCY DISTORTION due to unequal amplification of frequencies differing from the CARRIER frequency by amounts within the modulation frequency band. A circuit having a flat-topped response curve (see Fig. R-9(b)) introduces little frequency distortion in the frequency range $f_{-n} - f_{+n}$, but for radio-frequency applications is comparatively unselective.

The frequency response curve of an amplifier is usually drawn to cover the whole frequency range over which the amplifier is required to work, and thus indicates the degree to which the output is a faithful, undistorted version of the input signal.

Display of the response curve of a circuit, e.g. by means of an oscilloscope, is a valuable guide in diagnosing and tracing circuit faults and in making the necessary adjustments.

Retarding Field. Electric field the direction of which is such that electrons, previously accelerated and entering the field, tend to have their velocity decreased and eventually the direction of their travel reversed.

Retrace. See FLYBACK.

Retroaction. Regeneration or positive feedback, as defined under REACTION.

Return Line. See FLYBACK.

Reverberation. Acoustic effect at a given point due to the simultaneous arrival of sound waves of random phase, magnitude and direction resulting from multiple reflexion.

Reverse Feedback. Feedback of energy from the output to the input of an amplifier in such a sense that it opposes the original input signal. See NEGATIVE feedback. Also termed degeneration or degenerative feedback.

Reverse Grid Current. Current flowing in the control grid circuit of a thermionic valve and due to the emission of electrons from the grid resulting from overheating or bombardment, or as the result of the presence of positive ions in the space between cathode and grid as would occur if the envelope were imperfectly evacuated. Also termed BACKLASH.

Reversed Image. Image which appears on the television screen either as a negative picture (black-to-white inversion), or as a positive picture but with lateral inversion, i.e. left to right or top to bottom. A negative image is often due to low e.h.t. or low heater voltage on the cathode-ray tube; lateral inversion is the result of reversed connexions to one or both of the deflexion coils.

Rheostat. A VARIABLE RESISTOR.

Rhombic Aerial. A form of directional aerial consisting of four wires of equal length arranged in the form of a parallelogram. The transmitter or receiver is connected to two wires at one end of the major diagonal and the wires are connected together at the other end of this diagonal by a resistor. Usually mounted in the horizontal plane, the aerial has its maximum directional effect in the line of the major diagonal.

Rhumbatron. See RESONANT CAVITY.

Ribbon Microphone. MICROPHONE consisting of a thin strip of aluminium foil mounted vertically between the poles of a permanent magnet (see Fig. R-10). Movement of the ribbon when sound waves impinge upon it results in the generation of an electromotive force proportional to the rate of cutting of the lines of magnetic force by the ribbon.

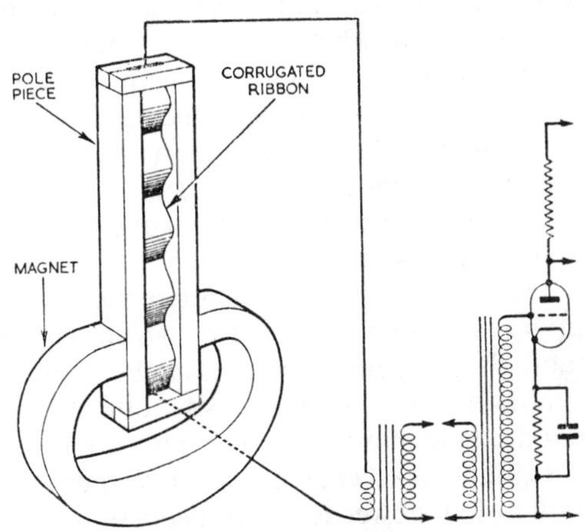

FIG. R-10.—DIAGRAMMATIC ARRANGEMENT OF A RIBBON MICROPHONE.

Ringing. Series of damped oscillations at the resonant frequency of the circuit which persist for a greater or less time after the exciting electromotive force is removed.

Ripple. Alternating current or voltage superimposed upon a direct current or voltage or upon an alternating current or voltage of lower frequency than the " ripple ". Ripple occurs in the output of a RECTIFIER prior to smoothing.

Ripple Filter. A network designed to remove ripple from a unidirectional current. A SMOOTHING CIRCUIT.

Ripple Frequency. The frequency of the ripple component of a voltage or current.

Ripple Voltage. The amplitude of the alternating (ripple) component of a unidirectional voltage.

Röntgen. (Symbol r) The unit of X-ray or gamma-ray radiation. It is defined as the quantity of X- or of gamma radiation which produces ions of either sign carrying a total of one electrostatic unit of electricity per cubic centimetre of dry air at 0° C and 760 mm of mercury pressure.

Röntgen Rays. See X-RAYS.

Root Mean Square Value. (Abbreviation r.m.s.) The effective value of an alternating current or voltage. Numerically equal to the square root of the mean value of the squares of the instantaneous values over a complete cycle. In the case of a sinusoidal waveform the r.m.s. value is equal to the amplitude (peak value) divided by $\sqrt{2}$.

Rotating-anode X-ray Tube. X-ray tube the anode of which is a shaped block of tungsten which, during operation, is made to rotate at high speed, so that the electron beam constantly impinges on a different part of the anode, thus reducing the risk of burning.

Rotor (of a Capacitor). That part of a VARIABLE CAPACITOR which comprises the moving plates attached to a spindle, rotation of which causes the moving plates to interleave to a greater or less extent with the fixed plates or stator.

Roving Eye. Mobile television transmitter consisting of a motor vehicle containing a television camera which can be elevated through the roof, thus permitting scenes to be televised while the vehicle is in motion. The vehicle also contains provision for recording a sound commentary, together with the necessary amplifiers and other equipment to enable the programme to be radiated to a main station at low power for re-transmission.

Rutherford Atom. Conception, due to Lord Rutherford, who invisaged the chemical atom as a nucleus with electrons revolving round it. See ATOM, STRUCTURE OF.

S

S-band. (10 cm band) Frequency band from 1550 to 5200 Mc/s employed in radar.

Saddle Coils. Coils of rectangular form, bent to fit on the neck of a cathode-ray tube, and carrying the currents producing magnetic deflexion of the beam. DEFLEXION COILS.

Saturated Diode. A thermionic diode operated under such conditions that increase of anode voltage produces no appreciable increase of anode current.

Saturation, Magnetic. Condition of a ferromagnetic material when the flux density has been raised to a value at which further increase of magnetizing force produces no appreciable increase of induction.

Saturation, Thermionic. Condition in a thermionic tube when all the electrons released from the cathode are collected by the anode and any other electrodes at a positive potential with respect to the cathode.

Saturation Current, Thermionic. The maximum value to which the anode current of a thermionic valve in the non-oscillating condition can be raised by increasing the steady direct potential applied to the anode, the cathode temperature and the potentials of all other electrodes being maintained at constant values.

Saturation Current (of a Transformer). The constant direct current which, circulating in a winding of an iron-cored transformer or other inductor, produces magnetic saturation of the core and hence reduces the inductance of the winding to a very low value.

Saturation Curve (of a Ferromagnetic Material). Graph showing the relation between the magnetizing force and the induction, and indicating the region of saturation. See also MAGNETIZING CURVE.

Saturation Curve (of a Thermionic Valve). A graph showing the relation between the anode current and anode voltage of the valve under conditions of constant cathode temperature and constant

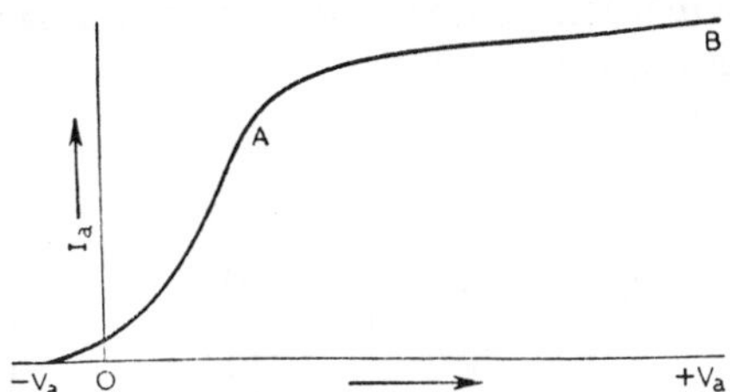

FIG. S-1.—SATURATION CURVE OF A HIGH-VACUUM THERMIONIC DIODE WITH CATHODE MAINTAINED AT CONSTANT TEMPERATURE.

potentials of all electrodes except the anode. Fig. S-1 shows the general form of the saturation curve of a thermionic diode, the condition of saturation setting in over the region A–B.

Sausage Aerial. Aerial consisting of a number of wires connected electrically in parallel and supported in parallel formation by attachment around the circumference of a number of circular SPREADERS.

Sawtooth Generator. A circuit in which voltages or currents of sawtooth waveform are generated, usually for use as a TIMEBASE in equipments incorporating cathode-ray tubes.

Sawtooth Waveform. Current or voltage waveform in which the amplitude increases uniformly with time over a period termed the STROKE (see Fig. S-2) and then rapidly falls to zero in a very short time termed the FLYBACK.

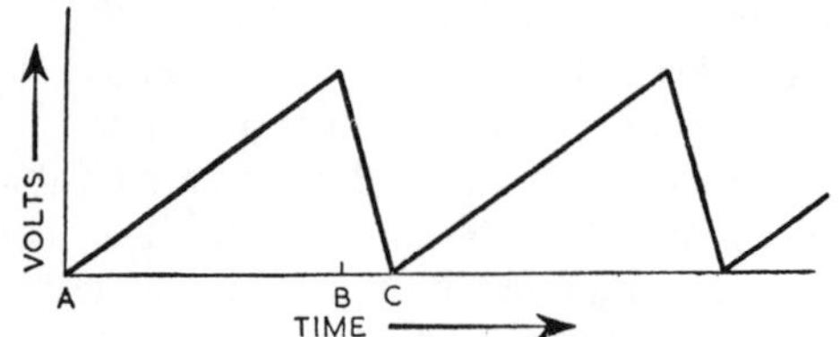

FIG. S-2.—WAVEFORM OF A SAWTOOTH VOLTAGE.
AB is the stroke and BC is the flyback.

Scalar. Said of a quantity which possesses magnitude but not direction or sense.

Scale of Notation. The base on which a system of indicating numerical quantities is arranged. Thus the decimal scale employs 10 digits (0, 1, 2, . . . 9) and the BINARY SCALE only two digits (0 and 1). The relation between the corresponding expressions for various quantities in the two scales is shown in the following table.

Decimal	Binary	Decimal	Binary
0	0	10	1010
1	1	11	1011
2	10	12	1100
3	11	13	1101
4	100	14	1110
5	101	15	1111
6	110	16	10000
7	111	17	10001
8	1000	18	10010
9	1001	19	10011

Scanner. A device or phenomenon whereby a fixed area is traversed point by point in succession until the whole area has been explored. A familiar example is the electron beam employed for " scanning " the picture area in a television picture tube.

Scanning. The process of sweeping the picture area of a television picture tube or a television camera, by the electron beam.

See also CIRCULAR SCANNING, INTERLACED SCANNING, RADIAL DEFLEXION, SEQUENTIAL SCANNING and SPIRAL SCANNING.

Scanning Beam. Electron beam, projected by an electron gun in a cathode-ray tube or television camera, and caused to sweep repeatedly over the whole of the picture area.

Scanning Coils. Coils mounted on the neck of a cathode-ray tube and carrying currents of sawtooth waveform and appropriate frequency to cause the electron beam to be deflected in such a way that it sweeps the whole picture area.

Scanning Line. The line illuminated by a single excursion of the scanning beam, e.g. horizontally across the picture area in a cathode-ray tube.

Scanning Spot. The light-spot on the screen of a cathode-ray tube produced by the electrons of the scanning beam at the point and instant of impact.

Scattering. Random re-radiation of wave energy when the incident ray impinges on an obstacle. A familiar example is the scattering which occurs when a radio wave enters an irregularly ionized region in the upper atmosphere (ionosphere).

Scheelite. An ore of tungsten, consisting of impure calcium tungstate.

Schmidt Optical System. Optical system in which the light from the object is mainly focused by means of a spherical mirror, a

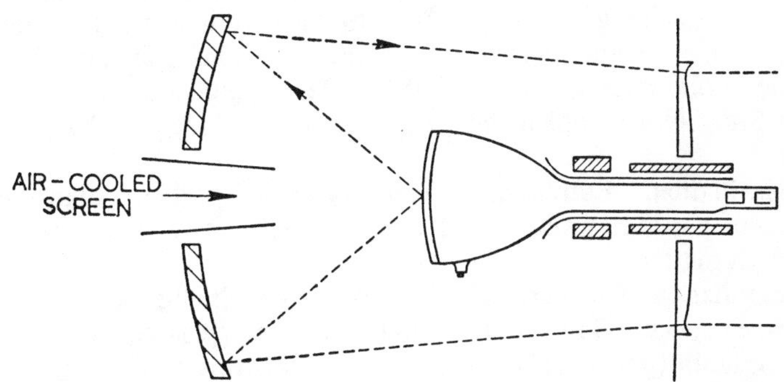

FIG. S-3.—SCHMIDT OPTICAL SYSTEM AS APPLIED TO PROJECTION TELEVISION.

" corrector " lens system being used to compensate the spherical aberration. A modified form of the Schmidt system is used in PROJECTION TELEVISION, the basic arrangement being shown in

Fig. S-3. To enable large-screen pictures to be obtained with a cabinet of moderate size, the path of the light beam is " folded " by means of two plane mirrors inclined at angles of 45° to the axis of the spherical mirror, as shown in Fig. S-4.

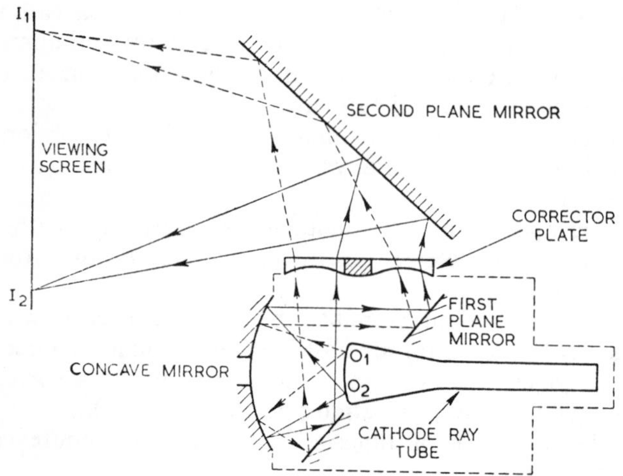

FIG. S-4.—SCHMIDT FOLDED OPTICAL SYSTEM.

Schottky Effect. Variation of the electron current in a thermionic valve due to changes in the WORK FUNCTION of the cathode material with change of anode voltage. These variations constitute NOISE in the anode circuit. The Schottky effect should not be confused with SHOT NOISE, which, however, is often included in the former term.

Scintillation. Luminous effect produced when high-speed charged particles (alpha and beta particles and protons) pass through matter.

Scintillation Counter. Device in which high-speed charged particles strike a PHOSPHOR so that their energy is converted into light quanta (photons) which may be detected by a photo-emissive cell.

Scrambling. System employed to secure secrecy in radio-telephony by changing the frequencies of the various fundamental and harmonic components of the speech transmitted, so rendering it quite unintelligible. At the receiving end the process is reversed, thus restoring the sounds to their original forms.

Scratch Filter. A LOW-PASS filter network which is inserted in the input circuit of an audio-frequency amplifier used for gramophone reproduction. It is designed to suppress signal components of frequencies exceeding say 7000 c/s and thus to eliminate noise resulting from the scratch of the stylus in the grooves of the record.

Screen (of a Cathode-ray Tube). Layer of luminescent material (phosphor) on the internal surface of the flattened end of a cathode-ray tube. Light is produced by the impact of the electron beam (cathode ray) on the screen material.

Screen. See SCREENING.

Screen (Television). Surface on which a television picture is reproduced and viewed. It may be the luminescent screen of a cathode-ray tube (direct viewing) or a reflecting or translucent surface upon which the image from the screen of a cathode-ray tube is projected.

Screen Burn. Deterioration of the luminescent screen of a cathode-ray tube due to bombardment by negative ions present in the tube. See ION BURN.

Screen Grid. An electrode in the form of a wire grid or spiral mounted between the control grid and the anode of a thermionic tetrode, or between the control grid and suppressor grid of a pentode. Maintained at a positive potential with respect to the cathode, the screen grid acts as an accelerating electrode. It is also so connected that it forms an earthed electrostatic screen, thus preventing feedback from the anode to the control grid within the valve via the anode-to-control-grid capacitance.

Screen-grid Valve. A thermionic high-vacuum valve having a screen grid. Applied originally to the tetrode, but now also applicable to screened pentodes for high-frequency circuits.

Screen Modulation. Method of MODULATING a radio-frequency carrier by applying the signal modulation to the screen-grid of the modulated amplifier valve.

Screened Pentode. PENTODE in which the screen grid is so formed and connected that it effectively reduces the electrostatic coupling between the anode and control grid to a very small value. Often termed simply a high-frequency or radio-frequency pentode.

Screening, Electrostatic. Reduction or prevention of penetration by an electric field into a given region, by means of a conducting screen, which may be of grid or mesh construction. A FARADAY CAGE.

Screening, Magnetic. Reduction or prevention of penetration by a magnetic field into a given region, by means of a screen of magnetically permeable material, e.g. mu-metal.

Sealing-in. The process of fusing the glass FOOT carrying the electrodes and lead-in wires of an electron tube to the glass envelope, forming a gas-tight joint.

Sealing-off. Operation in the manufacture of electron tubes whereby, after the tube has been evacuated or filled with the desired inert gas, the glass stem (pumping tube) by which the tube has been attached to the pump is heated and fused, thus closing the exit and severing the connexion.

Search Coil. A small inductor used in measuring magnetic fields. Its position and orientation in the field can be adjusted. Also termed an " exploring coil ".

Second-channel Interference. INTERFERENCE experienced in a superheterodyne receiver due to an unwanted station operating on a frequency which differs from the frequency of the wanted station by twice the intermediate frequency.

Second Detector. The true DETECTOR—rectifier or demodulator —in a supersonic heterodyne receiver. The term, which is seldom used now, was originally employed to distinguish the detector proper from the *mixer* section of the frequency changer, then called the " first detector ".

Second Harmonic. Component of a complex wave having a frequency twice that of the fundamental.

Second-harmonic Distortion. (Symbol d_2) Distortion of a waveform, particularly that of an audio-frequency signal, due to the generation of a second harmonic component as a result of the non-linear characteristic of a circuit component such as the grid-volts/anode-current characteristic of an amplifying valve.

Secondary Coil (Secondary Winding). An inductor which is penetrated by the magnetic field generated in another inductor (the PRIMARY COIL). Changes in the flux linkage due to changes of current in the primary, or relative movement between primary and secondary, cause corresponding voltages to be induced into the secondary coil.

Secondary Electron. Electrons which are emitted from a surface due to bombardment by swiftly-moving PRIMARY electrons.

Secondary Emission. The emission of electrons from a surface by bombarding it with swiftly-moving electrons. Dependent upon the velocity of the primary electrons and the nature of the material, the number of secondary electrons may be less or greater than the number of primary electrons.

Secondary-emission Factor. Ratio of the number of secondary electrons emitted from a surface to the number of primary electrons striking the surface.

Secondary-emission Multiplier. Electron tube in which the anode current is augmented by secondary electrons emitted from an auxiliary electrode. See ELECTRON MULTIPLIER.

Secondary-emission Valve. A thermionic valve operating on the principle of the electron multiplier as distinct from photocells using the same principle.

Secondary Voltage. Electromotive force generated in the secondary coil or winding of a transformer.

Secondary Winding. A SECONDARY COIL forming part of the windings of a static TRANSFORMER.

Selectance. A numerical expression of the SELECTIVITY of a tuned circuit or a complete receiver. It is usually taken as the attenuation in output voltage at some specified frequency off resonance, compared with the maximum voltage at resonance, the value being expressed in decibels.

Selective Resonance. Property of an oscillatory circuit which is designed to resonate at one or more definite frequencies, for example at frequencies corresponding to one or more harmonics of the fundamental frequency of an applied signal.

Selectivity. Ability of a circuit or receiver to respond more readily to signals of a particular frequency to which it is tuned than to signals of other frequencies.

Selector Switch. A switching device whereby a current can be diverted to one of two or more alternative paths, or whereby one of a number of alternative circuit elements can be introduced into a network.

Selenium. Non-metallic element existing in a number of allotropic forms, one of which, " grey selenium ", is a conductor of electricity when irradiated by light.

Selenium Cell. Photo-electric cell in which the sensitive material is the photo-conductive form of selenium.

Self-capacitance. The capacitance possessed by a circuit, or a circuit element or other device, included in a circuit for some purpose other than that of introducing capacitance. An example is the capacitance between the various turns of an inductor.

Self-excited Oscillator. Thermionic oscillator of the type in which the excitation of the grid is derived from positive feedback of alternating power from the anode circuit.

Self-inductance. Property of a conductor or arrangement of conductors whereby any change in the current flowing therein results in the generation of an electromotive force in such a direction as to oppose the change of current.

Self-oscillation. Production of sustained oscillation in electronic equipment due to excessive REGENERATIVE FEEDBACK.

Semiconductor. A material having electrical properties intermediate between those of good electrical conductors and those of insulators. Of particular interest are those whose conductivity varies with change of working conditions. The two most important types are THERMISTORS, whose conductivity varies greatly with change of temperature, the temperature coefficient being negative, and the UNILATERALLY-CONDUCTIVE type which conducts electricity more readily in one direction than in the reverse direction, and thus has a rectifying action.

Sender. A transmitting station.

Sensitivity. The input to a piece of apparatus, and particularly to a radio receiver, necessary to produce a specified output. For broadcast receivers the standard is generally taken as the input, expressed in decibels above or below 1 μV, required to give an output of 50 mW.

Separator. (1) A network, usually but not necessarily incorporating a thermionic valve, used for preventing variations of current, voltage or frequency in one circuit from affecting the performance or characteristics of other circuits. In this sense the term BUFFER STAGE is preferred.

(2) Network employed in television receivers for diverting the SYNCHRONIZING PULSES from the video signal proper. See SYNCHRONIZING SEPARATOR.

Sequential Scanning. System of scanning in television in which the lines of picture follow each other in strict sequence, the picture being completed in one FRAME as distinct from INTERLACED SCANNING, in which the picture consists of two frames, one containing the odd-numbered lines and the next the even-numbered lines.

Series. Method of connecting the elements of an electric circuit so that the same current passes through them.

Series Modulation. Method of impressing the signal modulation on a radio-frequency carrier by connecting the modulator valve and the modulated amplifier valve in series across the h.t. supply, as indicated in Fig. S-5.

Service Area. Area surrounding a broadcast (sound or television) transmitter over which the field strength is considered sufficient to permit signals to be received at good entertainment value.

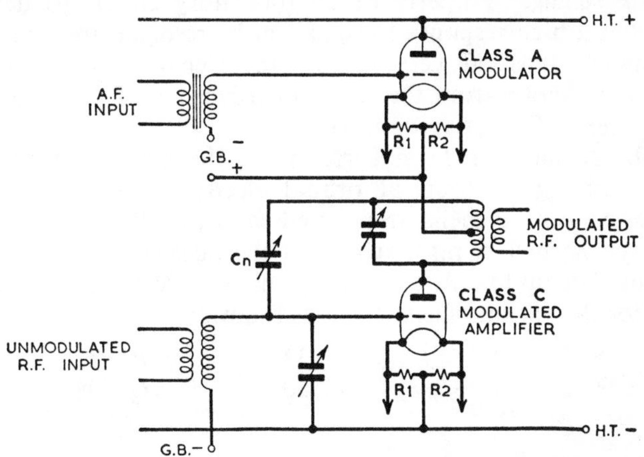

FIG. S-5.—BASIC CIRCUIT FOR SERIES MODULATION.

Shading. Blemishes in a television picture caused by non-uniformity of the field between different parts of the mozaic and the collector in the camera tube.

Shaping Network. Arrangement of circuit elements, usually capacitors and resistors, which can modify the shape or waveform of a pulse or succession of pulses. The two main forms of shaping circuits are the differentiating and the integrating networks, illustrated respectively at a and b in Fig. S-6. The extent to which the

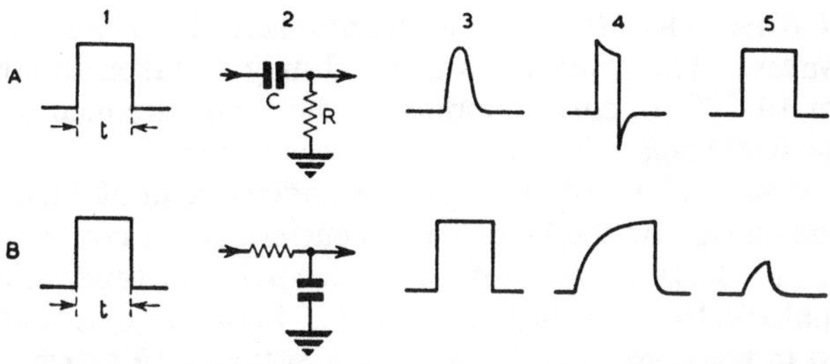

FIG. S-6.—EFFECTS OF TYPICAL SHAPING NETWORKS ON A SQUARE PULSE, FOR DIFFERENT RELATIONSHIPS BETWEEN PULSE DURATION t AND THE TIME CONSTANT $R \times C$ OF THE NETWORK.

(a) Differentiating network. (b) Integrating network.

pulse shape is modified depends upon the value of the time constant ($R \times C$) of the network compared with the duration of the pulse (t) as indicated in the figure.

Sharp Tuning. Property of an oscillatory circuit so designed that it has a high response to signals at its resonant frequency, but its response falls off very rapidly for signals whose frequency differs but slightly from the resonant frequency of the circuit. A high degree of SELECTIVITY.

Shell. A spherical layer surrounding the nucleus of an atom, and containing a group of orbital electrons. There are seven possible concentric shells, designated the *K, L, M, N, O, P* and *Q* shells, the *K* shell being that nearest the nucleus. Each shell can accommodate up to only a limited number of electrons, the complements for the various shells being as follows:

K	2	*N*	32	*P*	72
L	8	*O*	50	*Q*	98
M	18				

Shield. Alternative name for the WEHNELT CYLINDER or grid of a cathode-ray tube.

Shield, Electrostatic. See ELECTROSTATIC SCREEN.

Shield Grid Valve. A SCREEN GRID VALVE.

Shock Excitation. Production of oscillations at the natural frequency of a circuit or system due to the sudden application of energy from an external source.

Short-circuit. A connexion between two points by means of a conducting path of negligible resistance.

Shortening Capacitor. A capacitor connected in series with an aerial in order to reduce its natural wavelength.

Short Wave. Relative term to denote the order of wavelength of radio waves. The " short " waveband may be taken to cover the range of 10–100 m, corresponding to the " high-frequency band " of 3000–30,000 kc/s. The decametric waveband.

Shot Noise. NOISE occurring in the anode circuit of a thermionic valve and caused by the fact that the current is not continuous but consists of a large number of pulses occurring at random as each individual electron reaches the anode. Shot noise is sometimes included in the noise occasioned by the SCHOTTKY EFFECT.

Shottky Effect. See SCHOTTKY EFFECT.

Shunt. Method of connecting two or more circuit elements so that the same electromotive force is applied to each, the current being shared between the different elements in inverse ratio to their individual resistances. See also PARALLEL CONNEXION.

Sideband. A band of frequencies extending above and below the carrier frequency of a radio transmission, and of a total width equal to twice the highest modulating frequency. A radio CHANNEL ideally consists of the complete pair of sidebands.

Signal. Electric or electromagnetic manifestation, usually an electromotive force or a modulated wave, which is to be operated upon by a piece of apparatus such as a detector or amplifier. Originally applied to the information-carrying input to a receiving equipment, it is now commonly used also for any electrical effect which controls the output or operation of a piece of equipment.

Signal Frequency. The frequency of the CARRIER WAVE upon which the signal information has been impressed by the process of modulation. A preferable term when applied to telecommunication systems is STATION FREQUENCY.

Signal Generator. A device for producing electromotive forces of the same type of waveform as the signals encountered in radio, television, etc. These artificial signals are applied to receiving and other equipment under test or repair in order to simulate normal working conditions.

Signal-to-noise Ratio. The ratio of the strength of a wanted signal to that of the noise interference present, the ratio being normally expressed in decibels.

Silica. Dioxide of silicon. In its crystalline form it is known as quartz. Largely used in the manufacture of refractory materials and glass.

Silica Valve. Thermionic valve having an envelope of fused silica and thus able to withstand high operating temperatures.

Silicon. Non-metallic element having semiconductor properties and used in the manufacture of certain crystal diodes and transistors.

Silicon Diode. Semiconductor crystal diode in which the semiconductor is a p-type crystal of silicon, i.e. silicon containing a small and accurately controlled addition of boron, and usually also minute quantities of aluminium and beryllium.

Silver–Mica Capacitor. Capacitor having thin layers of mica as dielectric, the plates consisting of layers of silver fired on.

Simple Harmonic Motion. (s.h.m.) Form of mechanical vibration represented graphically by projecting on a diameter the successive positions of a point which travels at uniform angular velocity on a circular path. See Fig. S-7.

Simultaneous Broadcasting. Transmission of a single programme simultaneously from more than one transmitter, either on the same or at different carrier frequency.

Sine Wave. Waveform represented graphically by a curve the amplitude of which at any instant is proportional to the sine of the angular displacement of a point which travels at constant angular velocity on a circular path. See Fig. S-7.

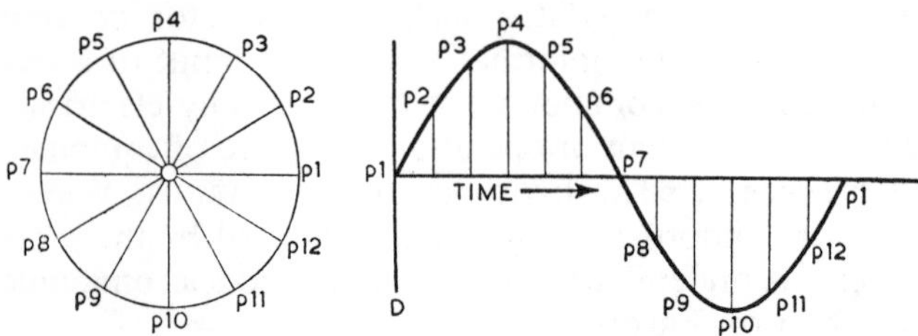

FIG. S-7.—SIMPLE HARMONIC MOTION.

A point p travels at uniform angular velocity on a circular path about centre O. p1, p2, . . . p12 are successive positions of p at intervals representing 30° of rotation. Projection of p1, p2, . . . etc. on a diameter represents simple harmonic motion, and these projections, plotted against a linear time scale, give the familiar sine wave.

Single-shot Recording. Recording photographically the luminous trace on an oscilloscope by making a single exposure during which the photographic film is stationary, as opposed to the moving-film method, in which vertical deflexion of the beam represents the phenomenon under investigation, the time element being obtained by continuous horizontal movement of the photographic film.

Single-sideband Transmission. Radio transmission in which only one of the SIDEBANDS is radiated, thus reducing the bandwidth occupied by a channel and permitting more channels to be accommodated in a given frequency band.

Single-wave Rectification. See HALF-WAVE RECTIFICATION.

Sintering. Process of heating strongly a quantity of more or less amorphous material, so causing it to coalesce into a single solid mass. Tungsten metal, prepared in powder form from its ore, is pressed into bar form and then sintered as an early stage in the manufacture of tungsten wire for lamp or electron-tube filaments.

Sinusoidal. Said of an alternating quantity the value of which, plotted against time, produces a SINE WAVE.

Skiagraph. Photograph taken by means of X-rays.

Skiatron. A form of cathode-ray tube sometimes employed in radar. Its screen is composed of potassium chloride and is white in colour but exhibits a magenta trace of long persistence. If the screen is illuminated by white light from an external source and its image projected by a conventional optical enlarger on to a viewing screen the enlarged reproduction of the trace will appear to be dark. See also DARK-TRACE CATHODE-RAY TUBE.

Skin Effect. The tendency of an alternating current of high frequency to travel near the surface of a conductor, thus increasing the effective resistance of the conductor.

Skip Distance. Minimum distance between a point at which the DIRECT WAVE from a radio transmitter is so attenuated that signals are inaudible, and a point at which, owing to the return of the INDIRECT WAVE reflected from the Appleton layer, signals are once more audible.

Skip Effect. See SKIP DISTANCE above. The effect is most noticeable at short wavelengths.

Sky Wave. Radiation which, after leaving the transmitter, is reflected from the ionized region of the upper atmosphere. See INDIRECT RAY OR WAVE.

Sliding-screen Pentode. Voltage-amplifying pentode, the amplification of which is varied by adjusting the potential applied to the screen grid.

Slope. Term sometimes applied to the MUTUAL CONDUCTANCE of a thermionic valve, symbol g_m. It is numerically equal to the " slope ", i.e. the tangent of the angle of inclination, of the grid-volts/anode-current characteristic of the valve.

Slot Aerial. A slot of length *a* and width 2*b* cut in a large conducting plate is equivalent, when fed across the centres of the long sides, to a normal half-wave dipole element of length *a* and diameter *b*, but with the plane of polarization turned through 90°. This form of construction offers advantages in certain cases and is, for example, commonly used in f.m. broadcasting.

Smoothing. Process of removing ripple or other small variations of voltage superimposed upon a steady direct voltage, and more particularly from the anode supply of thermionic tubes.

Smoothing Circuit (Filter or **Network).** Arrangement of series inductors or resistors and parallel capacitors, forming a low-pass filter for removing ripples from a d.c. supply. Typical basic circuits are given in Fig. S-8.

Socket, Valve. Device having a number of contacts arranged to mate with the connecting pins of a thermionic valve or other electron tube, enabling the tube to be connected in a circuit.

Soft Valve. Thermionic valve in which a small quantity of gas is deliberately left, as distinct from high-vacuum or HARD VALVES.

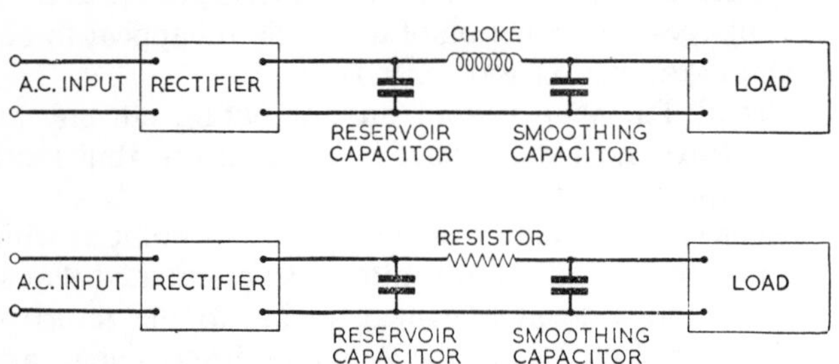

FIG. S-8.—TYPICAL FORMS OF SMOOTHING FILTERS.

Soft X-rays. Rays at the low-frequency end of the X-ray spectrum, having less power of penetration than the higher-frequency HARD X-RAYS.

Solenoid. Coil of wire consisting of many turns in one or more layers, wound on a cylindrical former.

Sound. The sensation experienced when the ear is acted upon by vibrations within a certain range of frequencies. Also the vibrations themselves.

Sound (Velocity of). The velocity of propagation of sound in air is 331·4 m/sec or approximately 700 m.p.h., varying slightly with change of pressure, temperature and humidity.

Sound Carrier. The radio-frequency wave which, modulated at sound frequency, carries the information which is re-converted in the receiver to sound vibrations.

Sound Channel. (1) The carrier frequency and its associated sidebands involved in the transmission of the sound accompaniment of a television programme.

(2) The term is also somewhat loosely applied to that part of a television receiver involved in the reproduction of the sound accompaniment of a television programme, i.e. the sound i.f. amplifiers, the audio detector and the audio amplifier stages.

Sound-on-vision. Intrusion of the sound signal of a television transmission into the picture-reproducing circuit of a receiver, producing alternate light and dark bands horizontally on the picture.

Space Charge. Negative electric charge due to the presence of an accumulation of electrons, e.g. in the neighbourhood of a heated cathode. Emission of electrons from the cathode leaves the latter with a positive charge which tends to attract the electrons back to the cathode. There is thus a continuous process of exchange, electrons leaving the cathode and entering the space-charge region, and other electrons returning from the space charge to the cathode.

Space-charge Limitation. Limitation of the electron current to the anode of a thermionic valve by the opposing forces represented by the attraction of the electrons from the region of the cathode by the anode, and the repulsion of electrons leaving the cathode by the negative space charge.

Spark Gap. Arrangement of two conductors the ends of which are separated by a space across which a disruptive spark discharge is caused to occur.

Spark Transmission. System of radio communication in which a succession of trains of waves are produced by disruptive discharges across a spark gap.

Spark Trap. Protective device forming part of an electron tube, and consisting of a subsidiary electrode through which any disruptive discharge due to overloading, etc., is conducted to earth.

Special-quality Valves (Special-service Valves). Thermionic valves having characteristics similar to those of corresponding conventional types, but specially designed to withstand more severe service conditions than are encountered in domestic or normal industrial applications. Typical conditions requiring special-service valves are those obtaining in aircraft, military vehicles, naval vessels and other mobile installations.

Specific Inductive Capacitance. Earlier term for DIELECTRIC CONSTANT.

Specific Resistance. Figure of merit for a conductive material. Equal to the resistance across opposite faces of a cube of the material having sides of 1 cm, the resistance being measured at a specified temperature. Also termed VOLUME RESISTIVITY.

Spectrum. The arrangement of radiations in order of their frequencies. Thus the spectrum of visible light covers frequencies from about 4×10^{15} to 8×10^{15} c/s. A general analysis of the electromagnetic spectrum is given in the Appendix.

Spherical Aberration. Lack of definition in the image produced by a lens or mirror having surfaces of spherical contour, and resulting from the fact that individual rays are not brought to a focus at the same point.

Spiral Scanning. System of SCANNING in which the cathode ray, and hence the light spot, sweeps over the scanning area in a spiral path, either starting at the centre and travelling outward, then returning rapidly to the centre, or starting at the periphery and travelling towards the centre, thereafter returning quickly to the periphery.

Spiral Timebase. System of deflexion voltages or currents which, applied to the deflexion plates or coils of a cathode-ray tube, causes the light spot to follow a spiral path at constant angular velocity.

Sporadic E Propagation. The propagation of waves above 40 Mc/s which are refracted by areas in the E-layer of the ionosphere during the intermittent periods when they become heavily ionized.

Spot Wobble. Device for improving the reproduced television picture by making less obvious the line structure resulting from imperfect interlace of adjacent lines. The improvement is achieved by causing the horizontal scanning line to assume a slightly sinusoidal formation, that is to say, by impressing on the normal horizontal travel of the electron beam a sinusoidal vertical deflexion having an amplitude slightly greater than the width of a line, and of such frequency that about 200–400 cycles of vertical deflexion occur in each line period. The slight defocusing effect thus caused considerably reduces the definition of the line structure of the picture.

Spread of Characteristics. Limits between which the properties of a device or circuit element, e.g. a thermionic valve, may vary from specimen to specimen, compared with the published "nominal" data for that particular type or make of device.

Spreader. Device for keeping the wires of a multi-wire aerial or transmission line spaced from each other and at the correct distances apart.

Spurious Oscillation. Oscillation produced in a circuit due to the circuit, or part of it, resonating at a frequency other than that of the signal. Also termed parasitic oscillation.

Sputtering. Process whereby the material of the cathode disintegrates under ionic bombardment and is deposited on some other electrode or on the walls of the envelope of an electron tube.

Square-law Capacitor. Variable capacitor the plates of which are so shaped that the capacitance is proportional to the square of the angular displacement of the moving plates.

Square Wave. Alternating current or voltage the waveform of which is approximately square or rectangular. See Fig. S-9.

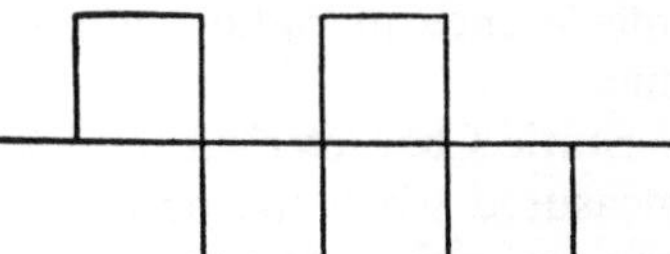

FIG. S-9.—IDEALIZED FORM OF A SQUARE-WAVE VOLTAGE OR CURRENT.

In practice, owing to circuit constants, only an approximation to a pure square wave can be attained.

Squegging. Mode of oscillation in a thermionic valve, in which oscillations of high frequency build up to a considerable amplitude and then suddenly cease, the process being repeated to give alternate bursts of oscillation and periods of quiescence.

Squegging Oscillator. Thermionic oscillator operating on the squegging principle, and sometimes used as a timebase generator for cathode-ray oscilloscopes.

Stacked Aerial. An aerial array in which the aerial elements are arranged in substantially vertical tiers.

Staggered Tuning. Method of obtaining wide-band amplification by using several tuned stages, the first of which is tuned to the desired centre frequency, the remaining stages being tuned to frequencies differing slightly alternately above and below the centre frequency, so that the overall response is approximately linear over the desired bandwidth.

Stampings. Thin plates of magnetic material of special form, used to build up the cores of iron-cored inductors and transformers. See also LAMINATIONS.

Standing Waves. Distribution of current and voltage in a conductor, e.g. in an aerial, which occurs when two sinusoidal waves of equal frequency are flowing in opposite directions. In these circumstances a number of fixed points are produced at which successive maximum and minimum values of current and voltage occur.

Start–Stop Control. Automatic control system in which the controlling element causes the process to be controlled either to continue or to cease. An example is a temperature-control system in which a source of heat is switched off when the temperature exceeds a pre-determined value by a specified amount, and is switched on again when the temperature has fallen below the desired value. Also termed ON–OFF and STOP–GO control.

Static. (1) Said of the relationship between two variable quantities when that relationship is not subject to change due to the variation of a third quantity.

(2) Alternative term for atmospheric disturbances producing interference in radio equipment, or for the interference so introduced.

Static Characteristics. The characteristics of a thermionic valve measured when the potentials applied to all the electrodes except one are maintained constant. Fig. S-10 is a typical anode-current/control-grid volts curve for a pentode operated under conditions of

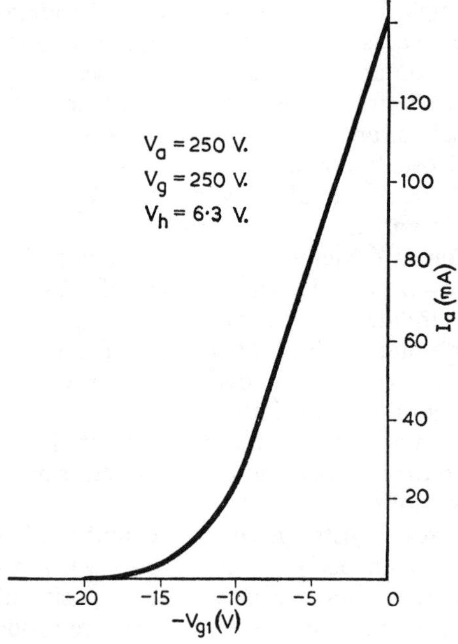

FIG. S-10.—STATIC ANODE CURRENT/GRID VOLTS CHARACTERISTIC OF A TYPICAL OUTPUT PENTODE (ANODE SCREEN AND HEATER VOLTS CONSTANT).

constant anode and screen-grid voltages. The inclusion of a load in the anode circuit of the valve operated with a varying signal voltage applied to the control grid introduces variations of anode voltage due to the varying voltage drop across the anode load.

Characteristics measured under such conditions are termed DYNAMIC CHARACTERISTICS.

Staticon. English name for the form of television camera tube known in America as the VIDICON.

Station Frequency. Preferred term for SIGNAL FREQUENCY, that is to say the frequency of the carrier wave on which a given station is transmitting.

Stator (of a Variable Capacitor). The assembly of fixed plates in a variable capacitor, as opposed to the moving plates which form the rotor.

Stem. Factory term for the PUMPING TUBE of a thermionic valve or other electron tube.

Stereophonic. Sound, from a radio transmission or a reproducer, is termed stereophonic when, because of the directional qualities, a listener gains the impression that the source of the sound is of considerable area. The resultant sensation should approximate to hearing the original sound with two ears. Stereophonic sound involves the use of two or more groups of microphones in the studio, two or more transmission or recording channels and, for reproduction, two or more independent amplifiers and speakers, suitably positioned.

Stereoscopic. Term applied to the transmission and reproduction of a scene or picture on a flat surface but giving a three-dimensional appearance. This is achieved by producing two images, taken from slightly different viewpoints, which are then so presented that they are either viewed by the separate eyes or are so combined as to produce the same effect.

Stop–Go. Alternative term for the START–STOP form of automatic control.

Stopper. A high-impedance circuit element, so connected as to reduce high-frequency potentials which might otherwise reach the grid (or anode) of a thermionic valve and set up parasitic oscillations.

Straight-line-frequency Capacitor. Variable capacitor the moving plates of which are so shaped that the capacitance is inversely proportional to the square of the angular displacement of the moving vanes. The frequency to which such a capacitor tunes a given inductor is directly proportional to the angular displacement of the moving plates.

Straight Receiver. Radio receiver in which all the pre-detector amplification occurs at station (signal) frequency, as distinct from a supersonic-heterodyne receiver in which some or all of the high-frequency amplification occurs at an INTERMEDIATE FREQUENCY. A tuned radio-frequency (t.r.f.) receiver.

Strain Gauge. Arrangement of fine resistance wires mounted on a paper strip. Cemented on to surfaces subjected to mechanical stresses, deformation of the specimen causes elongation of the wire and corresponding reduction of its diameter, thus increasing its electrical resistance. The change of resistance can be measured or displayed on a cathode-ray oscilloscope for determination of the mechanical properties of the material or specimen under test.

Stray Capacitance. Capacitance existing in a circuit other than that provided by capacitors deliberately included in the circuit. An example is the capacitance between two neighbouring conductors, the insulation forming the dielectric.

Stray Magnetic Field. Unwanted magnetic field set up by currents circulating in conductors or electrical apparatus, and having a deleterious effect on the operation of the circuit.

Stray Flux. The leakage flux from an iron-cored component such as an inductor or transformer.

Strays. Interfering signals resulting from natural phenomena. See ATMOSPHERICS.

Streaking. Alternative term for that form of television picture fault described under FLARE.

Stroke. That part of the complete period of a timebase voltage or current which causes the light spot in a cathode-ray tube to travel at uniform velocity across the luminescent screen. The rapid return of the spot is called the FLYBACK.

Strontium. Metallic element in the alkaline-earth group. Its oxide is one of the oxides used for coating thermionic cathodes.

Stub. A short section of transmission line, generally connected across an aerial feeder and used to facilitate impedance matching.

Sub-miniature Valve. Thermionic valve of very small dimensions, e.g. approximately 1 in. long and ¼ in. in diameter.

Submodulator. Audio-frequency amplifier which immediately precedes the modulator stage in a radio transmitter equipment. See MODULATION.

Super-conduction. The property of certain metals to lose their electrical resistance completely at temperatures of about 7° K. This effect is, however, destroyed in the presence of a magnetic field. Super-conduction is exploited in the device known as the CRYOTRON.

Superheterodyne Receiver (Superhet). Radio receiver in which all or most of the pre-detector amplification takes place at a frequency intermediate between the station frequency and the modulation frequency band. Full name SUPERSONIC-HETERODYNE RECEIVER (q.v.).

Supersonic Amplifier. Thermionic amplifier designed to amplify signals of a frequency greater than those of the audio waveband.

Supersonic Frequency. A frequency higher than those falling within the audio-frequency spectrum.

Supersonic-Heterodyne Receiver (Superhet). Radio receiver in which a high degree of sensitivity and selectivity is achieved by transferring the modulation of the radio-frequency carrier to a locally-produced carrier of lower (supersonic) frequency, this INTERMEDIATE FREQUENCY signal being subsequently amplified and detected. Not only is amplification at intermediate frequency more efficient than at radio frequency but, the intermediate frequency being of fixed value, the amplifiers can be pre-tuned, thus greatly simplifying the adjustment and operation of the receiver. The intermediate-frequency carrier is produced by the HETERODYNING of the station-frequency carrier with a locally-generated

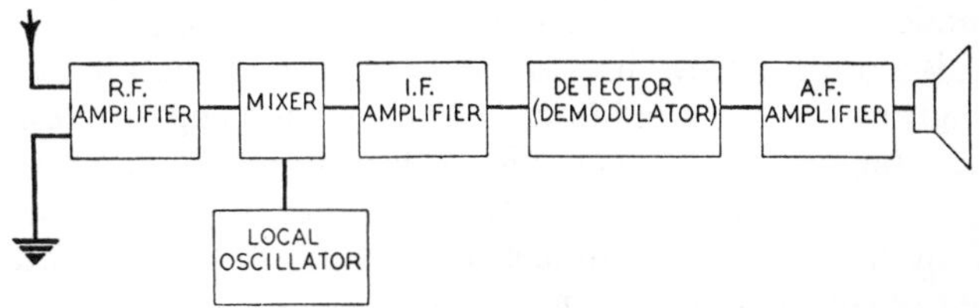

FIG. S-11.—BLOCK DIAGRAM OF A SUPERSONIC HETERODYNE RADIO RECEIVER.

The mixer and local oscillator together constitute the frequency-changer stage.

oscillation. A block diagram of a superhet receiver is given in Fig. S-11. The radio-frequency pre-amplifying stage is not always incorporated. It does, however, increase the sensitivity and selectivity of the equipment, and also serves as a buffer stage to reduce the risk of the local oscillation being radiated from the receiving aerial, causing interference in neighbouring receivers. See also FREQUENCY CHANGER and INTERMEDIATE-FREQUENCY AMPLIFICATION.

Suppressor. Device comprising one or more capacitors and possibly chokes and/or resistors, intended to prevent interference in radio or television receivers by radio-frequency waves generated by such equipment as electric motors, car ignition systems, etc., and transmitted either by radiation or via the electricity mains. Ideally, such interference should be suppressed at the source, but it is often necessary to fit a suppressor either at the mains input to the receiver or at the point where the mains enter the building. See INTERFERENCE.

Suppressor Grid. Electrode of grid formation located between the screen grid and anode of a thermionic PENTODE, and maintained at or near cathode potential. Its function is to repel secondary electrons emitted from the anode, thus preventing them from travelling to the screen grid. The negative resistance kink which characterizes the anode-current/anode-volts curve of a tetrode is thus avoided.

Surface-barrier Transistor. Type of transistor of similar type to the ALLOYED-JUNCTION, but with higher cut-off frequency. The method of construction is slightly different, by an electrolytic process.

Surge Arrester. Protective device for discharging the energy of electrical surges such as those resulting from lightning or accidental contact with high-voltage lines. It consists essentially of a gas-filled diode, the discharge through which, over a certain range of voltage, is a normal glow discharge, but changes to an arc discharge under higher over-volt conditions. The arc has a negative resistance characteristic, and is thus capable of discharging large amounts of energy. The connexion of a surge arrester to protect a radio receiver in the event of lightning striking the aerial is good practice, particularly with high outdoor aerials.

Sweep Circuit. Circuit supplying the deflecting voltage or current for a cathode-ray tube. A timebase generator.

Sweep Generator. A FREQUENCY-MODULATED OSCILLATOR or WOBBULATOR.

Symmetrical Deflexion. Deflexion of the beam in a cathode-ray tube by applying to a pair of deflexion plates a voltage which varies symmetrically above and below a mean value equal to the final anode voltage of the tube. Symmetrical deflexion minimizes the risk of trapezoidal distortion of the trace or image on the screen.

Synchronism. Strictly speaking, the condition in which two or more periodic phenomena have the same frequency and are also in phase. It is also used for a condition in which two periodic phenomena have frequencies, one of which is an exact multiple or submultiple of that of the other. Synchronism between the vertical and horizontal deflecting currents in the receiver and those at the transmitter is an essential pre-requisite for successful reproduction of television programmes and between the horizontal and vertical deflexion voltage for the display of periodic phenomena with a cathode-ray oscilloscope.

Synchronizing. The TELEVISION WAVEFORM contains, in addition to the video or picture information, two sets of pulses the functions of which are to control the phase and/or frequency of the horizontal and vertical timebases. After the composite signal has been amplified and detected, therefore, the synchronizing pulses must be removed from the video signal so that the latter can be applied to the modulating grid of the cathode-ray tube. The horizontal and vertical (line and frame) synchronizing pulses must then be separated from each other and applied to the appropriate timebases. These are two general forms of synchronizing circuit. In one, the synchronizing pulses trigger the timebase, thus determining the instant when the flyback commences. In the other, usually termed " flywheel " synchronizing circuits, the frequency or phase of the timebase is compared with the synchronizing pulses, any discrepancy producing a control signal which corrects the timebase frequency.

Synchronizing Pulse or Signal. Signal transmitted as part of every line and frame period of a television programme, and used to control the timebase generators, so ensuring synchronism between the scanning in the receiver and that at the transmitter.

Synchronizing Pulse Separator. The removal of the synchronizing pulses from the demodulated television signal can be effected by a valve-operated stage, the basic form of which is shown in Fig. S-12. The composite signal is applied to the control grid of a pentode in

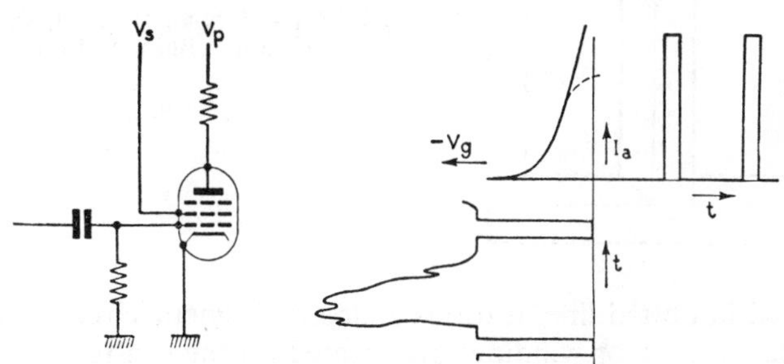

FIG. S-12.—BASIC CIRCUIT OF A SYNCHRONIZING PULSE SEPARATOR SHOWING A SIMPLIFIED CIRCUIT AND THE INPUT SIGNAL AND OUTPUT CURRENT.

the sense indicated, and the operating conditions of the valve are so adjusted that only the synchronizing pulses drive the valve above cut-off. If the anode voltage of the valve is so adjusted that the knee of the anode-current/anode-voltage characteristic corresponds with the tip of the synchronizing pulses (as shown in broken line) the valve also serves as a noise limiter. The vertical and horizontal synchronizing pulses are, of course, of equal amplitude, but they can be separated by means of an INTEGRATING or a DIFFERENTIATING CIRCUIT, as a result of which the two sets of pulses emerge with different amplitudes.

T

T-Aerial. AERIAL consisting of a vertical conductor attached to the mid-point of an elevated horizontal conductor.

T-Attenuator. ATTENUATOR comprising three resistors, one end of each being connected together, the free end of one being connected to one input terminal, the free end of another to one output terminal, and the free end of the third to both the second input terminal and the second output terminal. See T-NETWORK.

T-core. Ferromagnetic structure forming part of the magnetic circuit of an inductor or transformer, and having a form as illustrated in full line in Fig. T-1. In conjunction with a U-CORE, as

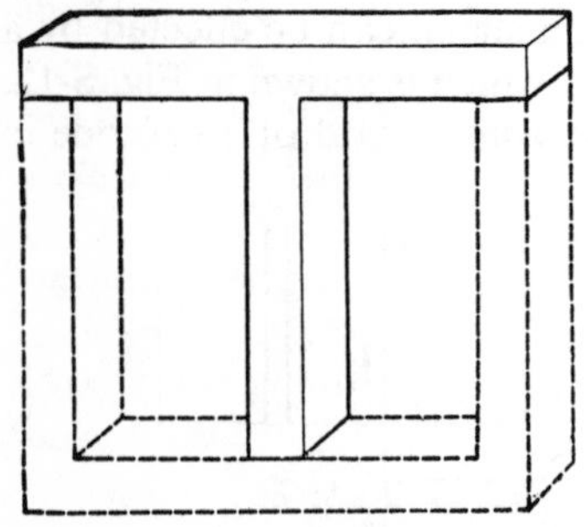

FIG. T-1.—T-CORE (FULL LINE) AND U-CORE (BROKEN LINE).

indicated in dotted line, it forms a closed magnetic circuit. In this case the winding or windings are located on the centre limb.

T-network. Also termed a Y-network or star network. An arrangement of three circuit elements possessing impedance, one end of each element being connected together. One free end is connected to one of the input terminals, another free end to one of the output terminals and the third free end to both the second input and the second output terminals, as indicated in Fig. T-2.

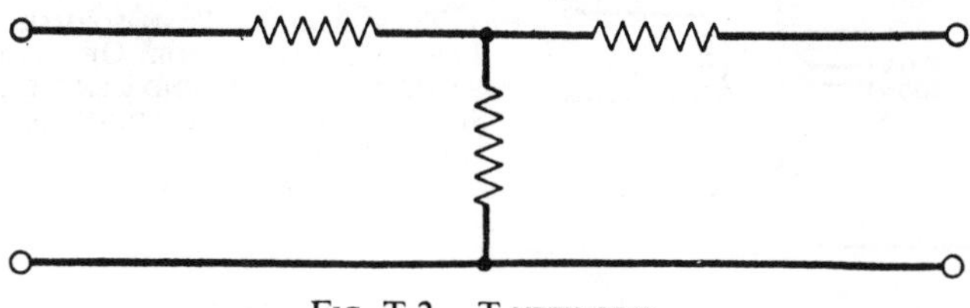

FIG. T-2.—T-NETWORK.

Tape Recording. System of recording sound (speech, music, etc.) in the form of variations of magnetization along a continuous tape of ferromagnetic material. Originally steel tape or wire was used, but modern systems often employ plastic tape impregnated or coated with magnetic material. In recording, the tape is drawn at constant speed through the airgap of an electromagnet energized by the audio-frequency current derived from a microphone. Each point on the tape is thus magnetized to a degree proportional to the strength of the audio-frequency current at the instant when it passes through the recording magnet or "head", the variations of magnetization along the tape thus corresponding to the waveform of the signal current. The sound is reproduced by passing the tape between the poles of a second electromagnet the coils of which are not energized. Changes in the magnetic flux in the core due to the varying intensity of magnetization of the tape induce a correspondingly varying voltage in the windings, and this voltage is applied to an amplifier and loudspeaker combination to reproduce the signal. Usually the tape is passed between the poles of an "erasing" magnet in order to remove any previous recording. Unless deliberately erased in this way, tape recordings are to all intents and purposes permanent. The quality of the recording and reproduction is very high and is practically indistinguishable from a "live" performance.

Tapping. A connexion taken to or from an intermediate point in a circuit element such as a resistor or inductor or a series chain of such elements. Usually employed for varying the potential applied to some other part of a network (see POTENTIAL DIVIDER) or for adjusting the value of a circuit element or adapting it for operation at a particular input voltage as in a POWER TRANSFORMER. See Fig. T-3.

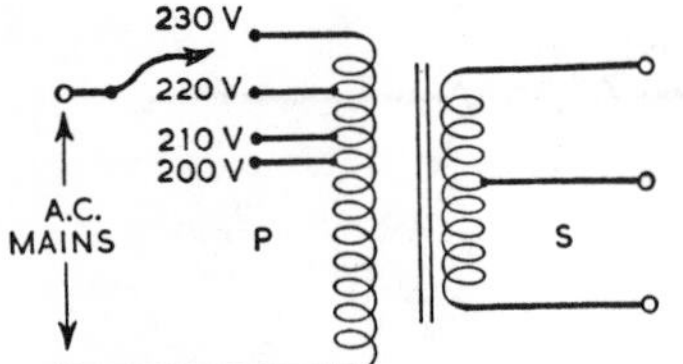

FIG. T-3.—MAINS TRANSFORMER WITH TAPPED PRIMARY FOR OPERATION AT VARIOUS VOLTAGES AND CENTRE-TAPPED SECONDARY FOR FEEDING A FULL-WAVE RECTIFIER.

Target. An electrode in an electron tube on which high-velocity electrons are caused to impinge. The anode of a thermionic valve is, in effect, a " target "; in a cathode-ray tube the target is the luminescent screen.

Target Specification. Statement of the desirable performance of a projected device or piece of apparatus, which the designer endeavours to realize.

Telecommunication. Omnibus term embracing all forms of communication in which signals consisting of writing, sounds or images are transmitted over a considerable distance by electric, radio or visual methods.

Telegraphy. Method of telecommunication in which the signals are transmitted as a series of impulses in accordance with a code and after reception, are translated into words, figures, etc.

Telemeter. Electrical measuring instrument the readings of which are transmitted by wire or radio to a distant point. Not only can electrical quantities, such as voltages and currents, be telemetered, but also any physical quantity which can be expressed in terms of an electrical quantity.

Telephony. Method of communication in which a sound signal, e.g. the human voice, is converted into electric variations of identical waveform and transmitted by wire or radio to a distant point at which it is reproduced as sound.

Teleprinter. A telegraph system in which the message is translated into, and transmitted as, a series of electrical impulses according to a code and, at the receiving end, used to operate a mechanism which prints the original message in words and figures on a continuous paper tape.

Teleradiography. A technique employed in taking X-ray photographs for medical purposes, in which the X-ray tube is at some distance from the body in order to minimize distortion.

Telescope, Radio. See RADIO TELESCOPE.

Television. The art of transmitting and of simultaneously reproducing at a distance a visible image of a picture or scene. It is the essence of television, as distinct from PICTURE TELEGRAPHY (facsimile telegraphy) that the reproduced television image is of momentary duration only but is repeated many times in rapid succession so as to appear to be continuous and to reproduce any movement or change incorporated in the original scene. The general principles of television are indicated in the following simplified description of the system employed for entertainment television in Great Britain. The systems used in other countries are basically similar but may differ in detail.

It is impossible to convey simultaneously on one CHANNEL all the information which constitutes a two-dimensional picture, i.e., the graduations of light and shade at all points in the scene. The light values of successive small elements of the picture area are therefore transmitted seriatim, the whole picture area being covered in a period of one-twenty-fifth of a second so that 25 pictures are reproduced every second. Owing to the PERSISTENCE OF VISION of the human eye, the picture appears to be continuous.

The picture content of the television signal is derived from a TELEVISION CAMERA in which the scene to be televised produces a corresponding pattern of electric charges on a suitably treated and prepared TARGET. The surface of the plate is swept or SCANNED in a series of horizontal lines by an electron beam, thus neutralizing the charge at successive points. Changes in the electric current in the plate circuit, brought about by this process of neutralization, produce a varying voltage drop across a load resistor, and these voltage variations constitute the video signal which is transmitted by wire or radio.

In the receiver the video signal is used to modulate the electron beam in a cathode-ray tube (PICTURE TUBE), thus producing corresponding variations of illumination, where the beam impinges on the luminescent screen. By means of a series of electromagnets energized by currents of sawtooth waveform and of appropriate frequency, the modulated electron beam is caused to scan the screen area in synchronism with the scanning beam in the television camera, so that the variations of illumination appear on the screen in the same relative positions as in the original scene. In addition to the video signal the television transmission includes certain pulses which control the frequency and phase of the deflexion currents and ensure synchronism between the scanning in the studio and in the receiver.

In the British system the picture is scanned in 405 horizontal lines, twenty-five times per second and with INTERLACED SCANNING, whereby the odd-numbered lines are scanned first, after which the even-numbered lines are traced, thus giving two FRAMES per complete picture. See Fig. T-4.

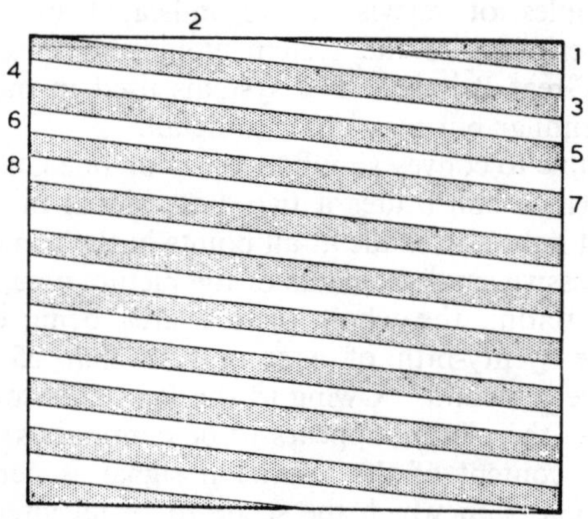

FIG. T-4.—THE STRIPS 1, 3, 5, 7, . . . ARE TRANSMITTED SERIATIM IN $\frac{1}{50}$ SEC TO FORM AN ODD FRAME, FOLLOWED BY STRIPS 2, 4, 6, 8, . . . IN SUCCESSION IN $\frac{1}{50}$ SEC TO FORM AN EVEN FRAME, THUS COMPLETING ONE ENTIRE PICTURE IN $\frac{1}{25}$ SEC.

The waveform of the television signal is illustrated in Fig. T-5. Variations of amplitude above the BLACK LEVEL correspond to variations of brightness at successive points on a particular horizontal line. Part of each line period is taken up by a negative-going line synchronizing pulse. During the last 14 line periods of each frame no picture information is transmitted, the time being occupied by eight broad negative-going frame synchronizing pulses at half-line intervals, followed by the normal line synchronizing pulses for 10 line periods. (See SYNCHRONIZING PULSES and TIMEBASE.)

For entertainment purposes the picture signal is used to modulate a carrier wave, as in sound broadcasting, but for industrial and similar applications the signal is often transmitted by wire (CLOSED CIRCUIT transmission). See also INDUSTRIAL TELEVISION.

Television Camera. Device in which the light content of successive picture elements, as scanned in a series of horizontal lines, is converted into a varying electrical signal which can be transmitted either by line or by radio and later re-converted into a visible picture. See also CAMERA TUBE. The principal forms of television camera are described under their different names—see EMITRON, ICONOSCOPE, IMAGE ORTHICON, ORTHICON, VIDICON, etc.

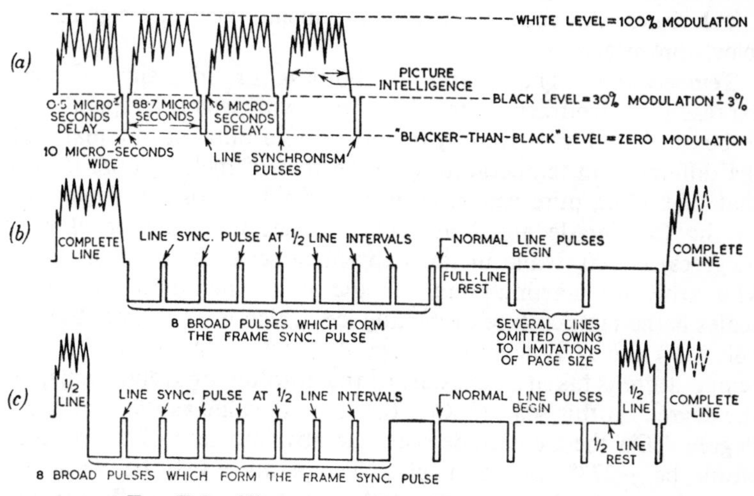

FIG. T-5.—WAVEFORM OF THE TELEVISION SIGNAL.

Television Microscope. Device in which a greatly enlarged image of a very small object is obtained by employing television techniques. In one form the FLYING SPOT SCANNER is employed, the moving light beam produced by scanning the screen of a cathode-ray tube by means of an unmodulated electron beam being made to scan the microscope slide. The light reflected from or passing through the slide is directed on to a photocell, the output of which, after amplification, forms the basis of a television signal. In an alternative method an image of the specimen to be examined is applied by a conventional optical microscope to a normal industrial type television camera tube.

Television Waveform. The waveform of the video signal in a television transmission comprises amplitude variations corresponding to the instantaneous light values of successive elemental areas of the picture area as scanned by the television camera, and a series of square pulses, termed SYNCHRONIZING PULSES for controlling or triggering the line and frame TIMEBASES. A LINE SYNCHRONIZING pulse is interposed between successive line periods, and a series of FRAME SYNCHRONIZING pulses at the end of successive frame periods. In the British television system 100 per cent modulation represents peak white, and 30 per cent modulation represents black level. The region below 30 per cent modulation is reserved for the synchronizing pulses. See Fig. T-5.

Televisor. An equipment for reproducing television signals. A television receiver.

Temperature. The degree of hotness or intensity of heat, expressed in arbitrary units. The scale with which temperature is to be measured is derived by dividing into a number of equal parts the difference in temperature between that of melting pure ice and that of boiling pure water, both at normal atmospheric pressure. In the Centigrade and " absolute " scales this number of parts (degrees) is 100, while in the Fahrenheit scale the number is 180. The arbitrary starting-point for the Fahrenheit and Centigrade scales is the temperature of melting ice, which is 32 degrees Fahrenheit (° F) and zero degrees Centigrade (° C). The absolute zero of temperature is taken as the start of the absolute or Kelvin scale, but the degree on this scale (° K) is the same in value as the Centigrade degree. On the Centigrade scale the absolute zero of temperature would be $-273°$ approximately. Temperature may be considered as analogous to electrical potential, since heat tends to flow from a point of higher to a point of lower temperature just as current flow (as distinct from the direction of electron flow) is considered to be from a region of high potential to one of lower potential.

Temperature Coefficient (of Resistance). Change in the resistance of an electrical conductor per degree Centigrade of temperature change, expressed as a fraction of its resistance at a temperature of 0° C.

Temperature Dependent Components. Circuit elements (e.g. resistors) the electrical properties of which change considerably with temperature. They can be employed to maintain stable performance or to avoid harmful effects resulting from changes in temperature. See THERMISTOR.

Tension. Term sometimes used, more particularly by continental authors, for POTENTIAL DIFFERENCE, e.m.f. or VOLTAGE. In Great

Britain it is used almost exclusively in such phrases as HIGH TENSION, LOW TENSION, etc.

Tera. Prefix denoting 10^{12}.

Terminal. Point in an electric circuit to which a connexion is made, e.g. the " input " or " output " terminals of a piece of apparatus. Also applied to the mechanical clamping device by means of which such connexions are made.

Terminal Velocity. The constant velocity attained by a moving body (including a charged particle) when the resultant of all the accelerating and decelerating forces acting on the body is zero.

Terminal Voltage. The p.d. generated by a source of electrical energy.

Tervalent. See TRIVALENT.

Test Card (Pattern). A pattern transmitted by television at stated times to assist manufacturers, service engineers and viewers in adjusting or testing television receivers. The most familiar test card is " Test Card C ". It contains a variety of shapes in a number of tones ranging from white to black, so designed and positioned as to permit the performance of a receiver to be checked in respect of ASPECT RATIO, picture size, frequency response, contrast, brightness, RESOLUTION and also focus at different parts of the picture area.

Tetravalent. Said of a chemical atom capable of combining with four atoms of hydrogen or their equivalent. A tetravalent atom has four electrons in the outer or valency shell. See ATOM, STRUCTURE OF.

Tetrode. Electron tube having four electrodes. The term is applied mainly, though not exclusively, to four-electrode high-

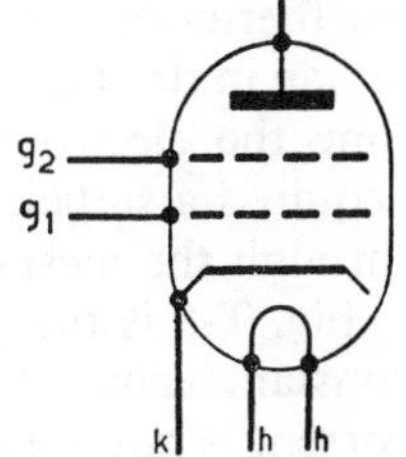

FIG. T-6.—CONVENTIONAL SYMBOL FOR AN INDIRECTLY HEATED TETRODE.

vacuum thermionic valves, termed SCREEN GRID VALVES, in which the electrode system comprises a cathode, two grids and an anode concentric with the cathode. The conventional symbol is shown in Fig. T-6. The functions of the cathode, grid No. 1 (nearer the cathode) and the anode are the same as in a TRIODE. The second grid or screen grid is located between the control grid and the anode and is maintained at a positive potential with respect to the cathode but usually somewhat lower than that of the anode. Fig. T-7 is a basic circuit for a tetrode of this type connected as a high-frequency amplifier. The screen grid acts as an electrostatic screen between

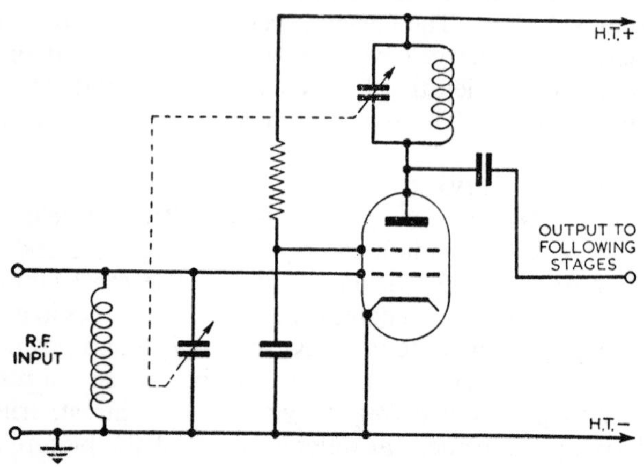

FIG. T-7.—BASIC CIRCUIT OF A TETRODE ARRANGED AS A RADIO-FREQUENCY AMPLIFIER.
In practice, a small negative grid bias would be applied.

the anode and control grid, so preventing FEEDBACK from the anode to the control grid within the valve via the anode-to-grid capacitance, and therefore reducing the risk of setting up oscillations which limit the performance of the triode as a high-frequency amplifier. Furthermore, the positive potential of the screen grid assists the anode in drawing electrons from the region of the cathode. By the time the electrons reach the region of the screen grid they have acquired a sufficiently high velocity to enable most of them to pass through the meshes of the screen and travel to the anode.

Fig. T-8 is the general form of the I_a/V_a curve of a tetrode for a constant value of screen voltage. Over the region CD the anode current is not greatly affected by variations of anode voltage so that the DYNAMIC CHARACTERISTICS of the valve in this region are much closer to the STATIC CHARACTERISTICS than in a triode. The " kink " in the characteristic curve in the region AC occurs at low values of anode voltage when " secondary " electrons, emitted from the anode due to the impact of high-velocity " primary " electrons which have been accelerated by the screen grid, form a reverse current to the screen. Over the region AB an increase of anode voltage actually results in a decrease of anode current, i.e. the valve behaves as if it possessed negative resistance. To ensure stable operation, therefore, the WORKING POINT of the valve, the anode load and the maximum input signal must be so selected that the anode voltage swing does not encroach on the lower part of the

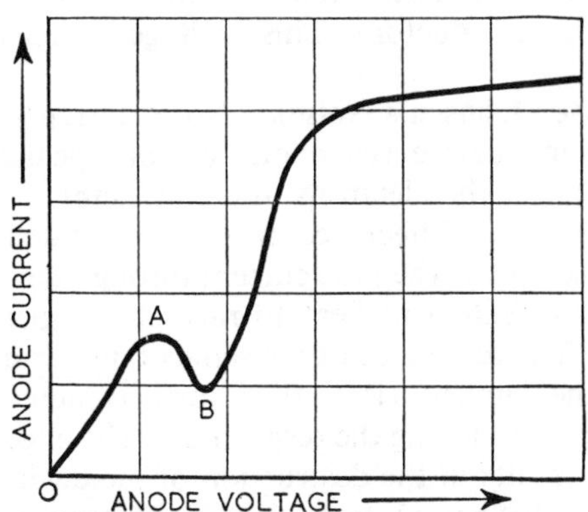

FIG. T-8.—GENERAL FORM OF ANODE VOLTS/ANODE CURRENT CHARACTERISTIC OF A TETRODE FOR CONSTANT VALUES OF CONTROL GRID AND SCREEN GRID VOLTAGES.

AB is the " negative resistance " region.

characteristic curve. This effect somewhat limits the usefulness of this class of valve, but is avoided in the BEAM TETRODE, which has auxiliary electrodes for this purpose, and in the PENTODE or five-electrode valve.

Theatre Television. Large-screen television reproduction suitable for theatres or large halls. In some systems the very bright picture produced on the luminescent screen of a cathode-ray tube operated at very high anode potential is magnified optically and projected on to a large screen (see PROJECTION TELEVISION). In other systems a normal arc projector illuminates a large viewing screen, its light being modulated by some form of " light valve " much in the same way as the beam is modulated by a lantern slide. One method of doing this is to produce a cinematograph film from the received television picture and to project this on to the viewing screen in the conventional way. In other systems modulation of the arc beam is by polarization of light, by defraction or by a series of transparencies produced by alternately bombarding a chemical screen with electrons and irradiating it with infra-red rays.

Thermal Agitation. Random movement of the electrons in a conductor, which increases as the temperature of the conductor rises.

Thermal Agitation Voltage. Varying voltage developed across the resistance of a conductor due to the varying electric current represented by the resultant of the random movements of individual electrons in the conductor. This voltage increases with temperature.

Thermal Noise (Johnson's Noise). Noise currents produced in a sound-reproducing device (telephone or loudspeaker) due to the thermal agitation of the electrons in a conductor.

Thermal Runaway. Effect occurring in a TRANSISTOR or other SEMICONDUCTOR device when the current through the semiconductor material generates sufficient heat to raise its temperature above a critical value. The resistance of the semiconductor decreasing with temperature, the current rises, thus further increasing the temperature and again reducing the resistance. The effect is cumulative and ultimately results in the destruction of the device.

Thermion. A little-used term for an electron emitted from a THERMIONIC cathode.

Thermionic Amplifier. AMPLIFIER incorporating one or more thermionic valves. A thermionic valve used as an amplifier.

Thermionic Cathode. A CATHODE from which electrons are emitted by the action of heat. A " hot cathode ". Early thermionic valves had cathodes composed of pure tungsten wire operating at a temperature of about 2500° K (bright emitter filaments) and heated by the passage of an electric current through them (directly-heated cathode). Tungsten filaments give an electron emission of about 0·3 A/sq. cm of cathode surface, and have an emission efficiency of about 4·27 mA/W of heating power. At a later date filaments of thoriated tungsten, i.e. tungsten with an admixture of thorium oxide, were introduced, and gave adequate emission at a dull red heat (dull emitter). Pure tungsten and thoriated-tungsten filaments are today used only in certain large valves employed in transmitting and industrial equipment. Most modern DIRECTLY-HEATED cathodes consist of tungsten or nickel wire coated with a mixture of the oxides of barium and strontium. Oxide cathodes give adequate emission at a working temperature of about 1050° K, and have an emission efficiency of approximately 1000 mA/W.

Thermionic cathodes for tubes intended to obtain their heating supply from the electricity mains are usually of the INDIRECTLY-HEATED type, consisting of thin-walled metal tubes coated externally with the emissive oxides, and heated by an independent heating element inserted in the bore of the tube and electrically insulated therefrom.

Thermionic Current. Electric current represented by the flow of electrons emitted from a thermionic cathode.

Thermionic Detector. High-vacuum thermionic tube employed for the detection of radio-frequency signals by the process of rectification.

Thermionic Emission. The emission of electrons from a substance when heated. Metals and other electrical conductors are thought to exist in an ionized state, with free electrons moving in the space between the positive ions. Due to the mutual repulsions between the free electrons and the forces of attraction between free electrons and positive ions, the movement of each individual electron is of a random nature, except in the presence of an ELECTRIC FIELD. (See also CONDUCTION.) The amount of this random movement is small within the body of the metal, since the numbers of positive ions and of electrons are approximately equal and the forces of attraction and repulsion almost entirely neutralize each other. At or near the surface of the material, however, neutralization of these forces is not complete, and those electrons which have the highest velocities may be able to leave the surface and to remain outside the metal for a brief period before being attracted back by the positive ions.

There is thus a continuous process of flow and return of electrons, and at any one instant there is a cloud of electrons just beyond the surface of the metal. This cloud is termed the SPACE CHARGE.

To permit a stationary electron to be released from the surface of the metal a minimum amount of energy must be imparted to it. The number of electrons acquiring sufficient energy depends upon the temperature of the metal, and it is possible to calculate, for a given substance, the maximum number of electrons which can leave unit area of the metal in one second at a given temperature.

Thermionic Oscillator. Device or circuit incorporating one or more high-vacuum thermionic tubes and used for generating electrical oscillations.

Thermionic Rectifier. A thermionic tube of either the high-vacuum or gas-filled type used for producing a unidirectional output current from an alternating input.

Thermionic Relay. A thermionic tube operated in such a way that the application of a comparatively small electrical impulse to the CONTROL ELECTRODE permits a relatively large current to flow between the anode and cathode. The term is chiefly applied to gas-filled triodes and tetrodes (THYRATRONS).

Thermionic Valve (Tube). A VALVE or other ELECTRON TUBE having a THERMIONIC CATHODE. See VALVE, ELECTRONIC.

Thermionic Voltmeter. Voltage-measuring device incorporating one or more high-vacuum thermionic valves. A VALVE VOLTMETER.

Thermionics. Primarily the study of the emission of electrons from heated bodies, but now loosely applied also to the study of the behaviour of electrons so emitted and particularly to their behaviour in high-vacuum and gas-filled tubes.

Thermistor. A RESISTOR composed of a synthetic material having a high negative temperature coefficient of resistance, that is to say, its resistance decreases rapidly with rise of temperature. The material is of a semiconductor nature and usually consists of a mixture of such oxides as those of manganese, cobalt, copper and nickel. Thermistors are employed as safety devices and as regulators in electric circuits. An example is shown in Fig. T-9,

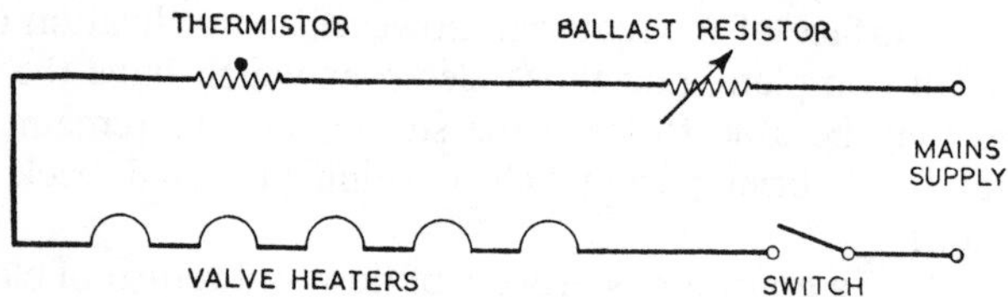

FIG. T-9.—BASIC CIRCUIT OF SERIES HEATER CHAIN WITH THERMISTOR.

where a thermistor is used to limit the current surge which occurs when a series chain of cathode heaters, having a low resistance when cold, is switched on.

Thermocouple. Junction of two dissimilar metals, across which an e.m.f. is developed when the junction is heated. Thermocouples form the basis of many temperature-measuring and controlling devices, some of which employ electronic methods for applying the control.

Thermo-electric Pick-up. Device in which changes of temperature produce corresponding changes of some electrical property such as e.m.f. or resistance, these changes then being used for purposes of measurement, control, etc.

Thermostat. Temperature-sensitive device which, when the temperature of its surroundings rises above or falls below a predetermined value, operates either an alarm or a control system so as to restore the temperature to the desired value.

Thoriated Filament. Wire consisting of tungsten with a small admixture of thorium, and used as a directly-heated cathode in certain thermionic valves. A thoriated filament gives satisfactory electron emission at a lower temperature than a pure tungsten filament.

Three-electrode Valve. A valve or other electron tube having three electrodes: a cathode, an anode and a control electrode. A TRIODE.

Threshold Frequency. The minimum frequency of radiation which will produce the emission of electrons from a photo-emissive metal. The threshold frequency is characteristic of the metal used.

Thyratron. Gas-filled triode or tetrode used as a THERMIONIC RELAY. Conventional graphic symbols are shown in Fig. T-10. At control grid potentials below a certain critical value, $V_{g\ crit}$, the

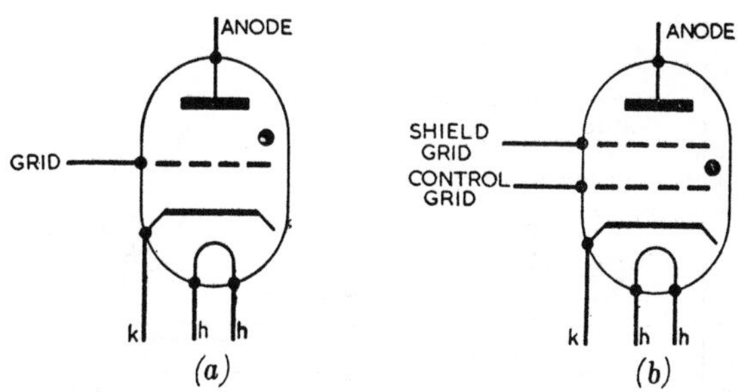

FIG. T-10.—GRAPHICAL SYMBOLS FOR (a) TRIODE THYRATRON, (b) TETRODE THYRATRON.

tube is non-conductive, but when the grid is raised to a potential exceeding the critical value, a small thermionic current flows (provided the positive potential at the anode exceeds the firing or striking value, V_{st}) and by reason of the ionization of the gas filling, the anode current rapidly rises to a maximum value governed only by the anode voltage and the resistance in the anode circuit. Once the tube has become conductive in this way the control grid can exercise no further control on the anode current, which will continue to flow until the control grid voltage is reduced below the critical value and the anode voltage is reduced to below the extinction or arc value.

There is a definite relationship between the critical value of grid voltage and the anode voltage, typical control characteristics being indicated in Fig. T-11. Fig. T-12 shows the voltage conditions before, at and after firing for a thyratron operated on direct current.

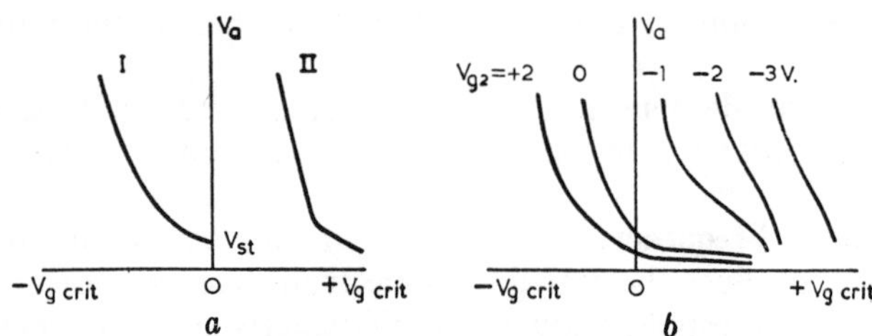

FIG. T-11.

(a) TYPICAL CONTROL CHARACTERISTICS OF THYRATRONS: I WITH NEGATIVE CONTROL CHARACTERISTIC; II WITH POSITIVE CONTROL CHARACTERISTIC.
(b) SHOWING HOW THE CONTROL CHARACTERISTICS OF A TETRODE THYRATRON CAN BE MODIFIED BY VARYING THE POTENTIAL AT THE SHIELD GRID.

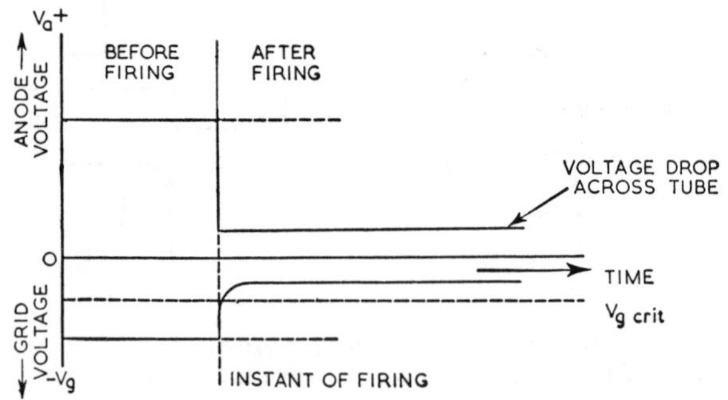

FIG. T-12.—VOLTAGE CONDITIONS BEFORE, AT AND AFTER FIRING, FOR A THYRATRON OPERATED ON DIRECT CURRENT.

In the more usual case, where a thyratron is operated with an alternating anode supply, the tube acts as a HALF-WAVE RECTIFIER passing current only during the positive half-cycles, and then only if the grid voltage is above the critical value. Since the critical value of the grid voltage at any instant depends upon the instantaneous value of the anode voltage, the critical grid voltage is not constant but varies throughout the cycle, as indicated in Fig. T-13. By adjusting the steady value of a direct grid voltage as indicated in Fig. T-14, therefore, the proportion of each positive half-cycle during which anode current can flow can be regulated, and thus the mean value of anode current can be controlled. Alternatively, the proportion of each positive half-cycle during which the tube conducts can be controlled by employing a combination of variable direct grid voltage and an alternating grid voltage as shown in Fig. T-15, or the direct component of the grid voltage may be kept below the critical value, and the phase of the alternating component varied, as shown in Fig. T-16. Control can also be effected by

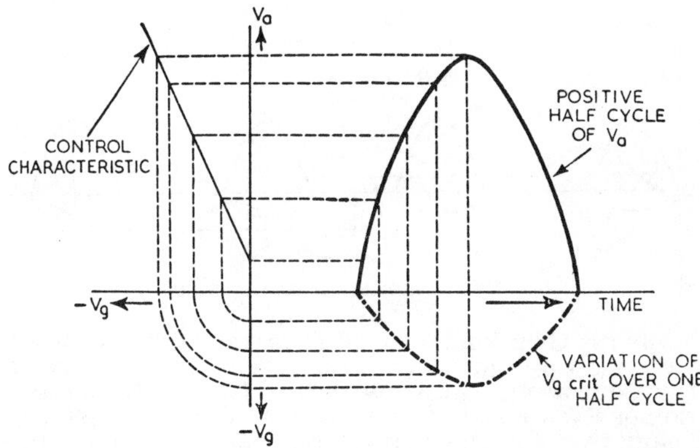

FIG. T-13.—CHANGE OF $V_{g\ crit}$ OVER A POSITIVE HALF-CYCLE OF ANODE VOLTAGE.

positive-going pulses instead of sinusoidal grid voltages. Thyratrons are employed as high-speed electronic switches and to control comparatively heavy currents, thus avoiding the heavy destructive sparking which accompanies the operation of mechanical switches or contactors.

Tight Coupling. COUPLING between two circuits such that the rate of transfer of energy from one circuit to the other is high.

Timbre. Tonal characteristic or quality of a sound due to the presence of various OVERTONES or HARMONICS of the fundamental frequency of the note.

Timebase. In a graph representing the variation of a quantity with time, the horizontal scale is the timebase. The term is, however, more generally applied to the voltages or currents of suitable waveform applied to the deflexion system of a cathode-ray tube in

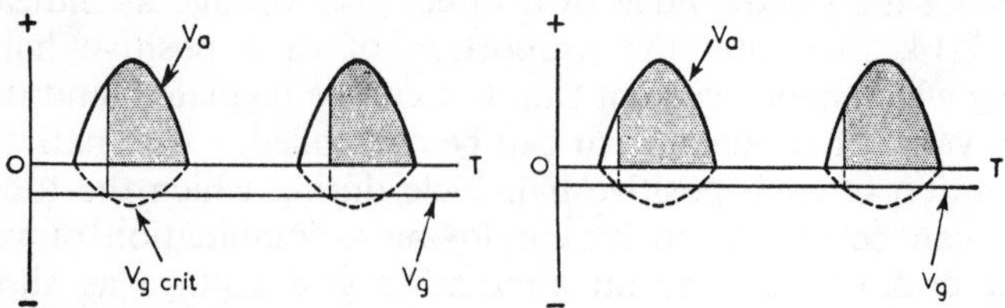

FIG. T-14.—IF A THYRATRON IS OPERATED ON AN ALTERNATING ANODE SUPPLY VOLTAGE THE PROPORTION OF THE POSITIVE HALF-CYCLE DURING WHICH THE TUBE CONDUCTS CAN BE REGULATED BY ADJUSTING THE GRID VOLTAGE V_g.

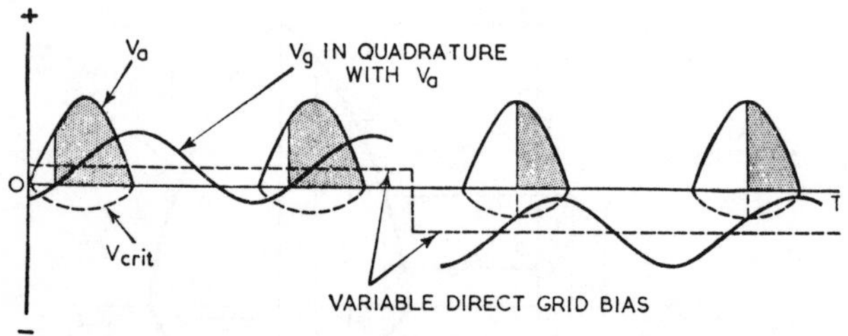

FIG. T-15.—IF THE GRID VOLTAGE OF A THYRATRON CONSISTS OF A CONSTANT ALTERNATING COMPONENT IN QUADRATURE WITH V_a AND AN ADJUSTABLE DIRECT COMPONENT, VARIATION OF THE LATTER REGULATES THE PROPORTION OF EACH POSITIVE HALF-CYCLE OF V_a DURING WHICH THE TUBE IS CONDUCTIVE, AND HENCE THE MEAN VALUE OF THE ANODE CURRENT (VERTICAL SHIFT CONTROL).

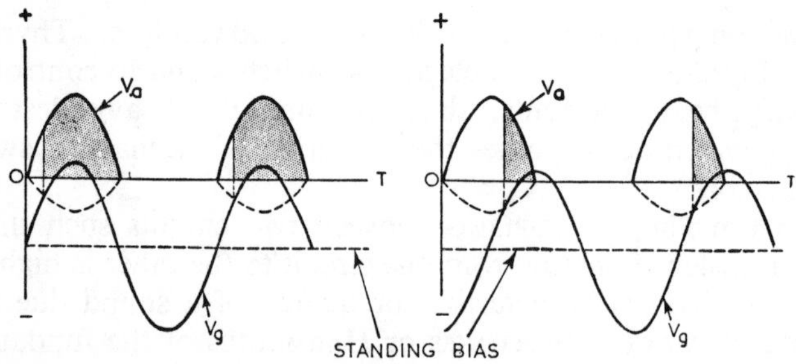

FIG. T-16.—HORIZONTAL SHIFT CONTROL OF A THYRATRON.

The grid voltage consists of a standing direct bias on which is superimposed an alternating voltage of the same frequency as the anode voltage. By shifting the phase of the alternating component, the proportion of each positive half-cycle of the anode supply during which the tube conducts can be controlled.

order to produce deflexion of the beam which is uniform with respect to time. In oscilloscopes one timebase may be used to provide linear deflexion of the beam in directions parallel to the x-axis (horizontal deflexion). For some applications, however, a radial, circular or even spiral timebase is required. In a television receiver two timebases are required, of sawtooth waveform, one to provide horizontal deflexion of the beam at LINE FREQUENCY, and the other to produce vertical deflexion at FRAME FREQUENCY and thus to ensure that each line is traced below the previous one.

Timebase Generator. Circuit for generating currents or voltages of suitable waveform for use as a timebase. Fig. T-17 shows a simple form of timebase generator in which capacitor C is charged

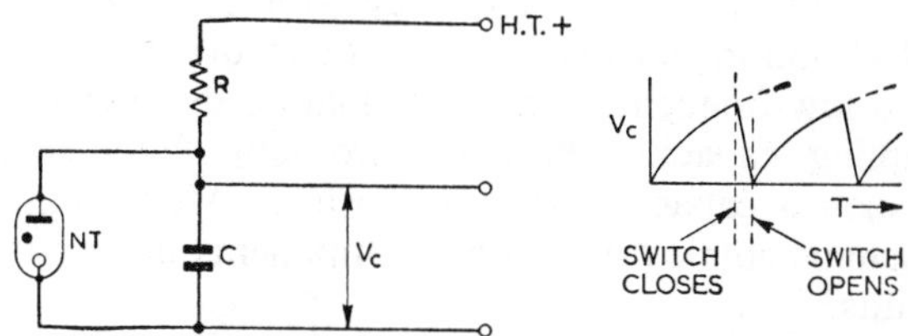

FIG. T-17.—CIRCUIT DIAGRAM OF A SIMPLE SAWTOOTH TIMEBASE GENERATOR, SHOWING THE WAVEFORM AS GENERATED.

during time t from a d.c. source via resistor R. As soon as the capacitor is charged to a voltage equal to the ignition voltage of neon tube NT, the tube conducts and the capacitor discharges rapidly through the tube. The waveform of the voltage across C is only approximately a sawtooth, as indicated. More satisfactory timebase generators can be made by using a pentode as charging resistor and a thyratron as the discharge tube. Still better performance is obtained from timebases using some form of thermionic oscillator. See BLOCKING OSCILLATOR, MULTI-VIBRATOR and TRANSITRON.

Time Constant. Time, in seconds, taken for the charge on a capacitor or the current in an inductor to decay to 0·3679 (i.e. $1/e$) of its initial value. It is numerically equal to RC or L/R, where C is in farads, L in henrys and R the circuit resistance in ohms.

Titration. Analysis or determination of the concentration of a solution by adding measured amounts of a standard solution of a suitable reagent until the chemical reaction between the two solutions is completed. Completion may be indicated by change of colour either of the solutions themselves or of a suitable chemical indicator. In electronic titration apparatus the indication of completion of the reaction is obtained by measurement of the potential between two electrodes dipping into the solution or by balancing it against a REFERENCE VOLTAGE, the null-point being shown on a simple form of cathode-ray tube.

Tone. Strictly speaking, a sound having one definite frequency, i.e. without overtones or harmonics; but the term is now often applied also to a more complex note having a constant fundamental frequency.

Tone Control. Circuit element or network included in an audio-frequency circuit, the FREQUENCY RESPONSE of which can be adjusted, so varying the tone colour or quality of the sound reproduced. For example, high-frequency (treble) attenuation can be obtained by shunting a capacitor across part of the audio-frequency circuit, and low-frequency (bass) attenuation by reducing the value of a coupling capacitor between two amplifying stages or by shunting such a capacitor with a resistor. More complete tone-control systems employ adjustable components in NEGATIVE FEED-BACK circuits.

Toroidal Winding. Inductor wound on a ring-shaped former or core.

Total Distortion. (Symbol D_{tot}) The sum of all the spurious harmonics present in the output of an amplifier, expressed as a percentage of the total output.

Total Emission. The maximum electron current (thermionic current) which can be drawn from a thermionic cathode at a given cathode temperature. See SATURATION CURRENT.

T/R Switch (Transmit/Receive Switch). A gas-filled diode having special characteristics, which conducts and short-circuits the signal input terminals of a delicate radio receiver when a nearby powerful transmitter is operating.

Tracking. (1) The movement of the needle in the groove of a gramophone record, or the control of the movement of the cutting stylus when making a record.

(2) Adjustment of the tuning characteristics of the oscillator valve circuit in a FREQUENCY-CHANGER by means of a small parallel capacitor (the trimmer) and a series capacitor (the padder) so that the frequency difference between the oscillator and the signal circuits is maintained constant over the whole tuning range of a receiver.

Train of Waves. A group of waves of limited duration.

Transconductance. The amplification factor of a valve (μ) divided by its anode resistance (r_a) and is measured in microhms. The term is preferred by American manufacturers to MUTUAL CONDUCTANCE. To convert transconductance to mutual conductance divide the number of microhms by 1000, this gives the mutual conductance in milliamps per volt.

Transducer. Device for transforming or converting power from one form to another, e.g. from electrical to mechanical, or vice versa. Thus, a microphone is a transducer which converts variations of air pressure into variations of electric current, and a loudspeaker is a transducer which transforms variations of electric current into variations of air pressure. See also MAGNETOSTRICTOR and PIEZO-ELECTRIC EFFECTS.

Transfer Characteristic. (1) Of a thermionic valve, the graph showing the relation between the voltage applied between the control grid and cathode and the current flowing in the anode circuit. The grid volts/anode current characteristic.

(2) Of a transistor, the graph showing the relationship between the current flowing to the control electrode and the current in the output circuit. For example, in the case of a transistor operated in common-emitter connexion the transfer characteristic is the base-current/collector-current curve.

Transfer Electrodes. Series of supplementary cathodes located between the true cathodes of a DEKATRON or cold-cathode decade-counting tube. A pulse applied to the transfer electrode causes the glow to be transferred from one effective cathode to the next.

Transformer. Device consisting of two or more inductors, more or less tightly coupled, often but not necessarily wound on a core of ferromagnetic material. If an alternating, or variable, or intermittent electric current is passed through one inductor (the primary winding), corresponding alternating, varying or intermittent voltages will be induced in the other (secondary) winding or windings. The ratio of the e.m.f.s appearing at the terminals of each winding to that applied to the primary is equal to the ratio of the number of turns in the secondary to the number of turns in the primary. Such transformers are sometimes referred to as static transformers to distinguish them from rotary transformers in which voltage transformation, and sometimes conversion from a.c. to d.c. or vice versa, is effected by rotating machinery. Transformers are used for many purposes, some of which are briefly described under the following headings: AUDIO-FREQUENCY TRANSFORMER, RADIO-FREQUENCY TRANSFORMER, INPUT TRANSFORMER, INTERMEDIATE-FREQUENCY TRANSFORMER, INTERVALVE TRANSFORMER, MATCHING TRANSFORMER, OUTPUT TRANSFORMER, POWER TRANSFORMER.

Transformer Coupling. Method of coupling two networks, e.g. the output circuit of one valve to the input circuit of a following valve, by means of a transformer.

Transient. Said of a phenomenon originated by a sudden change in conditions, and persisting for only a very short time after the change has taken place. In particular, the term is applied both as an adjective and as a noun to sudden sounds of short duration and to the corresponding voltages and currents in an electronic sound-amplifying and reproducing system.

Transient Response. Extent to which a circuit or other device can transmit, or reproduce without serious distortion, a transient signal.

Transistor. Device incorporating an arrangement of SEMICONDUCTOR material and suitable contacts which is capable of performing many of the functions of thermionic and photo-emissive tubes. The transistor principle can be explained with reference to Fig. T-18, which is a diagrammatic section of a typical form, the

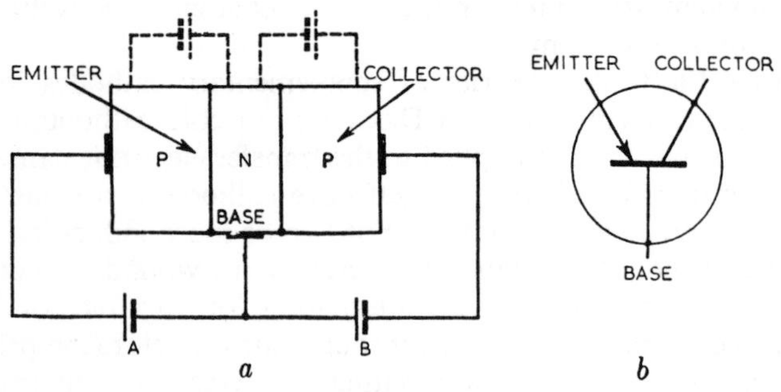

FIG. T-18.

(a) DIAGRAMMATIC REPRESENTATION OF A pnp JUNCTION TRANSISTOR WITH ITS BASIC CIRCUIT.

(b) CONVENTIONAL SYMBOL.

pnp JUNCTION TRANSISTOR. It consists of a composite crystal comprising a region of n-TYPE germanium termed the BASE, sandwiched between two regions of p-TYPE germanium known as the EMITTER and the COLLECTOR respectively. In the n-type base conductivity is due to the presence of mobile electrons while, in the p-type emitter and collector, conductivity is due to the predominance of positive charge carriers termed Holes. Since for every mobile charge carrier, electron or hole, there is a corresponding atom carrying an equal charge of opposite sign, the material as a whole is electrically neutral. In the absence of an electric field, therefore, there is no tendency for electrons to diffuse from the n-type base into the p-type emitter or collector, nor for holes to pass from the emitter or collector into the base, since any such infiltration would render the emitter or collector negative and the base positive. It is, therefore, as though a potential barrier existed across each junction between the n-type region and the adjacent p-type region, and this is represented in the figure by the imaginary batteries indicated in dotted line.

If, however, a real battery is connected between emitter and base in the sense shown at A in Fig. T-18, the emitter–base potential barrier is reduced, and holes can pass from the emitter to the base. If now a further battery is connected between base and collector in the sense shown at B, rendering the collector negative with respect

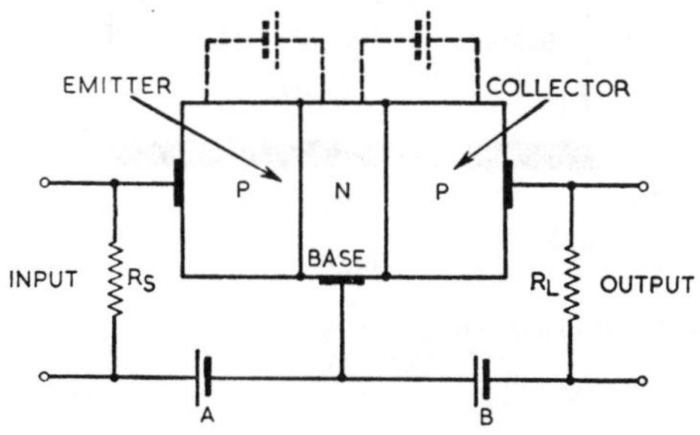

Fig. T-19.—Basic Circuit of Signal Source.
R_L is the load resistor and R_S is the resistance of the signal source.

to the base, some of the holes entering the base from the emitter will diffuse across the junction from the base to the collector. It is thus seen that variation of the emitter current, resulting, for instance, from the application of a signal voltage between the input terminals (Fig. T-19), produces a proportionate change in the collector current in the load R_L. Not all the holes representing the emitter current reach the collector, for some re-combine with electrons in the n-type base. In the arrangement shown, therefore, the current gain

$= \alpha = \left(\frac{\text{Change of output current}}{\text{Change of input current}}\right)$ is slightly less than unity. However, because of the low input impedance and high output impedance of this arrangement, substantial voltage and power gains are possible. Other circuit arrangements permit higher incremental gains.

Junction transistors can also be made with a p-type base and n-type emitter and collector (npn transistors), and there are also other combinations of p-type and n-type regions, including a tetrode arrangement. The POINT-CONTACT type of transistor, shown in diagrammatic form in Fig. T-20, consists of a base of

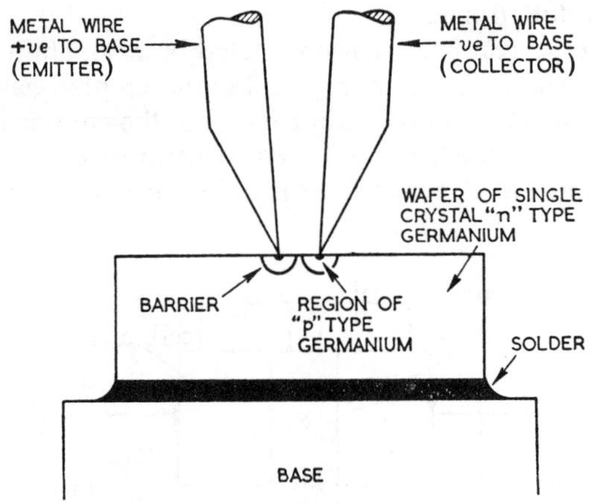

FIG. T-20.—DIAGRAMMATIC REPRESENTATION OF A POINT-CONTACT TRANSISTOR.

either p-type or n-type semiconductor material, the emitter and collector consisting of pointed wires or CAT'S WHISKERS just touching the surface of the base material.

Three modes of operating transistors were shown in Figs. C-16, 17 and 18. In the common-base or grounded-base arrangement the base connexion is common to both the input and output circuits, the input being connected between emitter and base and the output taken between collector and base. In the common or grounded emitter circuit the input is applied between base and emitter and the output is taken between collector and emitter. In the common or grounded-collector circuit the input is applied to the base circuit and the output is taken from the emitter circuit. The common-emitter arrangement is that most usually employed in amplifying applications, but the common-collector connexion has many of the characteristics of the thermionic CATHODE FOLLOWER, and can therefore be employed as an impedance-matching device.

The great advantages of transistors over thermionic tubes are their miniature dimensions, the very small requirements by way of battery power and the very small amount of heat generated by them.

Transistor Amplifier. Amplifier in which one or more transistors are employed instead of thermionic valves. In the basic circuit of Fig. T-21 variations of base current (I_b) in T1 caused by the application of a signal to the input terminals produce proportional changes

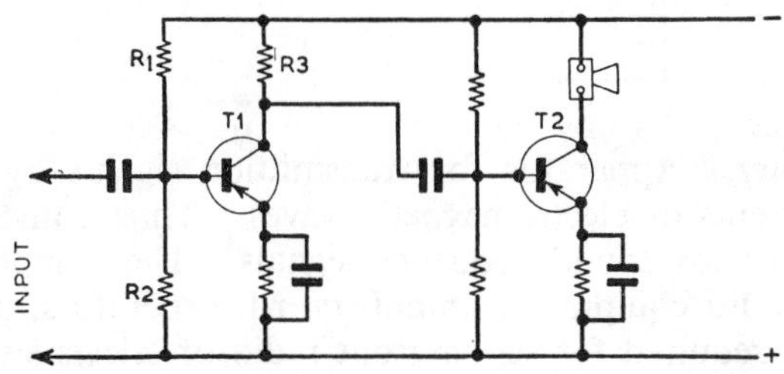

FIG. T-21.—BASIC DIAGRAM OF A TWO-STAGE TRANSISTOR AMPLIFIER.

in the current through load resistor R3. The corresponding voltage variations across R3 are applied to the base of T2 and the amplified output appears in the load (in this case a loudspeaker). Resistors R1 and R2 are bias stabilization resistors and permit the transistors to operate from a single battery.

Transistor Oscillator. A circuit in which a transistor is used for generating electrical oscillations. A basic circuit is given in Fig. T-22. Oscillations in the tuned circuit L1C1 are maintained by positive feedback via L2.

Transit Time. Time taken for an electron to travel from the region of the cathode to the anode of a thermionic valve. In high-frequency applications the transit time may be of the same order of magnitude as the periodic time of the signal, and thus limit the frequency at which a particular valve can operate efficiently.

Transitron Oscillator. Method of operating a thermionic pentode as a generator of oscillations by applying a negative bias to the suppressor grid.

Transmission. Process of conveying information by means of electrical or radio signals. Also applied to the information or programme transmitted.

Transmission Line. A non-radiating conductor or network of conductors joining an aerial either to the source of energy to be transmitted or to a receiving equipment.

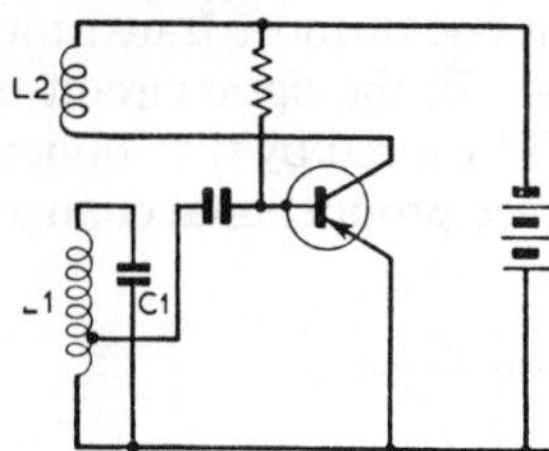

FIG. T-22.—BASIC CIRCUIT FOR A TRANSISTOR OSCILLATOR.

Transmitter. Apparatus for transmitting signals by means of electric currents or electromagnetic waves. Thus a microphone is a transmitter for sound-frequency signals. The complete assemblage of studio equipment, amplifiers, r.f. generators, modulators and aerials required for sending out radio or television signals or programmes is often referred to as a transmitter or transmitting station.

Transmitting Valve. Thermionic valve, usually of large power output, employed in radio or television transmitting equipment.

Trapezium Distortion. Distortion of the image or trace on the screen of a cathode-ray tube due to the use of deflexion voltages which are unbalanced or ASYMMETRICAL with respect to the final anode potential of the tube.

Travelling-wave Tube. Thermionic tube for use as a micro-wave amplifier. The input signal is caused to travel as a wave along a helix located axially in the tube, thus producing a travelling field which exchanges energy with an electron stream projected by an ELECTRON GUN along the axis of the helix. Interaction between the magnetic field of the helix and the electron stream modulates the stream and the energy delivered by the modulated stream to the collector electrode is greater than that of the original signal.

Triad. A TRIVALENT atom.

Trigger Electrode. Auxiliary electrode in an electron tube, an impulse applied to which initiates or terminates the flow of electron current between the main electrodes.

Trigger Tube. Electron tube such as a gas-filled triode in which an impulse of sufficient amplitude applied to an auxiliary electrode causes the tube to conduct or to cease to conduct, but thereafter exercises no control on current flow.

Trimmer (Capacitor). A small variable capacitor connected in parallel with one section of a ganged main tuning capacitor to compensate or to reduce the difference between the capacitances of two or more circuits so that they are all accurately tuned simultaneously to the desired frequency or frequencies by adjusting the single knob of the ganged capacitor.

Triode. Electron tube having three ELECTRODES. The term is mainly applied to three-electrode thermionic valves, but there are also cathode-ray tubes and some cold-cathode tubes with triode systems. In the triode valve the three electrodes are usually mounted concentrically, the cathode being in the centre and the

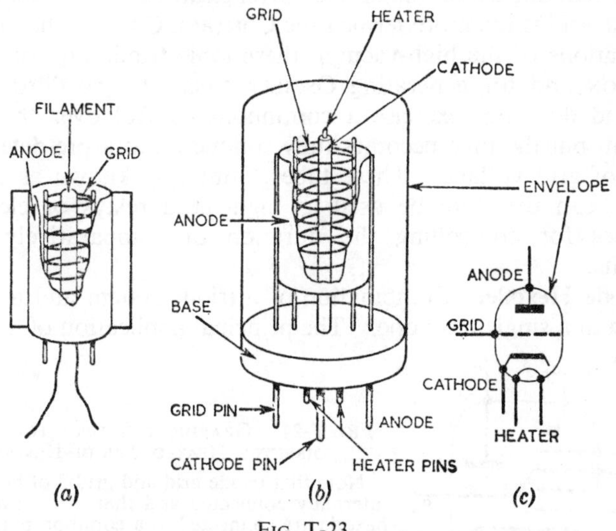

FIG. T-23.
(a) DIRECTLY HEATED TRIODE STRUCTURE.
(b) CONSTRUCTION OF INDIRECTLY HEATED TRIODE.
(c) CONVENTIONAL SYMBOL FOR TRIODE.

anode on the outside. The third electrode or GRID consists of a wire spiral or mesh and is situated between the anode and cathode. Fig. T-23 (a) and (b) shows typical constructions, and Fig. T-23 (c) the conventional symbol for a triode in circuit diagrams.

The action of a triode is shown by the characteristic curves reproduced previously in Fig. L-8. With the grid at the same potential as the cathode, and the cathode operated at its rated temperature, the relationship between the anode voltage and the anode current is as shown in the left-hand curve of Fig. L-8. A negative potential applied to the grid tends to neutralize the field due to the positive potential of the anode, and thus to reduce the rate at which electrons leave the region of the cathode, in other words, the anode current is reduced. The other lines in Fig. L-8 show the anode-current/anode-volts relationship for different values of negative-grid potential. Fig. C-21 showed the effect of the grid potential on the anode current of a triode at constant anode voltage. If a sufficiently large negative potential is applied to the grid, anode current ceases to flow and the valve is said to be CUT OFF.

By varying the potential difference between cathode and grid in a high-vacuum triode the anode current can be closely controlled, and the grid is therefore termed the CONTROL GRID. The principal applications of the high-vacuum thermionic triode are for AMPLIFICATION and for generating OSCILLATIONS. In gas-filled triodes the grid does not exercise a continuous control over the anode current, but the tube becomes fully conductive at a pre-determined value of grid voltage. These tubes, familiarly known as THYRATRONS, can therefore be used as high-speed relays or electronic switches for controlling the duration of comparatively heavy currents.

Triode–Hexode. Combination of a triode system and a hexode system in a single envelope. The principal application of a triode–hexode is as a frequency-changer, the triode section being used as the local oscillator and the hexode section as the mixer (Fig. T-24).

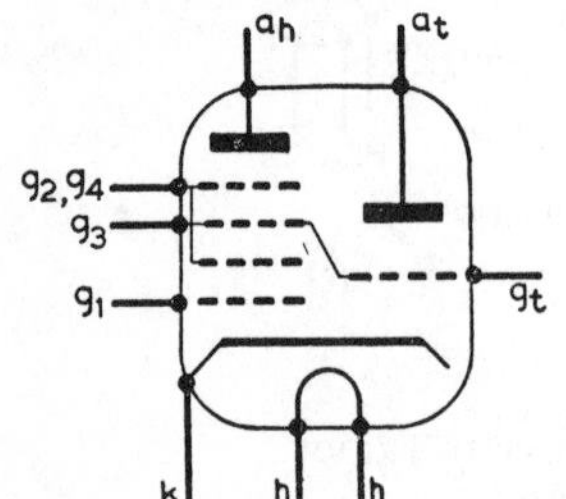

FIG. T-24.—GRAPHICAL SYMBOL FOR AN INDIRECTLY HEATED TRIODE-HEXODE.

Note that triode grid and grid 3 of hexode are internally connected and that grids 2 and 4 of hexode are connected to a common pin.

Trivalent. Said of a chemical atom capable of combining with three hydrogen atoms or their equivalent.

Troposphere. That region of the Earth's atmosphere below the ionosphere and extending to an altitude of about 5 miles. Radio transmission to distances of several hundred miles can be achieved in this region using very high frequencies.

Tube. Generic term for all forms of electron tube. See ELECTRON TUBE, CATHODE-RAY TUBE, COLD-CATHODE TUBE, GAS-FILLED TUBE, PHOTO-ELECTRIC TUBE, THERMIONIC TUBE, VACUUM TUBE, X-RAY TUBE, etc.

Tuned Amplifier. Amplifier incorporating one or more tuned circuits and so having maximum response to a particular frequency or band of frequencies.

Tuned-anode Circuit. Arrangement in which a tuned circuit is included in the anode circuit of a thermionic valve, thus forming a load which has maximum impedance at the resonant frequency of the circuit.

Tuned-grid Circuit. Arrangement in which a tuned circuit is connected between the control grid and the cathode of a thermionic valve.

Tuned Radio-frequency (t.r.f.) Receiver. Radio receiver incorporating one or more stages of radio-frequency amplification with tuned coupling between stages, as distinct from a SUPERSONIC-HETERODYNE RECEIVER or SUPERHET. T.r.f. receivers are sometimes called " straight " receivers.

Tuner or **Tuner Circuit.** Network consisting of an inductive and a capacitive element, one or both of which can be varied so that the circuit can be tuned to accept or to reject signals of a particular frequency.

Tungsten. Metallic element, also known as wolfram. Used as filaments and heaters in thermionic tubes and also for anodes of X-ray tubes.

Tuning Capacitor. Capacitor of variable capacitance used to tune a circuit to a particular frequency.

Tuning Coil or **Inductor.** Coil of fixed or variable industance forming part of a tuning circuit.

Tuning Curve. Graph showing the relation between the resonant frequency of a tunable circuit and the setting of the tuning capacitor.

Tuning In. Adjusting the tuner of a receiving equipment so as to obtain maximum response to a signal of a particular frequency.

Tuning Indicator. Device, which may be some form of galvanometer but more usually a simplified form of cathode-ray tube operated by voltages appearing in a radio receiver, which gives a visual indication as to whether the receiver is correctly tuned to a given signal.

Tuning Note (Tuning Signal). Musical note radiated at specified times from a transmitting station to facilitate the tuning of receivers to that particular station.

Tuning Out. Adjusting the tuner of a receiving equipment so as to minimize the response to an unwanted signal while still receiving the wanted signal.

Tunnel Diode. A two-terminal semiconductor device which can be used for amplification, oscillation and high-speed switching. These diodes can provide low-noise amplification up to about 2000 Mc/s. Due to the tunnelling effect in a semiconductor, these diodes exhibit a negative resistance characteristic over part of their operating range.

Turret Tuner. Tuning device for multi-channel television receivers, in which different circuits, pre-tuned to the frequency of different stations, are connected in turn to fixed contacts by a rotary mechanism, thus permitting the viewer to select the programme he wishes to see.

U

U-core. Ferromagnetic structure forming part of the magnetic circuit of an inductor or transformer. Sometimes termed a C-core. See Fig. T-1.

Ultra High Frequency. Radio frequencies in the range 300–3000 Mc/s, corresponding to wavelengths from 1 m down to 10 cm.

Ultra-linear Amplifier. A power output amplifier in which tetrode or pentode valves are used in a mode of operation intermediate between triodes and multi-grid valves by connecting the screen grids to a specified tapping on the primary winding of the output transformer. Usually employed in push–pull output stages of high-fidelity amplifiers.

Ultrasonic Cleaning. Method of cleaning metal objects by immersing them in a solvent through which high-frequency ultrasonic waves are passed. Particularly suitable for cleaning small metal parts of intricate shape.

Ultrasonic Drilling. Method of drilling hard or brittle substances such as glass, ceramics and die-steels. The drilling tool is caused to vibrate vertically in much the same way as a pneumatic road drill, and abrasive paste is applied to the tip of the drill. Holes of any desired shape can be made by using drills of corresponding cross-section. See Fig. U-1.

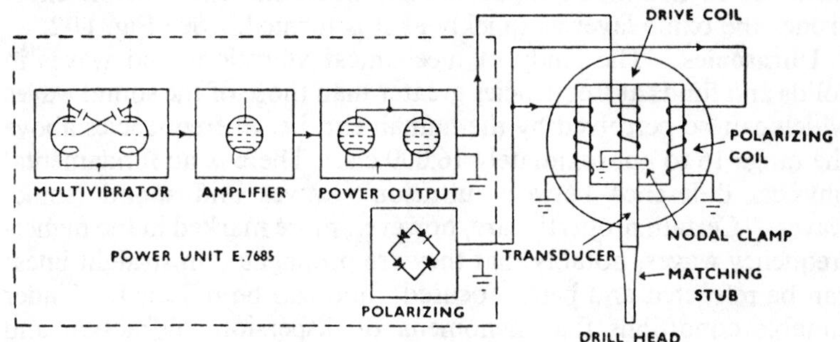

FIG. U-1.—FUNCTIONAL DIAGRAM OF AN ULTRASONIC DRILL.
(*Mullard Ltd.*)

Ultrasonic Frequencies. Frequencies higher than those of sound waves. Although the term "ultrasonic" is synonymous with "SUPERSONIC", the former is normally applied to mechanical vibrations in solids or fluids, and the latter to oscillating electric currents.

Ultrasonic Soldering and Tinning. Method of tinning and/or soldering metals such as aluminium which easily form an oxide

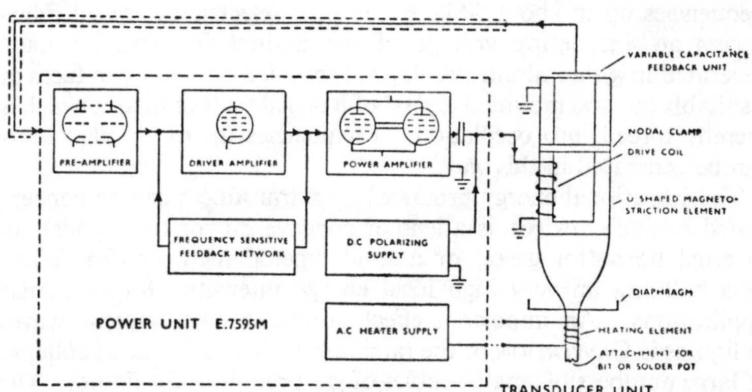

FIG. U-2.—FUNCTIONAL DIAGRAM OF AN ULTRASONIC SOLDERING EQUIPMENT.
(*Mullard Ltd.*)

coating, thus making difficult the satisfactory alloying of the solder and the metal. In the ultrasonic method ultrasonic waves are set up in the molten solder either between the soldering-iron and the metal or in a bath of liquid solder, when the CAVITATION effect erodes the oxide layer as quickly as it is formed. See Fig. U-2.

Ultrasonics. The study of mechanical vibrations and waves in solids and fluids at frequencies greater than those of the sound waves which can be perceived by the human ear, i.e. of frequencies above the range 16 to approximately 16,000 c/s. There is no fundamental physical difference between ultrasonic waves and sound (sonic) waves. Certain properties are, however, more marked in the higher-frequency waves, notably that they are propagated in straight lines; can be refracted and hence focused; and can be reflected. Under suitable conditions the phenomena of dispersion, diffraction and interference can also be demonstrated. All these properties of ultrasonic waves can be exploited in a large number of practical applications in industry, scientific research, etc.

Ultrasonic waves are usually generated by devices known as TRANSDUCERS the action of which is based on the changes of dimensions in certain materials when subjected to a varying magnetic or electric field. The principal forms of transducer are the MAGNETOSTRICTOR and the PIEZO-ELECTRIC transducer. In the former, mechanical vibrations are produced by passing an alternating current of the desired frequency through a winding surrounding a ferromagnetic core. This method is suitable for frequencies up to about 50 kc/s. In piezo-electric or crystal transducers an alternating voltage of the desired frequency, usually generated in a thermionic oscillator, is applied between two faces of a suitably cut and mounted crystal of Rochelle salt or quartz which is thereby forced into oscillation. Frequencies up to about 2 Mc/s can be generated in this way.

The vibrational energy produced by a transducer can be concentrated by such devices as a lens or concave mirror (in liquids), an inverted horn (for gases) or a solid tapered member (for solids) thus building up very high local energy intensities for particular applications. An important effect produced by ultrasonic waves in liquids is CAVITATION or the rapid expansion and sudden collapse of large numbers of small bubbles of gas present in the liquid. The pressure exerted by the liquid on the collapsing bubbles increases rapidly to very high values. Cavitation forms the basis of many of the practical applications of ultrasonics, the chief of which are:

blind guidance, depolymerization, dispersion of solids, elasticity measurement, emulsification, fatigue testing, flaw detection, smoke precipitation, ultrasonic cleaning, drilling, soldering and ultrasonic therapy.

Ultraudion. Name given in America to the early form of radio detector using a triode with REACTION.

Ultra-violet Radiation. Electromagnetic radiation of frequencies exceeding those of visible light, and corresponding to wavelengths ranging from 3900 down to 50 Ångström units. Ultra-violet waves affect photographic plates, can produce fluorescence and are able to ionize gases.

Undamped Oscillations (Waves). Oscillations, either mechanical, electrical or electromagnetic, which continue at constant amplitude.

Under-voltage. Operation of a piece of equipment at less than its rated working voltage. Under-running in this way usually results in some reduction of performance, and in some cases, particularly the cathode of a thermionic valve, may cause permanent damage. An under-voltage test is often included in the factory test and inspection routine for cathode-ray tubes and other devices to check that adequate performance will be obtained during periods when the electric supply voltage is below the nominal value.

Underwater Television. Equipment for obtaining television pictures of objects or events beneath the surface of the water; usually comprises a camera tube of the image orthicon type in a watertight housing which often also accommodates the lamps required for illuminating the scene. Remote control from the surface operates the focusing adjustment, aperture setting and lens selection. Such equipment has been made for operation at depths of 200 fathoms and to give satisfactory pictures at illuminations of one foot-candle or less. Typical applications include salvage operations, inspection of ships' hulls and underwater structures, the identification of objects located by such means as Asdic or echo-sounding, and marine biological research.

Unidirectional Aerial. An aerial designed to radiate or to intercept signals only, or mainly, in one direction.

Unidirectional Current. An electric current which flows always in the same direction. A direct current, as distinct from an alternating current. The value of a unidirectional current may not necessarily be constant. For example, the output from a rectifier valve is unidirectional, but varies between zero and a maximum, and may even have discontinuities. SMOOTHING NETWORKS are employed to level out the " hills and valleys " of such a current.

Unilateral Conductivity. Property of certain devices, notably thermionic tubes and some forms of crystals, of conducting electricity easily in one direction and not at all or only slightly in the opposite direction.

Unipolar Transistor. A new form of transistor, difficult to construct, but having high gain at very high frequencies.

Unipole. A quarter-wave vertical aerial fed against an earth plane which comprises either a conductive sheet of about quarter-wavelength radius or a number of quarter-wave rods. This type of aerial is commonly used in v.h.f. mobile work.

Unit. A value of a particular magnitude taken as the standard for quantitative measurements. The fundamental units are those of length, mass and time, the units of all other quantities being derived from, and capable of being expressed in terms of, these three fundamental units. See also FUNDAMENTAL UNITS, METRE-KILOGRAMME-SECOND SYSTEM.

Unit Electric Charge (Unit Quantity of Electricity). That charge which, if concentrated at a point, *in vacuo*, would exert a force of one DYNE upon an equal charge concentrated at a point one centimetre away. The quantity of electricity which passes a given cross-section of a conductor in one second when a current of one ampere is flowing is called the COULOMB. The charge carried by one electron is $1{\cdot}6 \times 10^{-19}$ coulomb.

Univalent. Said of a chemical atom which is capable of combining with only one atom of hydrogen or its equivalent. A univalent atom has only one electron in the outer or valency shell. Synonym MONOVALENT.

Universal (a.c./d.c.). Said of a piece of equipment, such as a radio or television receiver, which can operate equally well on a.c. or d.c. electric supplies.

Unmodulated Wave. A continuous radio wave of constant amplitude and frequency, i.e. one bearing no signal information.

Unstable. Said of an electric circuit when conditions are such that its performance in respect of conduction or oscillation is liable to large and sudden fluctuations.

Unstable Oscillation. Oscillations of electric current which continuously increase in amplitude with time.

Untuned Aerial. Aerial the resonant frequency of which has not been deliberately adjusted to equal that of the signal to be transmitted or received.

Untuned Circuit. An electrical circuit or network the resonant frequency of which has not been closely adjusted to a particular value. An APERIODIC CIRCUIT.

V

V-band. Frequency band from 46,000 to 56,000 Mc/s (wavelengths in the order of 6 mm) employed in radar.

Vacuum. Space from which gas has been removed. A perfect vacuum is one in which the gas pressure is zero, an impossible achievement. Pressures as low as 10^{-6} mm of mercury are readily obtainable with modern exhausting equipment, and vacua of this order are employed in high-vacuum valves and other electron tubes.

Vacuum (Photo) Cell. PHOTO-ELECTRIC CELL, the electrode system of which is enclosed in an evacuated envelope.

Vacuum Tube. Evacuated vessel containing two or more electrodes. The term includes high-vacuum thermionic valves, photocells, X-ray and cathode-ray tubes, as well as special forms of tube used in scientific research.

Valence. The force which joins atoms together to form a molecule. It is considered to consist in the mutual sharing of pairs of electrons.

Valency. The combining power of an atom or of a group of atoms, expressed in terms of the combining power of the hydrogen atom.

Valency Electrons. Electrons in the outer shell of an atom, and available for chemical bonding. See ATOMIC STRUCTURE.

Values. The value of an alternating electric voltage or current can be expressed in a number of ways, of which the most common are the CREST or PEAK value, the effective or ROOT MEAN SQUARE (r.m.s.) value, the mean value, the INSTANTANEOUS value and the PEAK-TO-PEAK value, each of which is defined elsewhere in this work.

Valve, Electronic. An ELECTRON TUBE intended primarily to exploit the property of unilateral conductivity, i.e. its ability to pass an electric current in one direction only, namely in the direction represented by the flow of electrons from the region of the cathode towards the anode. Most valves also incorporate means for controlling the intensity, duration, etc., of the electron flow, and thus of the current in the external anode circuit. The envelope of an electron valve may be either evacuated or gas-filled. High-vacuum valves have thermionic cathodes; gas-filled valves may have thermionic cathodes or cold cathodes. Valves are also classified in accordance with the number of electrodes they contain, as shown in the following table:

No. of Electrodes	Name
2	Diode
3	Triode
4	Tetrode
5	Pentode
6	Hexode
7	Heptode
8	Octode
9	Nonode

For descriptions and applications of the different types of valve see DIODE, TRIODE, TETRODE, etc.

Valve Adaptor. A device consisting of an insulating base carrying on its upper surface a number of metal sockets and on its lower side a number of metal pins, with conductive connexions between corresponding sockets and pins. The geometrical arrangement of the sockets and pins is such that a valve made with one type of base can be used in a valveholder designed for valves having some other type of base.

Valve Amplifier. An apparatus incorporating one or more thermionic valves and capable of amplifying or magnifying an electrical signal. See AMPLIFIER.

Valve Base. Lower end of the envelope of an electron tube, into which are sealed metal contacts, usually in the form of pins, connected internally to the tube electrodes. The tube is connected to the external circuit by plugging the base pins into mating sockets in a VALVEHOLDER. The principal standard forms of valve base are illustrated in the Appendix.

Valve Characteristics. Quantitative data concerning the properties and performance of a thermionic valve, expressed either in terms of certain properties exhibited under specified conditions (e.g. internal resistance, mutual conductance, amplification factor) or as the relationship between currents and/or voltages at the various valve electrodes, again under specified conditions. The principal characteristic curves for a thermionic valve are: (1) those showing the relation between anode current and anode voltage, and (2) those showing the relation between anode current and control grid voltage, in each case with the potentials at all other electrodes maintained constant. In order to permit the suitability of a given valve for a specific application to be assessed, and its performance under operating conditions to be estimated, complete "families" of characteristic curves are usually provided by valve manufacturers, showing how the required relationships are affected by a change in a third variable or "parameter". Fig. V-1, for example, shows

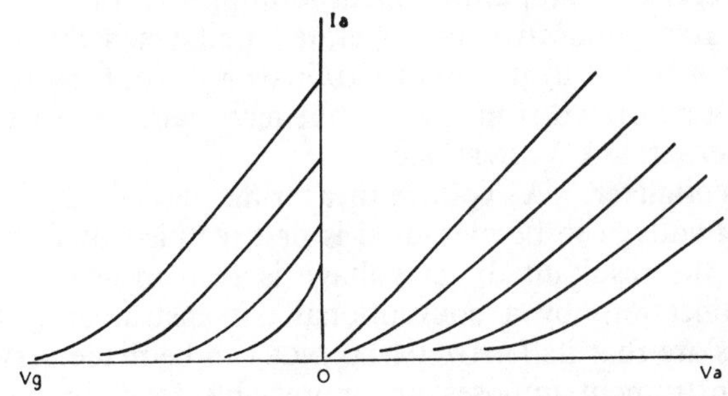

FIG. V-1.—I_a/V_g (*left*) AND I_a/V_a (*right*) CHARACTERISTICS OF A HIGH-VACUUM TRIODE.

on the left a family of anode-current/grid-volts characteristics with the anode voltage as parameter, and on the right the family of anode-volts/anode-current curves with the control-grid volts as parameter. The two sets of curves are for the same valve, which in this case is a typical triode.

Valve Heating Time. The time taken for a thermionic valve to attain minimum operating temperature after the rated voltage is applied to the heater. In the case of mercury vapour valves the valve heating time is usually longer than that required to raise the cathode to its normal operating temperature.

Valve Hiss. Random variations of anode current of a thermionic valve, manifest as a hissing sound in the telephone or loudspeaker. See VALVE NOISE.

Valve Noise. Voltage variations occurring in the output of a valve-operated apparatus, e.g. an amplifier, but not due to the application of the signal. Valve noise may be due to a number of causes, including agitation of the electrons in a conductor (particularly in the cathode) with random changes of temperature (Thermal Agitation); Shot Effect or variation in the rate at which electrons are emitted from the cathode; and Microphony. In apparatus employed for the reproduction of sound these effects are manifest as noise. In other valve-operated apparatus the disturbances are still referred to as "noise", although they produce no audible sound.

Valve Oscillator. Thermionic valve so connected and operated that electrical oscillations are generated in the circuit. See Oscillator.

Valve Rectifier. Apparatus incorporating one or more thermionic valves so connected and operated that when an alternating supply is connected to the input terminals a direct (uni-directional) current can be drawn from the output terminals. See Rectifier.

Valve Socket. A Valveholder.

Valve Voltmeter. A voltage-measuring device in which the alternating voltage to be measured is first rectified by a thermionic valve and the resultant direct voltage is then measured (possibly after amplification) by a conventional d.c. instrument. Its main advantages are that its Input Impedance can be made very high so that the instrument imposes no appreciable load on the voltage source to be measured, and that it can be used to measure alternating voltages of any frequency with equal accuracy.

Valveholder. Insulating base carrying a number of contact devices such as sockets or springs, arranged to mate with the contacts in the base of an electron tube, thus enabling the tube to be connected to the external circuit.

van der Graaf Generator. A machine for generating voltages in the order of a few megavolts for such applications as the production of high-energy X-rays and for nuclear research. In the machine static charges are continuously applied to an endless belt of insulating material at one point and are delivered to a metal electrode at another point.

Variable Attenuator. An Attenuator in which an electric signal can be reduced in strength either in a number of fixed steps or continuously.

Variable Capacitor. Capacitor whose capacitance can be adjusted between a minimum and a maximum value. Mainly used in tuning reasonant circuits in transmitting and receiving equipment and in measuring instruments. A typical construction consists of a number of fixed metallic plates (the stator) and a rotor composed of a number of similar plates mounted on a rotatable spindle, thus permitting the moving plates to interleave to a greater or less extent with the fixed plates, so altering the capacitance of the device.

Variable Coupling. COUPLING, which may be inductive, capacitive or resistive between two a.c. circuits such that the amount of energy transferred from one circuit to the other can be varied.

Variable Inductor. INDUCTOR the inductance of which can be adjusted by such means as varying the number of turns in circuit or by altering the position of a magnetic core or the extent to which the core is pre-magnetized.

Variable-mu Valve. A thermionic valve, usually of the tetrode or pentode type, the MUTUAL CONDUCTANCE of which can be varied smoothly over a considerable range by adjusting the grid bias. The I_a/V_g characteristic has a more gradual slope to its lower half than that of a " straight " valve. Variable-mu characteristics are obtained by suitable conformation of the control grid, e.g. by omitting one turn in the centre of the grid or by varying the pitch of the grid wires. Variable-mu valves are used, *inter alia*, for AUTOMATIC GAIN CONTROL.

Variable Resistor. Circuit component the resistance of which can be adjusted. Typical constructions include a carbon ring, or a high-resistance wire wound on a ring-shaped insulating former. Variation of the resistance is obtained by means of a radial contact arm.

Vario-coupler. Two inductors whose MUTUAL INDUCTANCE can be varied, usually by moving one coil with respect to the other, thus providing variable coupling between two a.c. (usually oscillatory) circuits.

Variometer. VARIO-COUPLER in which one of the inductors is rotatably mounted inside the other coil.

Vector. A quantity which has both a magnitude and a direction and sense is a vector, and may be represented by a straight line of length equivalent to the magnitude and drawn in a direction and sense corresponding to the quantity. Quantities without the properties of direction and sense are scalars.

Velocity. Rate of change of position, expressed in terms of the distance travelled in unit time, e.g. cm/sec.

Velocity Factor. The velocity of a radio-frequency current in a transmission line is less than it would be in free space (i.e. speed of light). The ratio of the actual velocity along a given line to that in free space is known as the velocity factor, and varies for different types of cables and lines, from about 0·65 to 0·95.

Velocity of Light. (Symbol *c*) And also the velocity of propagation of all forms of electromagnetic radiation *in vacuo* is approximately 3×10^{10} cm/sec.

Velocity-modulated Electron Tube. Electron tube (valve) in which the electron stream is MODULATED by varying the velocities of individual electrons, some being accelerated and others retarded, thus producing oscillatory energy.

Vertical Amplifier. Circuit for amplifying the voltage which produces vertical deflection of the beam in a cathode-ray tube. Also termed the Y-AMPLIFIER.

Vertical Deflexion. Deflexion of the electron beam, and hence of the light spot on the screen, of a cathode-ray tube in the vertical direction.

Vertical Frequency. Frequency of the VERTICAL TIMEBASE in an oscilloscope or television transmitter or receiver.

Vertical Hold. A control fitted in a television receiver for the purpose of keeping the picture held steadily on the screen. Sometimes called the FRAME HOLD. Cf. HORIZONTAL HOLD.

Vertical Scanning. Method of scanning the scene to be transmitted in a television system in a series of vertical lines as opposed to the horizontal scanning employed in present systems.

Vertical Timebase. Voltage or current of sawtooth waveform used to produce vertical deflection of the beam in a cathode-ray tube. In television, the vertical timebase generator is responsible for ensuring that the lines of horizontal scan appear one below the other from top to bottom of the frame, the sequence being then repeated, commencing from the top of the picture.

Vertically-polarized Wave. Radio wave in which the direction of the electric field is vertical. Cf. HORIZONTALLY-POLARIZED WAVE.

Very High Frequency. Radio frequencies in the range 30–300 Mc/s, corresponding to wavelengths from 10 down to 1 m.

Very Low Frequency. Radio frequencies below 30 kc/s, and corresponding to wavelengths above 10,000 m.

Vestigial Sideband Transmission. Radio transmission system, mainly used for television, in which one of the SIDEBANDS is almost entirely suppressed. In Fig. V-2 vestigial sideband and the normal double-sideband systems are compared. The system facilitates the wideband amplification required for television, and also permits a greater number of CHANNELS to be accommodated in a given waveband.

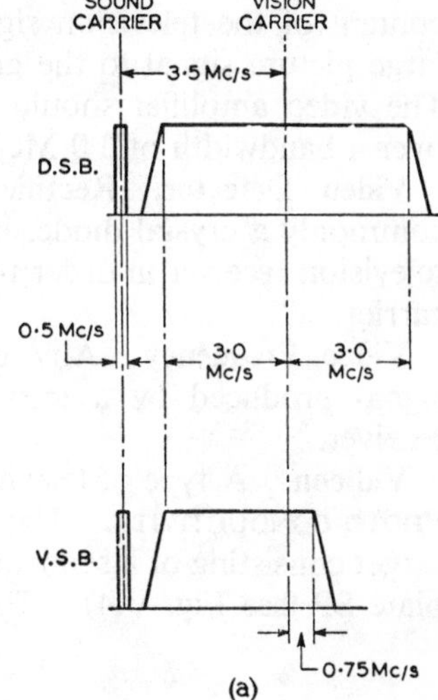

FIG. V-2.—COMPARISON OF TRANSMISSION CURVES IN DOUBLE SIDEBAND (D.S.B.) AND VESTIGIAL SIDEBAND (V.S.B.) TELEVISION TRANSMISSIONS.

Vibrator. Mechanical device for producing an alternating current by rhythmically interrupting or reversing a direct current by means of contacts carried on a tuned vibrating steel reed. A basic circuit is shown in Fig. V-3, in which an electromagnet

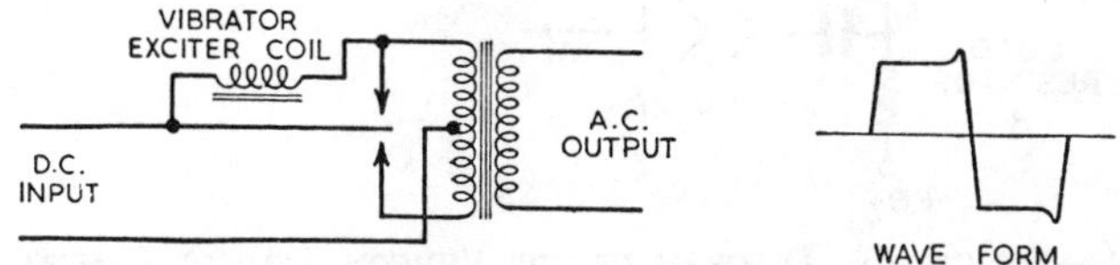

FIG. V-3.—TYPICAL VIBRATOR CIRCUIT FOR LOADS UP TO 30 WATTS. The output waveform is shown on the right.

operates a make-and-break device in much the same way as in an electric bell. A step-up transformer is provided, from the secondary winding of which an alternating supply can be taken. Chief application of vibrators is the production of h.t. supplies for mobile radio and similar equipment from low-voltage accumulators carried on the vehicle. In such applications the a.c. output at high voltage is rectified either by a thermionic diode, a metal rectifier or by further reversing contacts carried by the vibrating arm.

Video Amplifier. Thermionic amplifier which follows the VIDEO DETECTOR in a television receiver in order to amplify the picture content of the television signal and thus to provide a sufficiently large picture signal to the grid/cathode circuit of the picture tube. The video amplifier should give substantially linear amplification over a bandwidth of 3·0 Mc/s.

Video Detector. Rectifier unit, thermionic diode or more commonly a crystal diode, incorporated in the vision channel of a television receiver in order to separate the video signal from the i.f. carrier.

Video Frequency. Any of the frequency components of the signal produced by a television camera and reproduced in the receiver.

Vidicon. A type of television camera employing the principle of PHOTO-CONDUCTIVITY. The scene to be televised is focused on to a target consisting of a semiconductor backed by a transparent signal plate SP (see Fig. V-4). The semiconductor is scanned by a low-

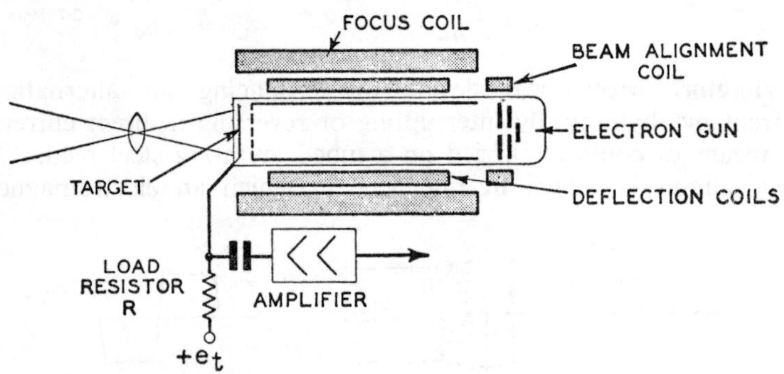

FIG. V-4.—FUNCTIONAL DIAGRAM OF THE VIDICON TYPE OF CAMERA TUBE.

velocity electron beam produced by an electron gun which serves to keep the surface of the target facing the cathode at cathode potential. The signal plate is maintained at a potential of some 20–30 V positive with respect to the cathode. The semiconductor acts as if each elemental area facing the cathode forms one plate of a small capacitor, the signal plate forming a common second plate for all the elemental capacitors. When no light falls upon an elemental area of the semiconductor the transverse resistance, i.e. the resistance between the scanned side and the side facing the signal plate, is so great that no appreciable current can flow and the elemental capacitor remains charged to the signal-plate potential. If light now falls on an elemental area the resistance at that spot decreases in proportion to the intensity of the light and the elemental capacitor discharges, the potential of the corresponding elemental area facing the cathode rising towards that of the signal plate until, when that area is again scanned, it receives sufficient electrons from the beam to restore its potential to that of the cathode. This action causes variations of current in the signal-plate circuit, and the corresponding variations of the voltage drop across the load R constitutes the video signal. The device known as the Vidicon in America is termed the Staticon in the U.K.

Virtual Cathode. A region (or strictly speaking a plane) within an electron tube which may be considered as the effective source of electrons. It is, in fact, a plane at which the electric field is zero, i.e. the potential more negative than on either side of it.

Vision, Persistence of. The ability of the eye to retain perception for a brief time after the stimulus is removed. See PERSISTENCE OF VISION.

Vision Carrier. The CARRIER WAVE which is modulated by the video signal in television transmission.

Vision Channel. (1) The carrier frequency and the associated sidebands constituting the bandwidth occupied by a particular television transmission.

(2) The term is also applied somewhat loosely to that part of a television receiver which handles the picture signal only, that is to say, the vision i.f. amplifier, video detector and video output valves and their associated circuits.

Vision Pick-up. See CAMERA TUBE.

Volt. Unit of potential difference or e.m.f. The final velocity of an electron which, starting from rest, traverses a space across which a difference of potential of 1 V exists, is 593 km/sec. The formula connecting electron velocity and the p.d. traversed is: $v = 5{\cdot}93 \times 10^5 \times \sqrt{V}$ m/sec where V is in volts.

Voltage. Difference of potential expressed in volts.

Voltage Amplifier. An AMPLIFIER the output of which is a varying voltage which is a magnified version of a varying input voltage.

Voltage Divider. A number of circuit elements, which may be resistors, capacitors or inductors, connected in series, and employed for obtaining a voltage which is a portion of that applied between the two ends of the series chain. Also called a POTENTIAL DIVIDER.

Voltage Doubler Rectifier. Device in which two rectifying elements operate alternately on the same a.c. source, their outputs being connected in series to give a potential difference twice that obtainable from a single rectifier. A basic circuit is shown in Fig. V-5.

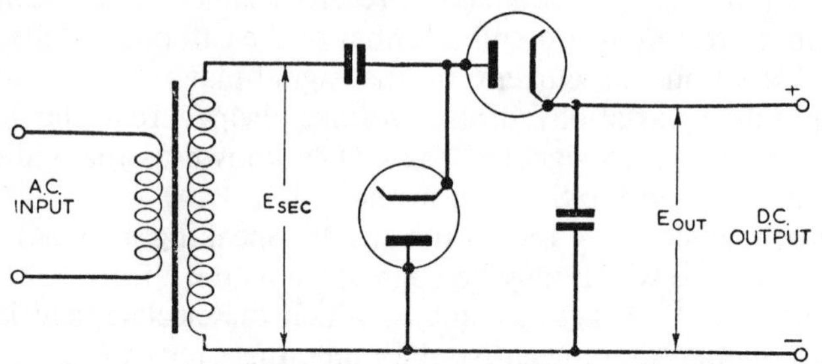

FIG. V-5.—BASIC CIRCUIT OF ONE FORM OF VOLTAGE DOUBLER.
The direct output voltage is $2\sqrt{2} \times E_{sec}$ approximately.

Voltage Drop. The difference of potential, expressed in volts, between two points in an electric circuit. In a d.c. circuit the voltage drop is equal to the current in amperes multiplied by the resistance in ohms between the two points. In a.c. circuits the voltage drop is equal to the current in amperes multiplied by the impedance between the two points expressed in ohms.

Voltage Dropper (Voltage Dropping Resistor). A device, usually a resistor, connected in a circuit in order to produce a VOLTAGE DROP.

Voltage Feedback. FEEDBACK of energy from the output of a device such as an amplifier to the input in such a way that the amount of energy fed back is proportional to the voltage across the output load.

Voltage Gain. The ratio of the output voltage to the input voltage of an amplifier.

Voltage Gradient. The difference of potential in volts per unit length in a conductor or in an electric field. In an electric field the term POTENTIAL GRADIENT is preferable.

Voltage Multiplier. A resistor connected in series with a voltmeter in order to increase the range of the instrument. For example, if the multiplier has the same resistance as the voltmeter the range will be doubled; if twice the resistance the range will be trebled and so on.

Voltage Reference Level. A potential which serves as a datum level for setting up electrical circuits or for measurements. For example, the potential of the cathode is usually taken as the voltage level to which the potentials of all other electrodes is referred.

Voltage Reference Tube. A VOLTAGE STABILIZER tube having very stable characteristics and employed to maintain the potential at one point in a circuit accurate to within very fine limits so that it may serve as a VOLTAGE REFERENCE LEVEL.

Voltage Stabilizer. An electron tube included in a circuit for the purpose of maintaining the potential difference between two

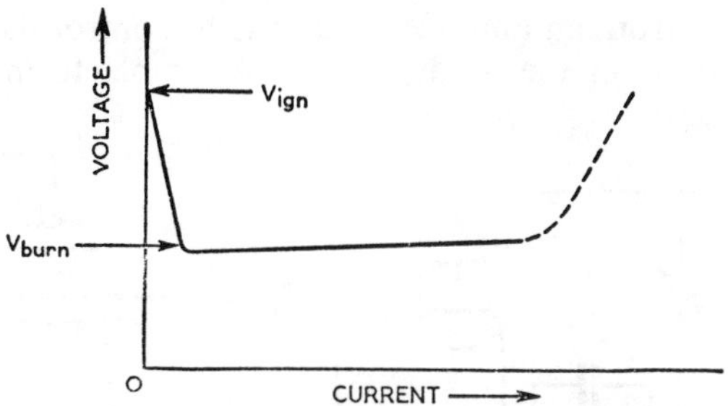

FIG. V-6.—GENERAL FORM OF CURRENT–VOLTAGE CHARACTERISTIC OF A VOLTAGE STABILIZER TUBE.

points very constant under conditions of fluctuating input voltage or of load. It consists of an envelope containing two electrodes and filled with an inert gas, usually xenon, at an appropriate pressure.

FIG. V-7.—BASIC VOLTAGE STABILIZER CIRCUIT.

R_L is the load and R1 is the resistance of V_{in} plus any current-limiting resistor.

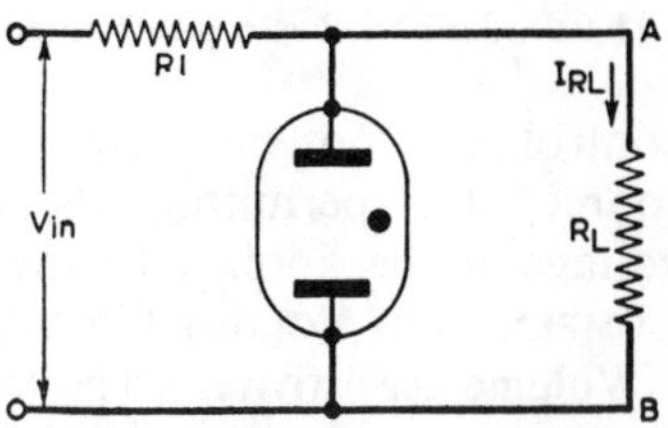

The tube becomes conductive, due to ionization of the gas filling, when the voltage applied between the two electrodes is raised to a value known as the ignition voltage (V_{ign}), and the discharge is characterized by a luminous glow at the cathode. Once ignited, the discharge can be maintained at a somewhat lower voltage, known as the burning voltage (V_{burn}), and the voltage drop across the tube remains constant at this value over a range of tube currents as indicated in Fig. V-6. The basic form of voltage-stabilizer circuit is shown in Fig. V-7, the voltage drop between points A and B remaining constant at V_{burn} over a range of fluctuations of V_{in} or of I_{RL}.

Volume, Sound. General term for the loudness of a sound. Volume may be expressed in terms of a unit called the PHON. The amount of audio-frequency power available to operate a sound-reproducing device such as a loudspeaker is also referred to as the "volume".

Volume Control. Circuit element or network used to vary the power output from an amplifier and thus to control the volume of sound produced in the loudspeaker. A simple form of volume

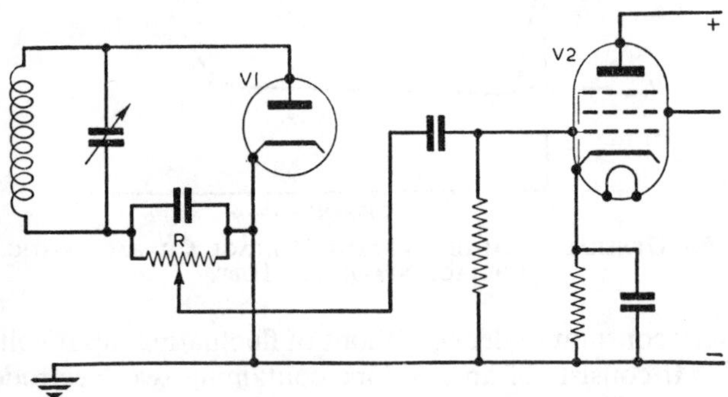

FIG. V-8.—BASIC CIRCUIT OF A DIODE DETECTOR V1, FOLLOWED BY A PENTODE AMPLIFIER V2.

The diode load R is a potentiometer which also serves as a volume control.

control is a potentiometer connected in parallel with the signal source, thus permitting the whole or only a part of the signal voltage to be applied to the amplifier. See Fig. V-8. See also COMPENSATED VOLUME CONTROL.

Volume Resistivity. The volume resistivity of a given material is the resistance, measured at a specified temperature, between opposite faces of a centimetre cube of that material. Also termed SPECIFIC RESISTANCE.

W

Wander Plug. Metallic plug, usually partly surrounded by insulating material, to which is connected a flexible conductor. Used for making a connexion to a terminal in the form of a mating socket, and particularly to one of several alternative sockets.

Water-cooled Valve. Thermionic valve of large power output, in which the heat generated is carried away by the circulation of cold water.

Watt. Unit of electrical power, equivalent to $\frac{1}{746}$ h.p. and corresponding to the rate at which work is done when the application of an e.m.f. of one volt results in the passage of a current of one ampere.

Wave. A disturbance, in space or time, in the form of an oscillation. Thus, sound waves consist of oscillating variations of air pressure; electric waves are oscillating variations of electromotive force or current; and all forms of radiant energy—heat, " radio ", light, X-rays, etc., are oscillating variations of electric and magnetic fields.

Wave Train. Unbroken group of waves of comparatively short duration.

Wave Trap. A parallel-tuned resonant circuit, connected in series with a signal source, e.g. between the aerial and the aerial terminal of a radio receiver. If tuned to the frequency of an unwanted (interfering) signal it will reject that signal while passing signals of other frequencies.

Wave Winding. A method of winding the coil of an inductor in such a way that there is appreciable air-spacing, thus decreasing the capacitance of the coil.

Waveband. A section of the electromagnetic spectrum covering a specified range of wavelengths. For example, the wavelengths between 200 and 550 m comprise the MEDIUM WAVEBAND used for sound broadcasts.

Waveform. Graphical representation of the variations of an oscillating quantity (e.g. a voltage) constituting a wave, plotted as a function of time. The most familiar waveform is the SINE WAVE. Other waveforms met with in applied electronics include SQUARE WAVES and SAWTOOTH WAVES.

Waveform, Television. Waveform of the video signal in a television transmission. It includes variations representing the picture information, i.e. variations of light and shade, and also the pulses required for maintaining the reproduction of successive picture elements in synchronism with the transmission. See TELEVISION.

Waveform Analyser. Instrument for measuring the amplitudes of the various frequency components of a complex waveform, the

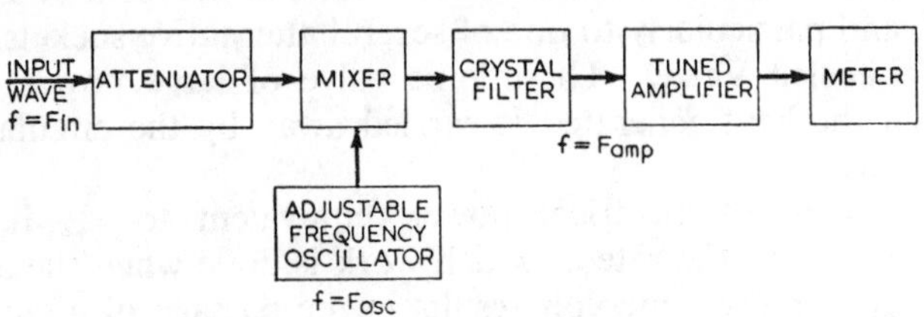

FIG. W-1.—FUNCTIONAL DIAGRAM OF WAVEFORM ANALYSER OF THE HETERODYNE TYPE.

The meter measures the amplitude of that sideband corresponding to the component of the input wave having a frequency equal to F_{osc}–F_{amp}.

measurements being either expressed directly in volts, or compared on a percentage or decibel scale with the amplitude of the fundamental frequency component. In one form of waveform analyser the wave to be analysed is combined with a local oscillation, the frequency of which can be adjusted. The " difference " waveform (see HETERODYNE) is applied to a multi-stage voltage amplifier via a crystal filter tuned to a fixed frequency. By adjusting the frequency

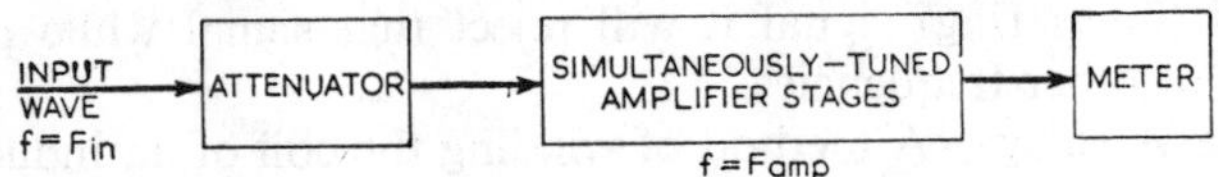

FIG. W-2.—FUNCTIONAL DIAGRAM OF A WAVEFORM ANALYSER EMPLOYING A SELECTIVELY-TUNED AMPLIFIER.

of the local oscillation, the various components of the wave under examination can be selected in turn. The output of the amplifier is connected to a suitable measuring instrument, such as a valve voltmeter (see Fig. W-1). In another form of wave analyser the wave under examination is applied, suitably attenuated if necessary, to a series of amplifying stages, the tuning of which is simultaneously adjustable, thus permitting the various frequency components to be selected and measured in turn (see Fig. W-2).

Waveguide. A waveguide may be simply defined as any device whereby an electromagnetic wave, particularly a wave in the microwave band, may be caused to travel between two points with less attenuation than would occur if the wave travelled in free space under otherwise identical conditions. The more academic definition is " an elongated enclosure, bounded by a conductor or by a discontinuity in a dielectric, along which energy is propagated over a distance by means of electromagnetic waves within the enclosure ". It must be understood that the energy travels through the space enclosed by the waveguide and not through the walls. The most usual form of waveguide is a metal tube of either round or rectangular cross-section, although a rod of insulating material in air can be used. The losses in dielectric waveguides are, however, considerable, and the use of this type of wave-guide is therefore restricted to short lengths. A wave may be propagated in a waveguide according to various modes. In the E-mode or transverse magnetic (TM) mode there is a longitudinal component of the electric field, but the longitudinal component of the magnetic field is everywhere zero. Similarly, in the H-mode or transverse electric (TE) mode there is a longitudinal component of the magnetic field, but the longitudinal component of the electric field is everywhere zero. These modes are further distinguished by the addition of two-figure subscripts to the letters E or H as the case may be. The first subscript indicates the number of half-wavelengths contained in the smaller dimension of the cross-section of the waveguide, and the second subscript the number of half-wavelengths in the larger dimension of the cross-section.

Wavelength. (Symbol λ) Distance between corresponding points in two consecutive waves. Thus, in Fig. W-3, the distance A–A′ or B–B′, etc., is the wavelength. Since the speed of propaga-

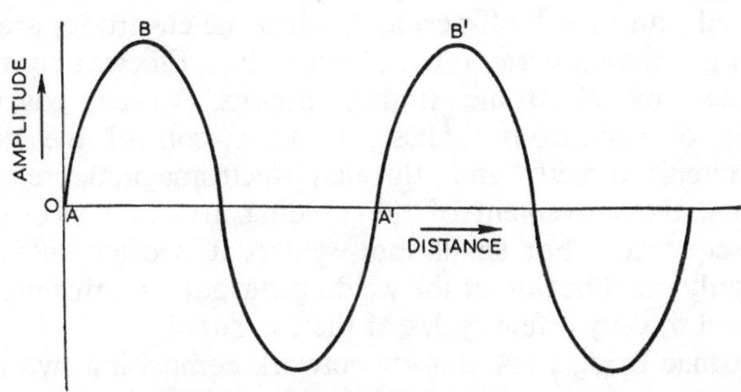

FIG. W-3.—AMPLITUDE OF A SINE WAVE PLOTTED AGAINST DISTANCE. AA′ or BB′ is one wavelength.

tion of electromagnetic waves is 3×10^8 m/sec, the wavelength of an electromagnetic wave can be calculated by dividing this figure by the frequency in cycles per second.

Wavelength–Frequency Conversion. The table reproduced in Appendix 5 facilitates conversion of wavelengths to frequency, and vice versa.

Wavelength of Light. Electromagnetic energy in the form of visible light is radiated at frequencies corresponding to wavelengths ranging from 3900 to 7600 ÅNGSTRÖM UNITS. Each wavelength corresponds to a characteristic colour. A table showing the relationship between the wavelength and colour of light is given in Appendix 4.

Wavemeter. Instrument for measuring the wavelengths of radio signals. Usually the instrument actually measures frequency, but is often calibrated either in frequencies, wavelengths or both.

Wehnelt Cylinder. A cylindrical electrode surrounding the cathode of a cathode-ray tube, and maintained at a negative potential with respect to the cathode. It has a focusing effect on the electron beam. By adjusting or continuously varying the cylinder potential the intensity of the beam can be controlled. Also termed the shield or grid of the cathode-ray tube. See CATHODE-RAY TUBE.

Welding. (Electronic control of electric spot-welding.) Complete control of electric spot-welding comprises accurate control of the " squeeze " time during which the welding electrodes close on the work and sufficient mechanical pressure is built up; control of the time during which current flows from the electrodes through the work rendering the material plastic; control of the " holding time ", when current is interrupted but the mechanical pressure is maintained; and the " off period ", when the electrodes are separated and positioned ready for the next weld. Efficient control can be effected by electronic timing circuits, which govern the operation of thyratrons. These, in turn, control the welding-current circuit directly and, through electromagnetic relays and contactors, the movement of the welding arm and electrodes in correct sequence. For small spot-welders it is often sufficient to control only the duration of the welding current, and this may often correspond to only a few cycles of the a.c. supply.

Wheatstone Bridge. A BRIDGE network comprising two parallel arms, each consisting of two resistors in series. In the circuit of Fig. W-4, if the ratio R1 : R2 is equal to the ratio R3 : R4, and an e.m.f. is applied between points A and B, the potential gradients in the two parallel arms are such that points C and D are at the same potential and the measuring instrument M shows no deflexion. The bridge is then said to be " balanced ". If R1 and R2 are known, R3 is variable and R4 unknown, the value of R4 can be ascertained by adjusting R3 until zero deflexion is obtained, when R4 = R2 × R3/R1. In electronic control systems R4 may be an element whose resistance varies with the quantity to be controlled

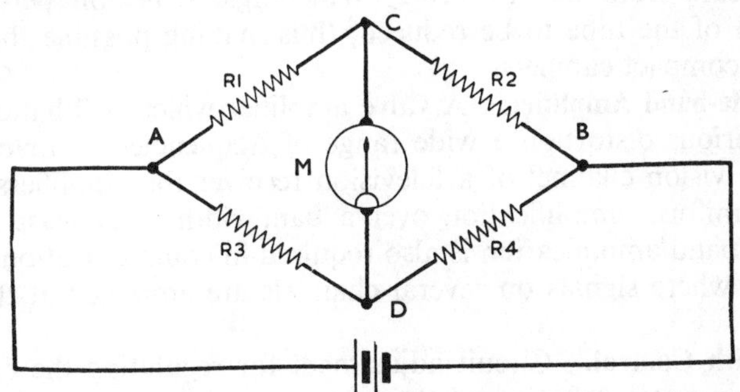

FIG. W-4.—BASIC WHEATSTONE BRIDGE CIRCUIT.

(e.g. temperature), and the amount of unbalance occasioned by variation of this resistance and indicated by a potential difference between points C and D can be applied as a signal to an amplifier, the output of which operates mechanism to correct the conditions causing the change.

Whistle. In radiotelephony, interference which appears as a high-pitched whistle in the loudspeaker. It may occur under any of the following conditions: if the frequency of the unwanted signal is approximately equal to the intermediate frequency of the receiver; if the difference between the frequency of the unwanted station and of the wanted station is approximately twice the intermediate frequency; if the frequency of the unwanted signal is approximately equal to the oscillator frequency in the receiver; if the frequency of the wanted signal is approximately twice, three times, etc., the intermediate frequency; if twice the frequency of the unwanted station is approximately equal to the frequency of the wanted signal; when there are one or more high-power interfering signals. The risk of these forms of interference is reduced by suitable selection of the intermediate frequency by the set designer.

and provision of adequately selective tuning circuits. It may, however, be necessary in individual cases to provide one or more wavetraps, including one tuned to the intermediate frequency.

Wide-angle Deflexion. Said of a television picture tube in which the beam must be deflected over a wide angle in order to cover the whole of the useful screen area. Successive improvements in the design of picture tubes, and particularly their electron-gun structures, have permitted the deflexion angle to be increased during the past ten years from 55° to 110°. Wide-angle deflexion permits the length of the tube to be reduced, thus making possible the use of more compact cabinets.

Wide-band Amplifier. A valve amplifier which will handle without serious distortion a wide range of frequencies. For example, in the vision channel of a television receiver the amplifiers should give uniform amplification over a bandwidth of at least 3 Mc/s. Wide-band amplification is also required in communications equipment, where signals on several channels are amplified at the same time.

Width Control. Circuit adjustment for regulating the extent of the horizontal deflexion of the beam in a cathode-ray tube. In a television receiver the width control, in conjunction with the HEIGHT CONTROL, permits the size of the picture to be adjusted and the correct ASPECT RATIO to be maintained. A typical form of width control in a television receiver is an adjustable inductor in the circuit of the horizontal scanning coils. In an oscilloscope the width control is usually a potentiometer by means of which the voltage applied between the horizontal deflexion plates can be regulated.

Wipe-out. Interference so severe that it makes reception of a desired radio signal impossible.

Wire Recording. Recording of speech, music, etc., as variations of magnetization along a thin steel wire. The sound can be reproduced by passing the wire through a REPLAY HEAD in which the variations of magnetization induce audio-frequency variations of current which, when amplified, operate a loudspeaker. To a great extent wire recording has been replaced by TAPE RECORDING, which permits more faithful reproduction.

Wireless. Popular name for all forms of radio communication, including broadcasting. It is being replaced to a great extent by the term " radio ". In technical circles there is a tendency to retain " wireless " as an adjective where the system of communication is primarily telegraphic, and the word " radio " where the system is telephonic. Thus: " wireless telegraphy " (W/T) and " radio telephony " (R/T). This usage avoids the confusion which would arise if the adjective " wireless " were used for both systems, since both would be abbreviated to W/T.

Wire-wound. Applied to resistors and potentiometers constructed of high-resistance metallic wire wound on an insulating former. For fixed-value resistors the former is usually cylindrical; for variable resistors and potentiometers the former is usually ring-shaped, a rotating radial contact arm being provided for adjustment.

Wobbulator. An instrument which generates an electrical oscillation the frequency of which varies rhythmically above and below a mean value which itself is adjustable. A FREQUENCY-MODULATED OSCILLATOR. It may be employed, in conjunction with an oscilloscope for such investigations as checking the response curves of the tuned circuits in radio and television receivers.

Wolfram. The original name for the metal TUNGSTEN.

Work Function. (Symbol ϕ) Potential difference which an electron traverses in performing sufficient work to permit it to leave the surface of a conductor as, for example, in THERMIONIC CATHODES. The work function differs for different metals.

Working Point. Operating point of a thermionic valve. The conditions in a thermionic valve when no signal is applied to the control electrode. It represents the simultaneous values of anode voltage and anode current corresponding to the application of the

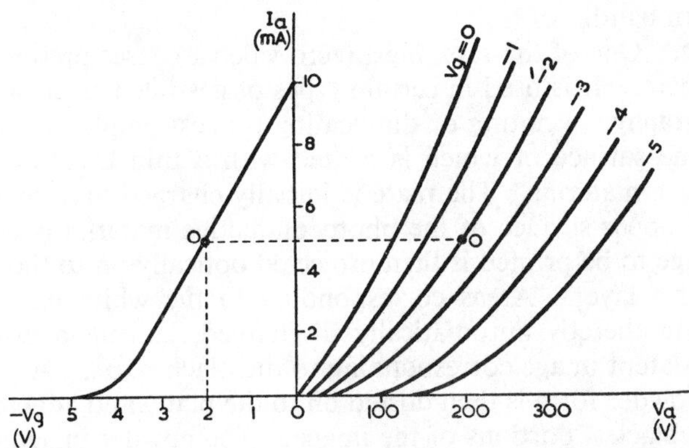

FIG. W-5.—CHARACTERISTIC CURVES OF TYPICAL THERMIONIC TRIODE. O represents the working point corresponding to a grid bias of −2 volts.

standing grid bias (if any) but without application of a signal. See Fig. W-5.

Wow. Slow variations of pitch of sound reproduced by a gramophone and due to variation of the speed of the turntable or other irregularities of drive either in the recorder or in the reproducer. More rapid changes are referred to as FLUTTER.

Writing Speed. The velocity with which the luminous spot moves on the screen of a cathode-ray tube. The higher the writing speed, the less the brightness of the trace for a beam of given intensity. For some types of investigations, and especially if the trace is to be recorded photographically, it may be desirable to modulate the electron beam in accordance with the variations of writing speed so that the trace is uniformly bright throughout its length.

X

X's. Symbol for ATMOSPHERICS. Also known as STRAYS or STATIC.

X-aerial. Form of aerial often used for television reception in which two pairs of arms radiate from a central junction unit. One pair acts as a V-DIPOLE and the other as a DIRECTOR.

X Amplifier. Thermionic amplifier for amplifying the voltage-producing horizontal deflexion of the beam in a cathode-ray tube.

X-Band. Band of radio frequencies from 5200 to 10,900 Mc/s. The 3 cm band.

Xenon. One of the rare, inert (zero valence) gases present in the atmosphere. It is used in certain types of gas-filled electron tubes.

Xerography. Printing or duplicating process employing a metal plate, one surface of which is coated with a thin layer of photoconductive material. The plate is initially charged in such a sense that the upper surface of the photoconductive material is positive. The image to be printed is then projected optically on to the photoconductive layer. Areas corresponding to the white part of the image are thereby automatically discharged, leaving a positively charged latent image corresponding to the black parts. A pigment in fine powder form is then dusted on to the plate, and adheres only to the " black " portions of the image. The powder image is then transferred to a sheet of paper and made permanent with a mechanical fixative.

X-plates. Pair of flat, parallel electrodes mounted vertically side-by-side in a cathode-ray tube. A difference of potential applied between the two plates produces horizontal deflexion of the beam.

X-rays (Röntgen Rays). Electromagnetic radiation of very high frequencies corresponding to wavelengths of 0·05–50 Å. X-rays are produced when electrons travelling at very high velocities strike a " target "—usually metallic. X-rays affect photographic plates, produce fluorescence and can ionize gases. They can penetrate many substances which are opaque to light, and have destructive effects on certain forms of organic tissue.

X-ray Analysis. (1) CRYSTALLOGRAPHY. Examination of the internal atomic structure of crystals by measuring the diffraction of X-rays directed on to them.

(2) SPECTROSCOPY. Method of chemical analysis by determining the wavelengths of the X-rays (characteristic X-rays) which a substance emits.

X-ray Spectrum. A wavelength pattern or scale, the lines appearing on which correspond to the wavelengths of the X-rays emitted by a body when bombarded by high-energy electrons.

X-ray Tube. High-vacuum electron tube containing a thermionic cathode, means for accelerating the electrons emitted from the cathode and a metallic target on which the high-velocity electrons impinge and from which X-rays are consequently emitted. In modern tubes a single electrode serves both as accelerating electrode (anode) and as target, that part of the surface of the anode upon which the electrons impinge being machined at an angle to the electron path. In order to avoid overheating, and consequent destruction of the tube, the anode is of massive construction and made of tungsten. Water-cooling may be employed. In many large tubes burning of the anode is avoided by causing the anode to rotate at high speed, so that the electrons do not always strike it at the same spot.

Y

Y-amplifier. Thermionic amplifier for amplifying the voltage producing vertical deflexion of the beam in a cathode-ray tube.

Y-plates. Pair of flat parallel electrodes mounted horizontally, one above the other in a cathode-ray tube. A difference of potential applied between the two plates produces vertical deflexion of the beam.

Yagi Aerial. A particular form of directive end-fire aerial array in which the director and reflector elements are parasitically excited. Most television receiving aerial arrays are of this type.

Yoke (Deflexion Yoke). System of electromagnets mounted on the neck of a cathode-ray tube and energized in such a way as to produce deflexion of the beam.

Z

Zener Diode. Special type of SILICON DIODE, the voltage drop across which is constant over a considerable range of reverse current. It can therefore be used as a voltage stabilizer or as a voltage reference level device.

Zone Refining (of Germanium). Process in the preparation of very pure crystals of germanium. The ingot of germanium is placed in a boat-shaped container and slowly passed through an electric furnace, the heating elements of which consist of a number of coils carrying high-frequency currents. As the metal passes through each coil it is heated by eddy-currents, the progressive movement of

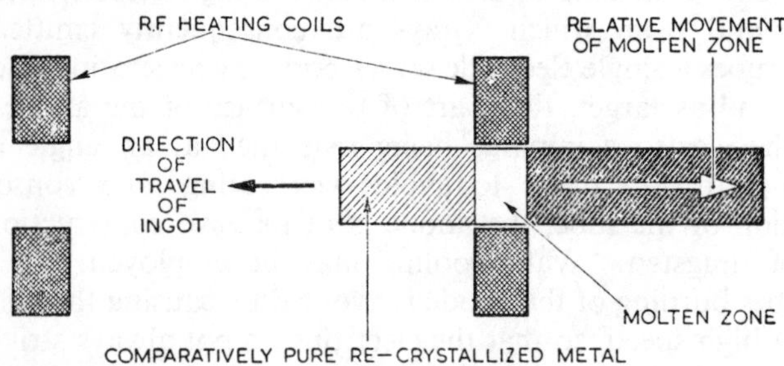

FIG. Z-1.—DIAGRAMMATIC REPRESENTATION OF THE ZONE REFINING OF GERMANIUM.

the ingot ensuring that only a limited portion or " zone " of the metal is in a molten condition at any one time, this molten zone travelling, as it were, towards the rear end of the ingot, in other words, in the opposite direction of the movement of the metal (see Fig. Z-1). Since the impurities tend to congregate in the molten zone, leaving the newly solidified portion comparatively free from impurities, several sweeps of zone melting along the ingot result in an extremely pure crystal of germanium, ready for further processing to convert it into p- or n-type germanium for use in transistors and crystal diodes.

Zoom Lens. A lens system employed in some television cameras which allows the focal length, and hence the angular field, to be continuously adjusted over a range of about 5 : 1, thus avoiding the momentary interruptions of picture which occur when using a lens turret. With the adjustment of focal length the magnification is altered, thus giving the impression that the camera is approaching or receding from the scene.

ADDENDA

Note: Words printed in small capitals are defined elsewhere in this Dictionary. Where the definition appears in this Addenda, a small superior s is added after the word, e.g. AVALANCHE EFFECT[s].

α **Cut-off Frequency.** The frequency at which the current gain of a transistor has decreased to $1/\sqrt{2}$ of its low frequency value (the gain of a transistor decreases as the frequency at which it is operating increases).

Accumulator. Used in COMPUTERS, the accumulator stores a digit and on receipt of a second digit adds the two and stores their sum.

Adjacent Channel Interference. The simultaneous reception of a "wanted" signal and the whole or a distorted part of another signal transmitted on the next higher or lower wavelength to that of the wanted signal. The risk of adjacent channel interference is in general reduced as the SELECTIVITY of the receiver is increased, but may be unavoidable if the strength of the interfering signal approaches or exceeds that of the wanted signal. Some mitigation can also be achieved by incorporating in the audio-frequency amplifier a LOW PASS filter or a tone control which eliminates or severely attenuates the higher audio frequencies.

Alloy Diffusion Transistor. TRANSISTOR in which the width of the base is made very small—in the order of a few thousandths of a millimetre, thus rendering the device suitable for high frequency application, since the frequency at which a transistor operates satisfactorily is limited by the time taken for charge carriers to diffuse from the emitter to the collector through the base. In the manufacture of pnp diffusion transistors an n-type layer is first applied to the p-type collector crystal. Two small germanium pellets are then fused to the n-type layer in close proximity. One pellet is of n-type and, ultimately, forms the base; the other is doped with both n- and p-type additives, and ultimately forms the emitter. A carefully controlled heating cycle follows, during which the n-type additive penetrates the crystal to a greater depth than the p-type, thus forming a base layer of graded concentration which has an accelerating effect on the charge carriers.

Aluminized Cathode-ray Tube. CATHODE-RAY TUBE in which the luminescent screen is backed by a thin deposit of aluminium to increase the forward emission of light. See also METAL BACKING.

Amplidyne. When more elaborate and sensitive control of electrical equipment is required than that obtainable by simple switching, devices such as the amplidyne may be used. The principle of this device is indicated in Fig. 1. If a small current is applied to the

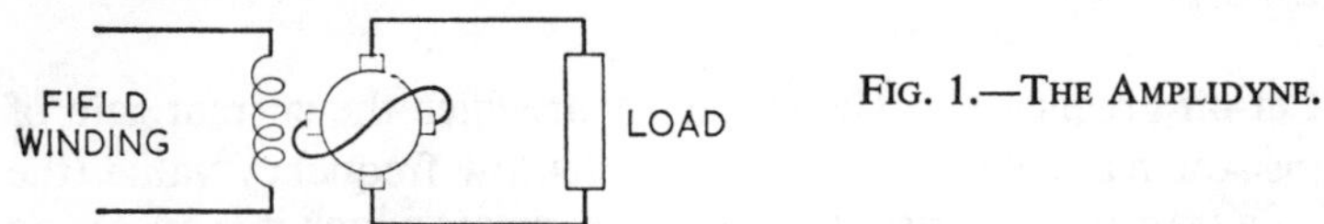

FIG. 1.—THE AMPLIDYNE.

field winding, the flux in the armature induces a voltage across the two shorted brushes, and a large current flows through the shorted windings setting up a reaction field which generates an output voltage across the output brushes. Thus from a small current the amplidyne produces a large current which varies greatly with small variations of the field current. Other names for this type of machine are: Metadyne, cross-field generator and rotary amplifier. See also SERVO AMPLIDYNE[s].

AND Gate. A gate arrangement, with several inputs and one output, which delivers an output only when there is an input to all input terminals.

Anderson Bridge. A network used in evaluating the inductance of a CHOKE. See also OWEN BRIDGE[s].

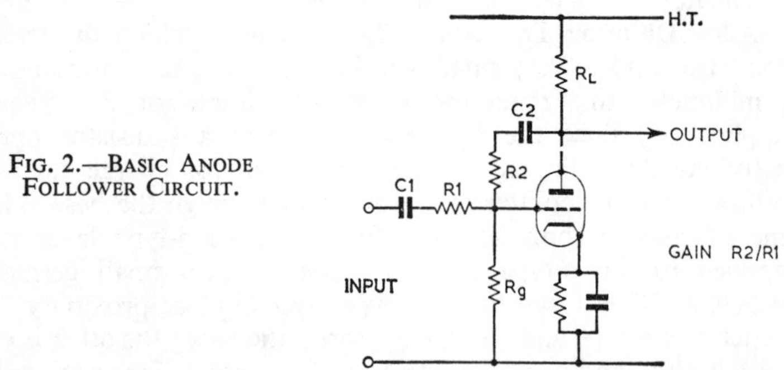

FIG. 2.—BASIC ANODE FOLLOWER CIRCUIT.

Anode Follower. A circuit (see Fig. 2) used to provide amplification with stable gain by means of a high degree of negative feedback.

Addenda

Ascultoscope. An electronic stethoscope which provides a visual trace on an oscilloscope of the heart-beat waveforms in addition to an audible signal. It consists essentially of a sensitive microphone which, when placed on the chest, produces an output current which is fed to associated amplifier equipment.

Astable. Said of a system or circuit which cannot be maintained for an appreciable time in one condition but rapidly changes to another condition, e.g. a free-running MULTI-VIBRATOR.

Avalanche Effect. When relatively high voltages are applied across the p–n junction of a TRANSISTOR or CRYSTAL DIODE, the charge carriers are accelerated to such an extent that they liberate further charge carriers from the semiconductor lattice by a collision process. The newly-liberated carriers, themselves being accelerated by the electric field, release yet more carriers. This process is analogous to GAS AMPLIFICATION.

Avalanche Transistors and Diodes. SEMICONDUCTOR devices exploiting the AVALANCHE EFFECTS. A typical application is for the production of high-speed, large-current pulses. A typical avalanche TRANSISTOR can produce a 60 mA pulse in 10^{-9} seconds.

Avalanche Voltage. The critical voltage above which the AVALANCHE EFFECT[s] takes place.

β. The current amplification factor of a transistor in the COMMON EMITTER configuration.

Backfire. An effect which can occur in the MERCURY ARC RECTIFIER, when a discharge takes place between the two anodes. The full explanation of this effect is not known, but it appears to be some form of electron emission from one anode which occurs at times when this anode is at a negative potential with respect to the other anode.

Bistable. Said of a system or circuit which may be in either of two stable conditions, and can change from one condition to the other on the application of a suitable pulse or signal.

Bit. (*Bi*nary dig*IT*.) A single digit of a BINARY SCALE number.

Black Body. Hypothetic body possessing the properties of a perfect radiator and which, therefore, at any given temperature radiates at all wavelengths the maximum amount of energy which any radiator could radiate at the same temperature.

Bleeder (Bleed Resistor). If the load resistance of a RECTIFIER circuit is disconnected, the peak voltages in the device may rise to a value which will endanger the components. It is therefore considered good practice to connect a bleed resistor or bleeder permanently across the output terminals to prevent this. The value of the bleeder is normally chosen at about ten times the working load resistance.

Bolometer. A device for the detection and measurement of infra-red radiation. Now virtually superseded by the more sensitive PHOTO-CONDUCTIVE CELL.

Bootstrap Circuit. General term applied to circuits in which feedback obtained by utilizing the MILLER EFFECT is used to increase the gain. Among other applications, the bootstrap principle is employed in many types of amplifier and also in one form of saw-tooth oscillator.

Bottoming. In certain active circuit elements—transistors and thermionic pentodes—the curve relating the voltage at, and the current delivered by, the output electrode (collector or anode) is of the general form shown in Fig. 3. If the circuit and instantaneous

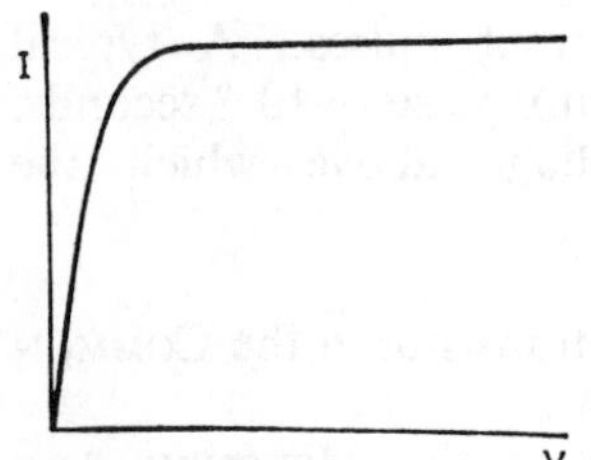

FIG. 3.—OUTPUT ELECTRODE CURRENT/VOLTAGE RELATIONSHIP OF SOME ACTIVE CIRCUIT ELEMENTS.

conditions are such that the transistor—or valve—attempts to draw a heavy current, practically all the available voltage is dropped across the output load, the potential at the collector—or anode—falls almost to zero, and practically no current will pass. This condition is known as "bottoming". In normal amplifiers this is, of course, a source of series distortion. However, the effect is exploited in other types of circuit where the rapid change from full conduction to bottoming is equivalent to a switching action. One familiar example is in MULTI-VIBRATORS where two active elements are so connected and operated that one is conducting while the other is cut off, this condition being reversed either rhythmically or by the application of external pulses. The output of such an arrangement is of approximately square waveform.

Brimistor. Proprietory name for a device having properties similar to those of the THERMISTOR.

Addenda

Cadmium Sulphide Cell. A PHOTO-CONDUCTIVE CELL consisting of a tablet of cadmium sulphide with a small proportion of activating additives. The electrodes are formed by depositing a metallic film in the form of two inter-locking combs. The DARK RESISTANCE of the cadmium sulphide cell is high—from 10^6 to 10^8 ohms. The maximum response is to radiation of wavelengths of about 700 mμ in the red region. See also LIGHT.

Carey Foster Bridge. An improved form of WHEATSTONE BRIDGE.

Centre-Fed Aerial. Another name for a DIPOLE aerial.

Channelling. A system of communication by TELEGRAPHY in which several channels may be operated simultaneously on a single link.

Chopper. Any device for continuously interrupting a physical phenomenon. In photo-electric applications it is often necessary to interrupt a beam of light at some convenient frequency, for example by a rotating perforated disc or other form of shutter. The resultant series of light pulses, falling on the sensitive surface of a PHOTOCELL, produces current pulses which are then applied, usually via a SHAPING NETWORK, to a thermionic or transistorized amplifier. Electro-mechanical choppers, e.g. a VIBRATOR, are often used to chop a d.c. signal into a series of pulses which can then be amplified by an a.c. amplifier: this is done to overcome drift which is often a problem with d.c. amplification.

Coercive Force. The MAGNETIZING FORCE which must be applied to a piece of magnetic material in order to destroy its residual magnetism. In the magnetizing curves, Figs. M-2 and M-3 on page 174, the residual magnetism is indicated by point X and the coercive force by point Y.

Coherent Light. Coherent light can be produced by devices such as the LASER, and is radiated in a single plane and direction. It is therefore many times more intense than normal or INCOHERENT LIGHTS of the same power.

Coherent Oscillator (Coho). A stable oscillator which is triggered by the transmitter (in Radar) to ensure that a correctly phased oscillation is available for comparison with the echo signal.

Coincidence Detector. Circuit providing an output that depends on the degree of coincidence of two or more inputs. A common system is to feed inputs to grids one and two of a pentode, the amount of current flowing in the anode depending on the phase difference of the inputs.

Addenda

Colour Temperature. The colour value of a light source is often quoted as its " colour temperature ", that is to say the ABSOLUTE TEMPERATURE at which a BLACK BODY[s] would emit radiation giving the same impression on the human eye as does the light source under consideration.

Complementary-symmetry Circuit. A transistor circuit in which a pnp and an npn transistor with matched characteristics are connected in parallel.

Conduction Band. Range of ENERGY LEVELS[s] within which electrons are sufficiently dissociated from the ATOM to permit them to move at random in the inter-atomic space and, under the influence of an electric field, to drift towards the positive pole, thus forming an electric current. The conduction band is the lowest of the EXCITATION BANDS[s].

Corona Discharge. Phenomenon sometimes seen or heard on or near high-voltage electricity lines or high-power transmitting aerials, etc. A faint blue flickering spark, accompanied by a crackling sound, corona discharge results from partial IONIZATION of the air surrounding the conductors.

Counting Circuit. A circuit which counts by, say, providing one output pulse for every two fed to it. The ECCLES-JORDAN bistable circuit provides one output pulse for every two input pulses and is much used for counting in COMPUTERS, etc.

Cross-field Generator. See AMPLIDYNE[s].

Cut-off Frequency (of a transistor). The current amplification factor of a TRANSISTOR is limited by various effects, some of which are frequency-dependent. The cut-off frequency of a transistor is that operating frequency at which the current amplification factor has dropped to $1/\sqrt{2}$ of its low-frequency value.

Data Storage. See STORE[s].

Data Transmission. Broadly speaking, any process of transmitting information, but the term now has a specialized meaning, namely the transmission of information via telecommunication circuits in some code, such as the BINARY SCALE, for DATA STORAGE[s] and processing. Also used to describe transmission of information by means of a SELSYN SYSTEM[s].

Dead Time. The short period of time which elapses after a GEIGER–MÜLLER TUBE has been ionized by a radiation and before it is able to return to its equilibrium state. See also DE-IONIZATION TIME and QUENCHING[s].

Addenda

Delay Time. The time taken for the leading edge of a pulse to rise from 0 to 10 per cent of its maximum value.

Difference (or Differential) Amplifier. An amplifier having two independent d.c. inputs and one output, the output voltage being an amplified version of the difference between the two input voltages. Basically, as is seen from Fig. 4, the difference amplifier is very similar to the LONG-TAILED PAIR.

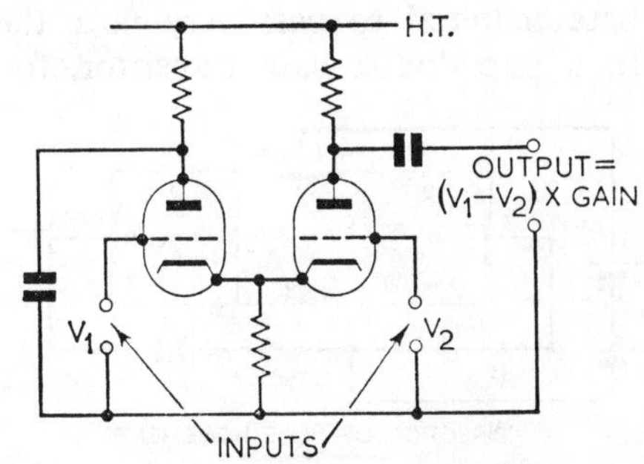

FIG. 4.—BASIC DIFFERENCE AMPLIFIER CIRCUIT.

Differential Magslip. A MAGSLIP with three windows on both stator and rotor used where it is necessary for the receiver in a magslip transmission system to indicate the sum or difference of two separate inputs.

Diplexing. A method of CHANNELLING[s].

Dissociation. The process in which a moving ELECTRON instead of IONIZING a MOLECULE on impact, causes it to break up into its component ATOMS.

Doorknob Valve. A type of thermionic valve designed for operation at ultra-high frequencies. The electrode spacing is very small resulting in its characteristic shape. C.f. LIGHTHOUSE VALVE.

Doppler Effect. To an observer approaching the source of any wave motion (e.g. sound, radio waves, or light) the frequency of the wave motion appears higher than to an observer moving away. The effect is only obvious if the observer and the source are approaching or receding at a speed comparable to the propagation velocity of the wave-motion. An example of the Doppler effect is the whistle of a moving train, which appears to be of high pitch when approaching and of much lower pitch when receding. Doppler effect has to be considered in RADIO ASTRONOMY, since the velocity of stars emitting radio waves is comparable to the velocity of the radio waves. Doppler effects have also to be taken into account in satellite communication.

Dose-meter. An instrument for measuring the quantity of X, gamma or beta radiation in the atmosphere. Unlike the RATE-METER[s], the dose-meter records the total energy of the radiation falling on it.

Double-base Transistor. A conventional JUNCTION TRANSISTOR with two BASE contacts, one being connected in the conventional manner and the other so biased as to cause charge carriers in the base material to pass very near the conventional base contact. In a pnp double-base transistor, for example (see Fig. 5), holes

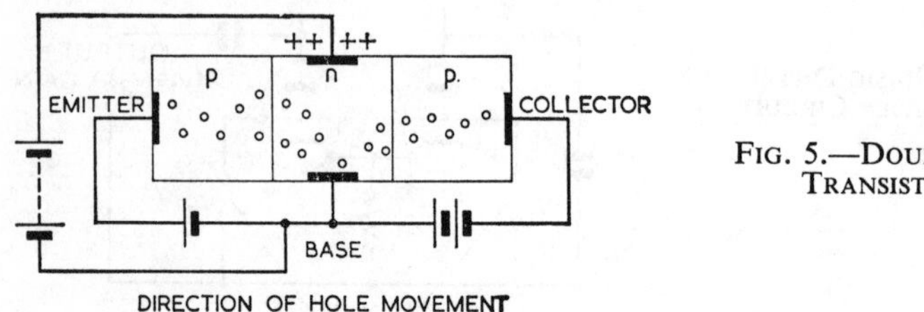

FIG. 5.—DOUBLE-BASE TRANSISTOR.

crossing from the emitter to the collector are repelled from the second base contact, which is positively biased, and thus pass near the conventional contact. The effect is to lower the base resistance of the transistor and thus to improve the frequency response.

Driftless Amplifier. To overcome the problem of drift in D.C. amplifiers, the d.c. signal is often passed through a chopper so that it can be amplified by an a.c. amplifier. This arrangement is termed a driftless amplifier.

Driver Stage. In general, the stage in a valve-operated or transistorized equipment which supplies the signal that controls or stimulates the operation of the succeeding stage. The term was originally, and is still more properly, applied to the MASTER OSCILLATOR in a transmitting equipment. This may be a valve operating under closely controlled conditions (valve drive), or an oscillator the frequency of which is determined by the vibration of a piezo crystal (crystal drive) or by some other electro-mechanical device incorporating, for example, a tuning fork. The term is now frequently used also for the last amplifying stage before the power amplifier of an amplifier or receiver and also for the penultimate stage of a transistorized amplifier, particularly where the final stage operates under CLASS B or CLASS C conditions in which grid current is drawn so that the previous stage must deliver an appreciable amount of power.

Duplex. A loud speaker array designed for efficient operation over a wide range of audio frequencies. It comprises a large loudspeaker for the lower range of frequencies, with a smaller TWEETER[s] mounted inside the cone.

Electrocardiograph. Medical instrument for recording the fluctuating electrical potentials produced in various parts of the body as the result of the heart beat. The potentials picked up by electrodes placed on the skin are then amplified and finally displayed on an oscilloscope or on a pen recorder.

Electro-encephalograph. A medical instrument for detecting, amplifying and recording the minute electrical currents in the human brain. Electrodes are placed around the skull, and the voltages picked up are displayed on an oscilloscope or on a pen recorder.

Electrostatic Store. A STORE[s] employing a distribution of electric charge as a means of representing and retaining information. See also MAGNETIC MEMORY[s].

End-Fed Aerial. Aerials, such as vertical rods, into which the signal current is injected at one end are called end-fed aerials to distinguish them from centre fed aerials such as the DIPOLE. The effective length of an end-fed aerial is twice the actual length of the aerial, due to reflection from the ground.

End Fire Array. An AERIAL system comprising two or more aerials placed in line with a critical separation distance (a quarter of a wavelength) and energized by signal currents with a progressive phase-shift of 90° from aerial to aerial. The effect is to transmit a very strong signal in one direction only—along the line of the aerials.

End Window Counter. A type of GEIGER–MÜLLER TUBE in which the ionizing particles enter the tube via a small mica window at one end.

Energy Band. In an aggregation of atoms (e.g. a crystal), the ENERGY LEVELS[s] of the various orbital electrons occupy semi-continuous ranges or " energy bands ", these bands being separated by so-called FORBIDDEN BANDS[s]. An electron cannot move from one energy band to a higher energy band unless it is given sufficient additional energy to traverse the intervening forbidden band.

Energy Level. Each orbital ELECTRON in an ATOM possesses a certain amount of energy, this amount being in direct ratio to the distance between the electron and the nucleus. The amount of energy, usually expressed in electron-volts, is termed the " energy level " of that electron.

Epitaxial Transistor. A type of JUNCTION TRANSISTOR with a non-ohmic resistor in series with the COLLECTOR, resulting in a device which can operate at high voltages without damage to the BASE region.

Epoxy Resins. A range of man-made resins used for bonding, sealing and impregnation. Used in electrical and electronic components for mechanical protection and for insulation against extreme climatic conditions.

Eraser. A circuit used to eliminate sound signals already recorded on magnetic tape by a TAPE RECORDER. It employs a high-frequency oscillator to produce an oscillating magnetic field which destroys the magnetism on the tape.

Excitation Band. The range of ENERGY LEVELS[s] beyond the VALENCE BAND[s], and thus normally unoccupied in a neutral atom. If an electron is elevated into the excitation band by the acquisition of additional energy the atom is said to be EXCITED. The return of the electron to its former energy level is accompanied by the emission of electromagnetic radiation.

Fall Time. The time taken for the amplitude of a pulse to decrease from 90 to 10 per cent of its maximum value.

Forbidden Band. An interval in the energy spectrum of the orbital electrons of a material. Electrons cannot reside in a forbidden band, but in certain circumstances can traverse it.

Foster-Seely Discriminator. One form of detector which converts an input signal consisting of frequency deviations into an output voltage variation.

Four-Pole or Four-Terminal Network, or Quadripole. It is often convenient to predict the behaviour of TRANSISTORS and other complex electronic devices or networks by considering them as " black boxes " with two input and two output terminals. Various characteristics of the device may then be expressed in terms of input and output conditions. See also h-, y- and z-PARAMETERS[s].

Gated A.G.C. A.G.C. system used in television receivers enabling the receiver gain to be varied independently of picture content. This may be achieved by basing the control bias on the black level of the television waveform.

Addenda

Goniometer. A device used for DIRECTION FINDING in conjunction with a complex AERIAL array. It gives fairly accurate bearings of the signal source, usually in the horizontal plane.

Greinacher Circuit. One of the many possible VOLTAGE DOUBLER circuits. It consists of two diodes and two capacitors connected as shown in Fig. 6, and produces a no-load output voltage of $2\sqrt{2}$ V, where V is the r.m.s. value of the input alternating voltage.

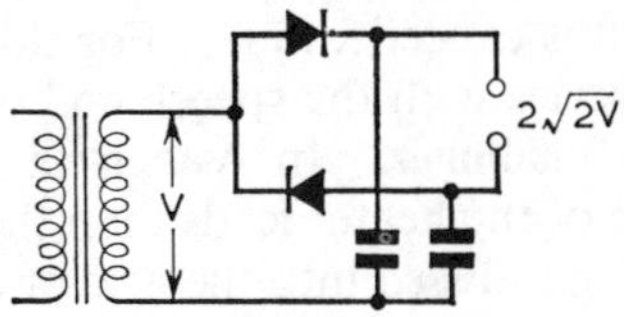

FIG. 6.—GREINACHER CIRCUIT.

Grid-dip Oscillator. Basically an oscillator with a very low-value of grid resistor. It can be used for measuring frequencies in the radio range. The basic circuit is shown in Fig. 7, from which it is

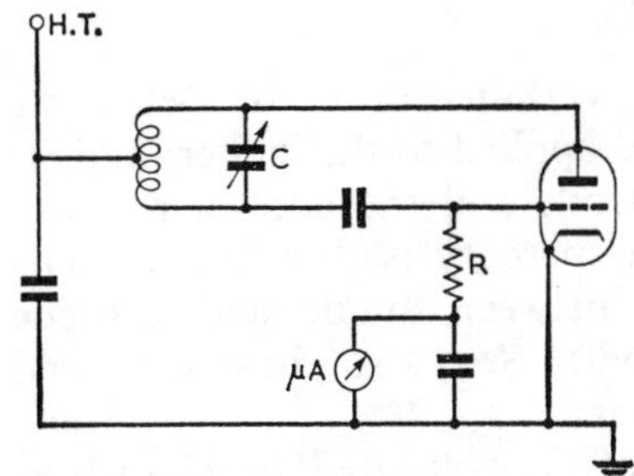

FIG. 7.—GRID DIP OSCILLATOR.

seen that, if the grid resistor R is of low value, grid current will flow; this is measured by the micro-ammeter. In use, the oscillator is loosely coupled to the circuit under examination, and the tuning capacitor C, which is previously calibrated in terms of frequency, is adjusted for maximum reduction or "dip" in the grid current reading. A second application is the rough checking of the resonant frequency of a passive inductance–capacitance circuit.

h-parameters. A set of characteristics used when determining the behaviour of a FOUR POLE (QUADRIPOLE)[s] such as a TRANSISTOR, in terms of the slope of the various characteristic curves. See also y-PARAMETERS[s] and z-PARAMETERS[s].

Addenda

Half-power Points. Frequencies at which the gain of an amplifier falls to 0.7 (−3dB) of the maximum gain.

Hole Storage. The form of MINORITY CARRIER STORAGE[s] applicable to an n-type semiconductor.

Hum-bucking coil. A coil, usually wound on the same core as the smoothing choke of a POWER PACK, and so adjusted and connected that the ripple (hum) voltage generated in it is equal to but in anti-phase with the hum voltage present in the equipment which is thus cancelled out. For this purpose, the coil may be connected in series with the speech coil of the loudspeaker.

Humdinger. In AMPLIFIER circuits the grid lead is often nearer one of the heater leads than the other, resulting in a 50 c/s " hum " being induced into the grid circuit of the valve. This may be overcome partially by connecting a POTENTIOMETER of low resistance, say 50 Ω, across the heater with the slider connected to earth. Such a potentiometer is called a humdinger. Adjustment of the slider to one side or the other of the centre point will often neutralise the hum or reduce it to a very low level.

Igniter. Auxiliary electrode in certain forms of MERCURY VAPOUR TUBE. A positive potential applied to the igniter initiates an arc discharge between this electrode and the pool of mercury forming the cathode. Some of the mercury is therefore vapourized so that the main discharge between anode and cathode can commence and maintain itself. See also IGNITRON and EXCITRON.

Implosion. When the envelope of an evacuated vessel such as a cathode ray tube is ruptured, the atmospheric pressure first forces the fragments inward. This is termed " implosion " as distinct from " explosion " when a vessel containing, say, gas at high pressure is ruptured and the fragments are forced outwards.

Incoherent Light. Ordinary light, comprising a mixture of various wavelengths, and radiated in all planes from a point source is termed " incoherent light ". C.f. COHERENT LIGHT[s].

Insertion Loss. The theoretical Q-FACTOR of an inductor can never be achieved in a working circuit since connecting the coil into circuit will slightly alter its resistance, and possibly also its inductance. The reduction in Q-factor for an inductor in a circuit is termed " insertion loss ", and is calculated from the expression: Loss $= Q_0/(Q_0 - Q_w)$ decibels, where Q_0 is the theoretical Q and Q_w the working Q.

Addenda

Ionisation Level. That ENERGY LEVEL[s], beyond the VALENCE LEVEL[s], at which an electron has sufficient energy to place it beyond the influence of the nucleus and thus, in the case of a crystal, to leave the surface of the material. Such electrons are then termed " free electrons ". The energy difference between the highest occupied level in the VALENCE BAND[s] and the ionization level is termed the WORK FUNCTION.

Kelvin Effect. See THOMPSON EFFECT[s].

Laser. A development of the MASER which operates at light frequencies. In principle, bursts of INCOHERENT LIGHT[s] illuminate a large crystal of ruby, stimulating the emission of a very narrow and intense beam of COHERENT LIGHT[s] from one of the crystal faces. A possible application of the laser is an improved form of LIGHT TELEPHONE[s].

Lead Sulphide Cell. PHOTO-CONDUCTIVE CELL the sensitive material of which is lead sulphide deposited on a glass plate. The

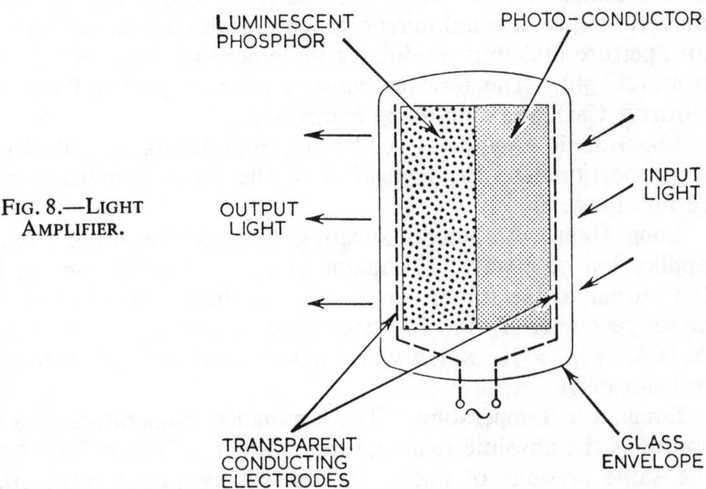

FIG. 8.—LIGHT AMPLIFIER.

maximum sensitivity of this type of cell is to radiation of wavelengths in the order of 2.5 μ, i.e. in the infra-red (heat) region. For this reason lead sulphide cells are often called " temperature dependent resistors ".

Light Amplifier. A form of IMAGE INTENSIFIER in which the light output is of the same wavelength (colour) as the light input, but of greater intensity. One very compact SOLID STATE[s] version is the panel amplifier consisting of a PHOTO-CONDUCTIVE layer superimposed on a luminescent layer, the whole sandwiched between two transpararent conducting electrodes as shown in Fig. 8. Alternating current is applied to the two electrodes, producing light in the luminescent layer. This layer is, however, effectively in series with the photo-conductive layer, the resistance of which varies with input light intensity. Thus the intensity of the light output after amplification is governed by the intensity of the input light.

Light Current. The total current flowing in a photo-cell, and thus the sum of the PHOTO CURRENT and the DARK CURRENT.

Light Dependent Resistor. A term which could be quite properly applied to any photo-conductive cell, but is normally reserved for cells of the CADMIUM SULPHIDE[s] type.

Light Telephone. A communication device first used by the Afrika Corps in Libya during the Second World War, using light as a CARRIER WAVE. The speech currents from a microphone are made to deflect a small mirror which deviates a beam of light over an aperture and thus modulates the emergent beam of light from a searchlight. The receiver consists essentially of a PHOTO-CONDUCTIVE CELL and amplifying equipment.

Logarithmic Amplifier. A form of amplifier the output of which is proportional to the logarithm of the input amplitude over a certain range.

Loop Gain. A factor indicating the gain resulting from the application of positive FEEDBACK in an OSCILLATOR circuit, from the output to the input. In a valve oscillator, for example, with anode reactance X_L and MUTUAL CONDUCTANCE g_m, the loop gain A_o is $A_o = g_m \times X_L \times 1/n$, where n is the turns ratio of the feedback transformer.

Luminance Temperature. The luminance temperature of a light source is the absolute temperature at which a BLACK BODY[s] emits the same amount of energy as the source under consideration (cf. COLOUR TEMPERATURE[s]).

Magnetic Drum. A type of MAGNETIC MEMORY[s] consisting of a drum on which several tracks of magnetic tape are laid. Information can be stored in the form of electrical impulses applied to the tape. See also MATRIX STORE.[s]

Addenda

Magnetic Memory. A collective term for a number of different magnetic devices which can STORE information for COMPUTERS. See also MAGNETIC DRUM[s] and MATRIX STORE[s].

Marconi Aerial. Popular name for an END-FED AERIAL[s] of actual length equal to a quarter of a wavelength.

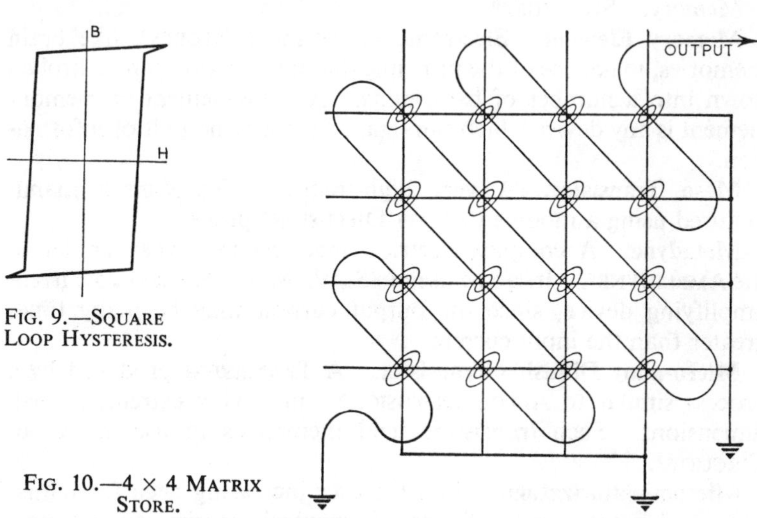

FIG. 9.—SQUARE LOOP HYSTERESIS.

FIG. 10.—4 × 4 MATRIX STORE.

Matrix Store. A STORE[s] device used in COMPUTERS comprising a large number of small FERRITE rings each having a rectangular MAGNETIC HYSTERESIS loop (see Fig. 9). Each single ring in the matrix can be used as a BINARY store, the information being retained in terms of its retentivity (see MAGNETIC HYSTERESIS), positive retentivity being used to represent 1 and negative retentivity to represent 0. Fig. 10 shows a simplified 4 × 4 matrix store. Information is written in (see WRITE IN[s]) to any of the rings by applying current pulses to the horizontal and vertical wires which pass through the ring, so putting it into a magnetic state of +B or −B. To READ OUT[s] the information from the core, a small current is applied to the same two wires, and the induced e.m.f., which varies according to the magnetic state of the core, is detected via the output (diagonal) wire. Practical matrix stores may contain up to 196,608 rings.

Mean-level A.G.C. Simple form of television receiver A.G.C. in which the waveform at the grid of the sync. separator is sampled and fed back to vary the gain of the receiver.

Meacham Bridge Oscillator. A very stable form of OSCILLATOR using a bridge feedback system in which increase of output voltage reduces the positive feedback, thus tending to maintain oscillations of constant magnitude and frequency independent of the current drawn.

Memory. See STORE[s].

Memory Element. Electronic or magnetic STORES[s], like brain memories, make use of the principle that information can be broken down into a number of basic units. A store element or memory element is any device which can retain such a basic unit of information.

Mesa Transistor. A very high-frequency TRANSISTOR manufactured using a modified ALLOY DIFFUSION[s] process.

Metadyne. A complex electrical machine somewhat similar to the AMPLIDYNE[s]. It can be used in SERVO MECHANISMS[s] as a current amplifying device, since the output current may be many times greater than the input current.

Micro-alloy Diffusion Transistor. A TRANSISTOR produced by a process similar to ALLOY DIFFUSION[s], but having extremely small dimensions. Such transistors lend themselves to use in MICRO CIRCUITS[s].

Microminiaturization. With the ever increasing need for miniature equipment various forms of microminiaturization are now being used. The three basic techniques are as follows:

(*a*) Micro modules (or micro stacks). Miniature resistors, capacitors and other components are mounted individually on thin wafers. The complete circuit is in the form of a stack of wafers interconnected by riser wires soldered to the edges. The stack can be encapsulated in resin if necessary.

(*b*) Micro circuits. Micro circuits use film resistors and capacitors deposited on to a wafer together with their interconnexions. Active components such as transistors and diodes are set into the wafer.

(*c*) Solid circuits. The solid circuit uses a piece of semiconductor material which is etched and doped to give the required electronic performance.

Minority Carrier Storage. Term used to account for the time delay which occurs between the instant at which the voltage applied to a semiconductor device is changed from the forward direction to the reverse direction and the instant at which the current reaches its final value. It is due to the fact that it takes a finite time for the MINORITY CARRIERS to leave the material or to re-combine within the material.

Mismatch. If the impedance of a load is several orders of magnitude greater or smaller than the output impedance of the driving device a mismatch occurs resulting in a considerable loss in power. See also MATCHING TRANSFORMER.

Monostable. Said of a circuit, e.g. a MULTI-VIBRATOR with one side biased in a non-conductive state, which, upon being triggered by a suitable pulse, undergoes a single cycle of oscillation before returning to its stable state.

Multiplexing. A method of CHANNELLING.

N.T.C. Resistor. (Negative Temperature Co-efficient Resistor.) A resistor the resistance of which decreases with rise in temperature.

N.T.S.C. System. A system of COLOUR TELEVISION transmission and reception which originated in the U.S.A. The system is "compatible", that is to say that black-and-white receivers can accept the colour signals and reproduce them in monochrome.

NAND Gate. A transistor gating circuit with several inputs and one output, see Fig. 11. An output is provided when there is

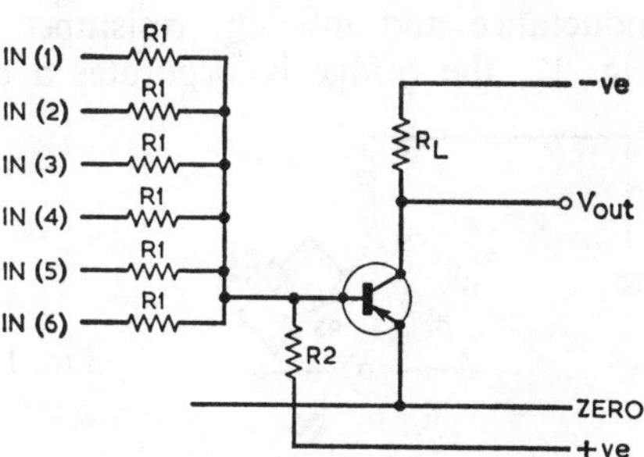

FIG. 11.—BASIC TRANSISTOR NOR OR NAND GATE CIRCUIT. With positive input signals an output is obtained when there is NOT an input to IN (1) AND all other inputs. With negative input signals an output is obtained when there is NOT an input to IN (1) OR any of the other inputs.

NOT an input at the first AND each of the other inputs. For use with positive input signals.

Near Visible Rays. That region of the ELECTROMAGNETIC SPECTRUM from the far infra-red to the far ultra-violet corresponding to wavelengths from 100 microns to 300 Å. This region, of course, includes the visible light spectrum.

Addenda

Nevitron. A type of single anode mercury arc tube. The construction is such that the cathode spot is anchored to the side of the mercury pool and the tube can therefore be used under conditions (e.g. movement and vibration) where it would be difficult to use other types of mercury arc tube.

NOR Gate. A transistor gating circuit with several inputs and one output, see Fig. 11. It provides an output when there is NOT an input at IN (1) OR any of the other inputs. For use with negative input signals.

NOT Gate. A gate arrangement with two or more inputs and one output which provides an output only if all the inputs are short-circuited to earth (c.f. GATE).

Numerical Indicator Tube. A COUNTER TUBE which displays actual images of numerals.

Octet. A group of eight electrons occupying the VALANCE BAND[s] of an atom. Such a group forms a very stable configuration, and atoms having eight valence electrons, e.g. neon, krypton, argon, etc., are chemically inert.

Omegatron. A miniature form of CYCLOTRON.

OR Gate. A gate arrangement with two or more inputs and one output: an output is obtained when a signal is applied to one or more of the inputs.

Owen Bridge. A circuit designed for measuring values of the inductance and inherent resistance of chokes. As indicated in Fig. 12, the bridge incorporates a detector (e.g. a magic eye or

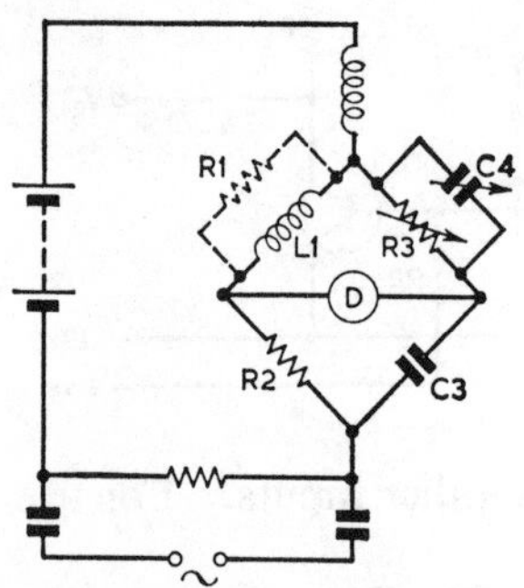

FIG. 12.—OWEN BRIDGE CIRCUIT.

earphones) across one diagonal, the energizing current (a.c. *and* d.c.) being applied across the other diagonal. Values of C_4 and R_3 are adjusted until no current flows in the detector. The impedance

(L1) and the resistance (R_1) of the choke can then be calculated from the expressions R1 = R2.C3/C4 and L1 = R3.R2.C3.

P.T.F.E. Polytetrafluoroethylene—a man-made plastic material with useful mechanical and electrical properties. It has low friction, is water-repellent and has excellent dielectric and insulation properties.

Parallel-T Filter. A filter network (see Fig. 13) which may be used to give a theoretical true null output. C.f. BRIDGED-T FILTER.

FIG. 13.—PARALLEL-T FILTER.

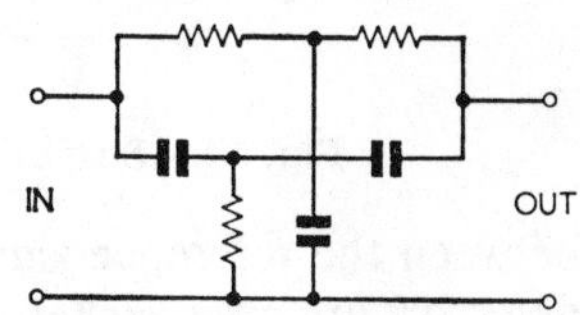

Pauli Exclusion Principle. Certain properties concerning the motion of orbital electrons in an ATOM are indicated by four quantities termed " quantum numbers ". The Pauli exclusion principle states that no two electrons in a neutral atom can possess the same set of four quantum numbers.

Peak Detector. A detector biased so that it only provides an output during that part of a signal which exceeds a certain value.

Peltier Effect. The heating or cooling of a junction between two dissimilar metals when an electric current is passed across the junction. Heat is either produced or absorbed according to the direction of the current, and its amount depends upon the quantity of electricity passing through the junction. The Peltier effect is thus the converse of that which occurs in a THERMOCOUPLE.

Penetrating Waves. Electromagnetic waves at the high-frequency end of the SPECTRUM beyond the ultra-violet region. This range includes X-rays and gamma rays and such radiations are termed penetrating waves on account of their ability to pass, to a greater or lesser extent, through materials which are opaque to visible light.

Peripheral Device. Term sometimes used to describe components such as resistors and capacitors when associated with valves or tubes in electronic circuits.

Phantastron Timebase. A modified form of MILLER TIMEBASE circuit.

Phase-sensitive Detector. A detector which provides an output which is dependent upon both the phase and the amplitude of the input signal. To achieve this a reference signal is applied to the circuit (an example is given in Fig. 14) as well as the input signal. The polarity of the output is dependent upon the phase relationship

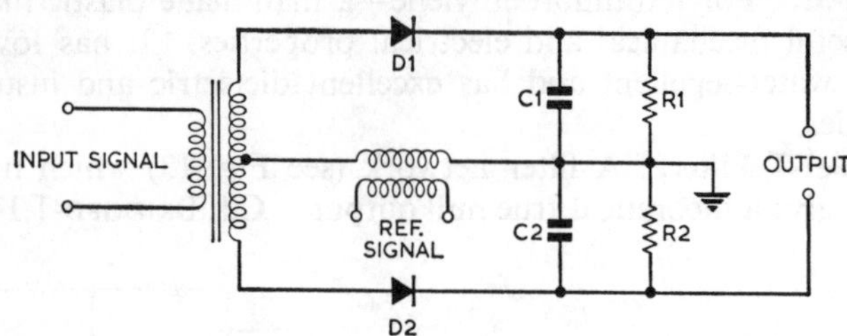

FIG. 14.—SIMPLE PHASE-SENSITIVE DETECTOR CIRCUIT.

between the reference signal and the input signal. Phase-sensitive detectors are necessary in many control systems where it is necessary to know both the degree and direction of displacement of the element being controlled.

Phase-shift Oscillator. See resistance–capacitance oscillator.

Photo-magnetic Effect. A difference of electrical POTENTIAL produced when a block of semiconductor material has one surface irradiated by light and is at the same time located in a magnetic field

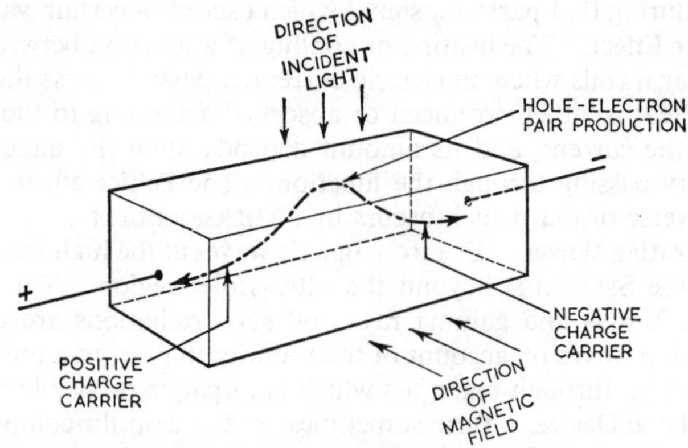

FIG. 15.—THE PHOTO-MAGNETIC EFFECT.

the direction of which is perpendicular to that of the light rays. The direction of the photo-magnetic voltage is at right-angles to both the direction of the light and the direction of the magnetic field. The phenomenon is illustrated in Fig. 15. The incident light initiates

PAIR PRODUCTION at the irradiated surface. As the charge carriers thus produced diffuse into the bulk of the material they are deflected by the magnetic field, holes in one direction and electrons in the opposite direction. Opposite charges thus accumulate at the ends of the block, setting up the photo-magnetic voltage.

Photo-voltaic Effect. The generation of a POTENTIAL DIFFERENCE between two metal electrodes in contact with certain materials when irradiated by light. The simplest form of photo-voltaic cell is the selenium cell, consisting of a coating of selenium on a metal base, a

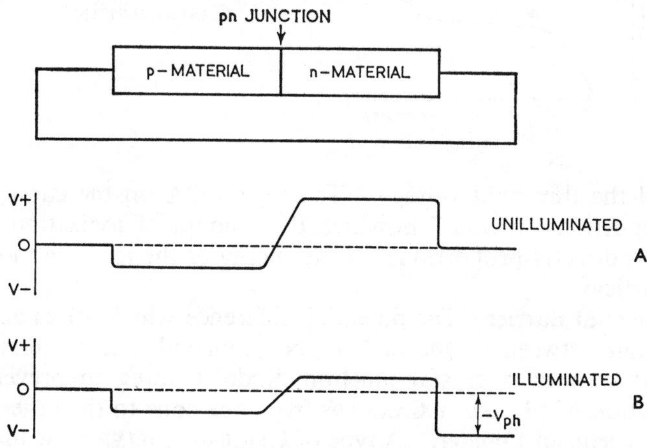

FIG. 16.—THE PHOTO-VOLTAIC EFFECT.

thin, transparent film of one of the precious metals, e.g. gold, being deposited on the upper surface of the selenium. A POTENTIAL BARRIER[s] exists at the gold-selenium junction. Light traversing the transparent film sets up PAIR PRODUCTION in the selenium, and electrons are drawn from the selenium to the gold by the barrier potential. The gold therefore attains a negative potential with respect to the metal base. Cells of this type are used, for example, in photographic exposure meters and lux-meters. Another form of photo-voltaic cell consists essentially of a semiconductor pn junction, for which silicon is usually employed. The potential distribution across such a device when unilluminated is shown at A in Fig. 16, the broken line indicating the barrier potential gradient at the junction. When the cell is illuminated, PAIR PRODUCTION occurs in the material and the potential distribution becomes as illustrated at B, so that a potential difference is set up between the external electrodes.

Plateau. The flat portion of the characteristic curve of a GEIGER–MÜLLER TUBE. It is also known as the " Geiger region ". As shown in Fig. 17 the voltage at which the plateau commences is

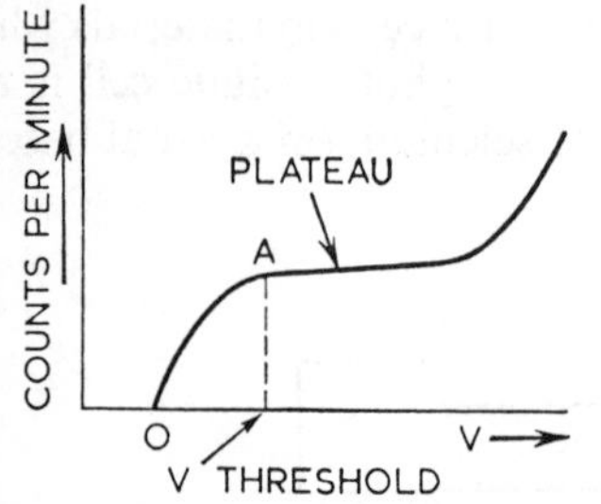

FIG. 17.—GEIGER–MÜLLER TUBE CHARACTERISTIC.

called the threshold voltage. The region OA on the curve is the " proportional region " in which the amount of ionization in the tube is directly proportional to the energy of the ionizing radiation or particle.

Potential Barrier—The potential difference which arises across a junction between p-type and n-type semiconductor material in a TRANSISTOR or a crystal junction diode, tending to prevent the migration of MAJORITY CARRIERS from one zone to the other.

Proportional Counter. A type of GEIGER–MÜLLER TUBE in which the energy of the ionizing radiation is measured directly from the amount of ionization it produces. See also PLATEAU[s].

Proportional Region. See PLATEAU[s].

Q-meter. A complex instrument used to measure the Q FACTOR of an inductor.

Quenching. Term applied in general to the sudden suppression of an electrical oscillation or a discharge through a gas. For quenching oscillations in a circuit, purely electrical methods must be used such as, for example, the inclusion of resistance—the circuit is then said to be damped. For quenching a gas discharge such as, for example, in a GEIGER–MÜLLER tube used as a radiation counter, when the discharge started by IONIZATION must be quenched before the next burst of energy reaches the tube, quenching may be achieved by the external circuit or, as is more usual, by mixing certain other gases or vapours with the normal permanent gas filling.

R.B.E. Relative biological effectiveness (see REM[s]).

Rad. A unit of X, gamma, or beta radiation (see also REM[s]).

Radiation Monitor. A circuit using a GEIGER–MÜLLER TUBE with the function of continuously measuring the X or gamma radiation near, say, an atomic reactor, and giving a visible or audible warning if the radiation intensity should rise to a dangerous level.

Rate Meter. An electronic circuit or device used for step-by-step counting, and in particular a device used in conjunction with a GEIGER–MÜLLER TUBE to indicate the number of pulses occurring in a tube during a certain period of time.

Read or Read Out. The process of extracting information from a MEMORY OR STORE.

Rediffusion. The process of relaying radio or television signals to the home by means of cable. This system is used to advantage in areas where the signal strength is very low. Signals are picked up by a single aerial placed on high ground, amplified where necessary, and then distributed to subscribers by wire.

Reluctance. Term indicating the degree of opposition which magnetic flux meets in a given piece of magnetic material, or part of a magnetic circuit. Reluctance is thus the magnetic analogue of electrical resistance. It is numerically equal to the length of the specimen divided by the product of its cross sectional area and its PERMEABILITY.

Rem. A unit of X, gamma or beta radiation as absorbed by human tissue. See also RAD[s]. 1 rem = 1 rad × relative biological effectiveness (R.B.E.).

Resistance–capacitance Oscillator. Oscillator in which the positive feedback is applied via a frequency-determining RC network. Also known as a Phase shift OSCILLATOR.

Ring Modulator. A MODULATOR circuit using four thermionic or crystal DIODES, see Fig. 18.

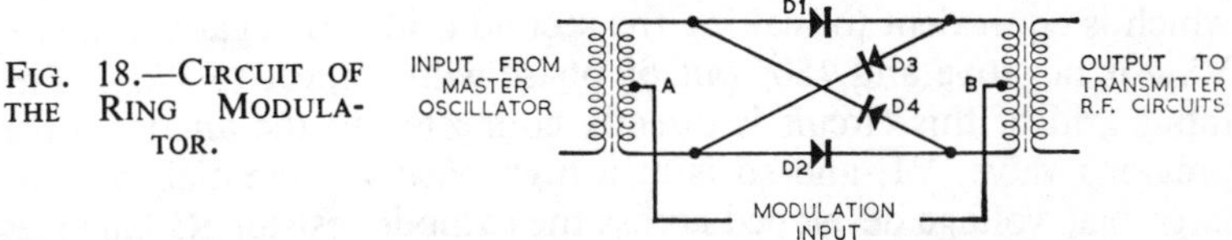

FIG. 18.—CIRCUIT OF THE RING MODULATOR.

Rise Time. Time taken for the leading edge of a pulse to increase from 10 to 90 per cent of its maximum value.

Addenda

Rotary Amplifier. See AMPLIDYNE[s] and METADYNE[s].

Ruggedized Valves. Another term used in describing SPECIAL-QUALITY VALVES.

Sarah. The " Search And Rescue And Homing " apparatus is a portable RADIO BEACON which is attached to the life-jackets of airmen. After a crash or parachute descent into the sea, rescue teams can locate the survivors by homing on to the characteristic signals transmitted by the apparatus.

Saturable Reactor. A transformer or choke with an additional winding. The alternating current in the normal winding or windings can be modified by variable direct current, tending to SATURATE the core, applied to the additional winding. Also known as a TRANSDUCTOR. See also MAGNETIC AMPLIFIER.

Scaler (Scaling Circuit.) An electronic circuit used for counting electrical pulses and employing specially designed valves with many electrodes such as the DEKATRON OR TROCHATRON[s].

Schmitt Circuit. One of the many types of PARAPHASE amplifier. As seen in Fig. 19 a negative pulse applied to the input grid of valve

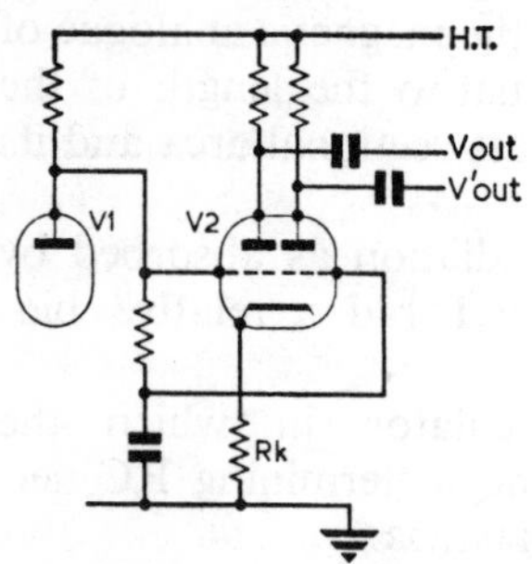

FIG. 19.—SCHMITT AMPLIFIER CIRCUIT.

V2 produces a positive pulse at the first anode so that V_{out} is positive. The common cathode then becomes more negative, which is equivalent to making the second grid less negative; hence V^1_{out} is negative and 180° out of phase with respect to V_{out}. The input grid of this circuit is directly connected to the anode of the previous valve, V1, and so is at a high positive potential, but the large bias voltage developed across the cathode resistor R_k balances this.

Selective Amplifier. An amplifier incorporating tuned circuits or filters to limit its BAND WIDTH.

Selsyn System. The selsyn unit consists of two or more small electric induction motors each having three-phase stator windings and a single-phase salient pole rotor. Generally, only two poles of the rotor are wound, so that the system has only one position of correspondence per 360° revolution. The motors are connected in parallel, as shown in Fig. 20, through pilot wires, and the normal

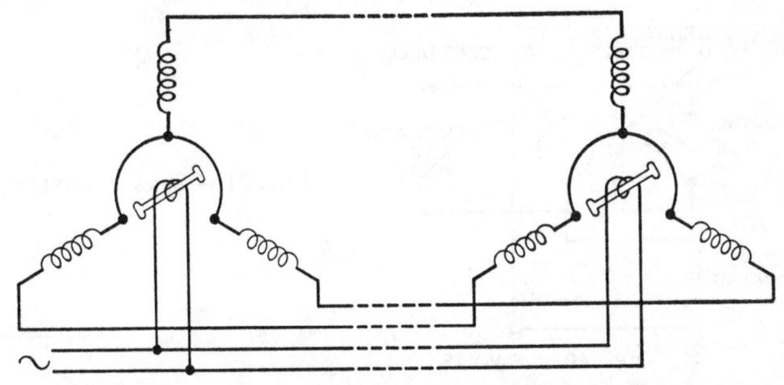

FIG. 20.—ARRANGEMENT OF A SIMPLE SELSYN SYSTEM.

state of equilibrium is that in which all the rotors are in the same position when the electromagnetic forces induced in the rotors are in opposition and no rotor current flows. Any relative displacement of one rotor in the system upsets this balance, and circulating currents are set up in the other rotors, resulting in torques which restore the units to the equilibrium position of mutual correspondence. Such systems have obvious applications in SERVO MECHANISMS[s].

Sensistor. Proprietary name for a resistor of high positive temperature co-efficient of resistance. See also SILISTOR[s].

Servo (Servo Mechanism). A mechanism, partly or completely electromagnetic or electronic, which automatically controls the operation of some mechanical, electrical, or even chemical process. See also AUTOMATION and SERVO AMPLIDYNE[s].

Servo Amplidyne. A typical SERVO[s] application of the AMPLIDYNE[s] lies in the automatic control of the output voltage of a d.c. generator. As shown in Fig. 21, the field current of the generator is supplied from the output of the amplidyne, and the amplidyne field corresponds to the difference between a fraction of the generator output and a fixed reference field. A small deviation in generator output voltage alters the field current of the amplidyne. This in turn adjusts the generator field current until the generator output voltage is restored to the correct value.

Servo Selsyn. See SELSYN SYSTEM[s].

Sheath. The layer of positive gas IONS which accumulate around any negatively-charged electrode in a gas-filled valve. In the THYRATRON, it is the sheath which prevents the grid from influencing the behaviour of the main electron stream once this has started to flow.

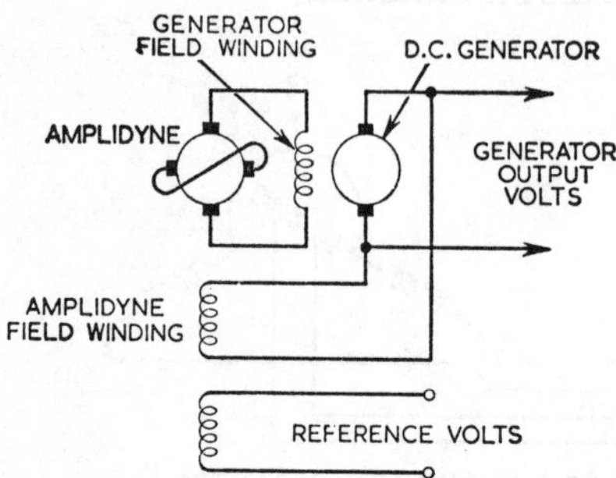

FIG. 21.—SERVO AMPLIDYNE.

Shockley Diode. Another name for TUNNEL DIODE.

Silicon Controlled Rectifier. The SOLID STATE[s] equivalent of the THYRATRON. Current conduction in the forward direction cannot occur until either a critical forward voltage is reached or a triggering signal is applied to the " gate " or trigger electrode. Once conduction has started, the trigger electrode has no further control until the current is reduced to below a critical value referred to as the " sustaining current ".

Silistor. A resistor with a very high positive temperature coefficient, used to prevent damage to circuits during sustained overload.

Sine-cosine Potentiometer. A POTENTIOMETER in which the resistance between one extremity of the track and the slider varies as the sine (or cosine) of the angle through which the spindle has been rotated.

Slide-back Voltmeter. A type of VALVE VOLTMETER in which the grid bias of a TRIODE valve is adjusted by a POTENTIOMETER until the anode current is reduced to a low value. The alternating voltage to be measured is then applied to the grid in series with the bias which is further reduced until the anode current again falls to the original set value. The difference in applied bias is then a measure of the peak value of the alternating voltage.

Slug. Small piece of magnetic material, consisting either of iron dust in a binding medium or of one of the magnetic ferrites, which is inserted into a coil and its position adjusted in order to vary the INDUCTANCE.

Softening Voltage. The critical collector voltage of a JUNCTION TRANSISTOR above which the current increases more and more rapidly with increasing voltage. Transistors to which voltages much greater than the softening voltage are applied may show the AVALANCHE EFFECT[s].

Solar Battery. Semiconductor device in which the PHOTO-VOLTAIC[s] effect is exploited to produce electrical power from solar energy. Each cell consists of a pn silicon junction diode, and a number of cells can be connected in series or series-parallel to form batteries delivering considerable power output. Among practical application is their use as power supply sources in artificial satellites. For this application it is usually necessary to provide protection from destructive proton radiation which is met with at certain altitudes. For solar radiation the power conversion efficiency may be as high as 10 per cent.

Solid State Device. An electronic device such as a SILICON DIODE, a TRANSISTOR or a PHOTO-CONDUCTIVE CELL which exploits the special behaviour of HOLES and ELECTRONS in elements or compounds in their solid state. See also SEMICONDUCTOR.

Sonar. A system for the detection and location of objects under water. Analogous to RADAR, sonar employs bursts of sound waves in place of radio waves which cannot be transmitted in liquid media. Sonar is used for depth sounding, for the location of shoals of fish, and for submarine detection.

Spectral Distribution. The relative amounts of energy at different wavelengths emitted by a radiator at a given temperature. Fig. 22 shows the general form of the spectral distribution curves of a BLACK BODY[s] at three different temperatures.

Spectral Response. The relative sensitivity or response of a system or device to radiation of different wavelengths within a certain range or SPECTRUM. The term is applied principally to the response of PHOTO-ELECTRIC CELLS to indicate their sensitivity to light (and heat) radiation over the wavelength range of 25 to 4,000,000 Å. Figs. 23, 24, and 25 show the spectral response curves of three types of photo cells.

Split-load Output Stage. In valve practice, an output stage in which part of the load is in the anode circuit and part in the cathode circuit.

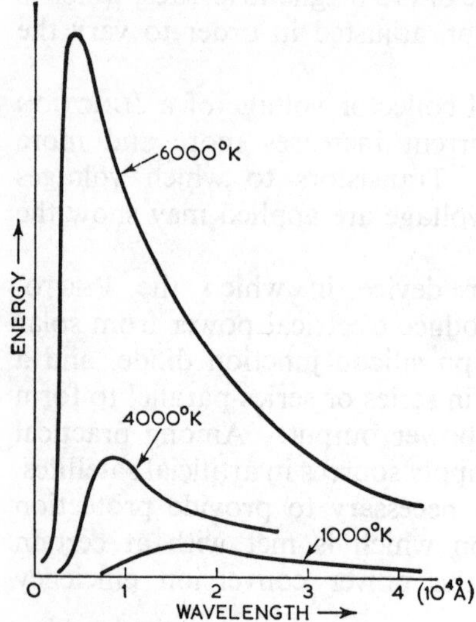

FIG. 22.—GENERAL FORM OF SPECTRAL DISTRIBUTION CURVES OF A BLACK BODY AT VARIOUS TEMPERATURES (NOT TO SCALE).

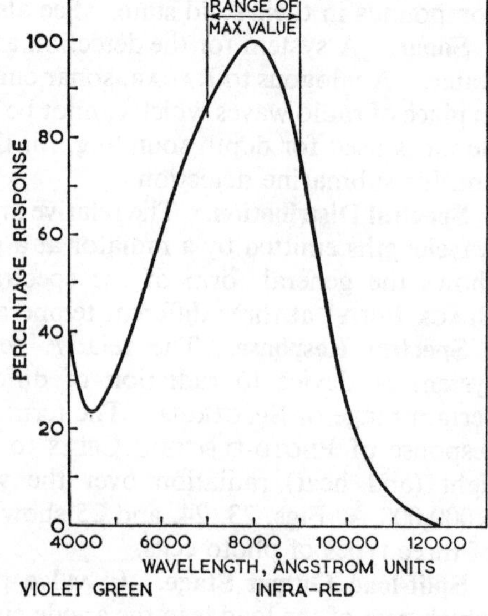

FIG. 23.—SPECTRAL RESPONSE OF A PHOTO-EMISSIVE CELL WITH CAESIUM ON OXIDISED SILVER CATHODE.

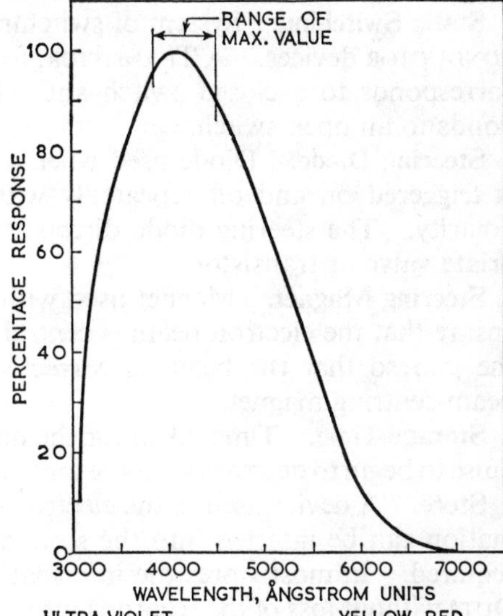

FIG. 24.—SPECTRAL RESPONSE OF A PHOTO-EMISSIVE CELL WITH CAESIUM ANTIMONY CATHODE.

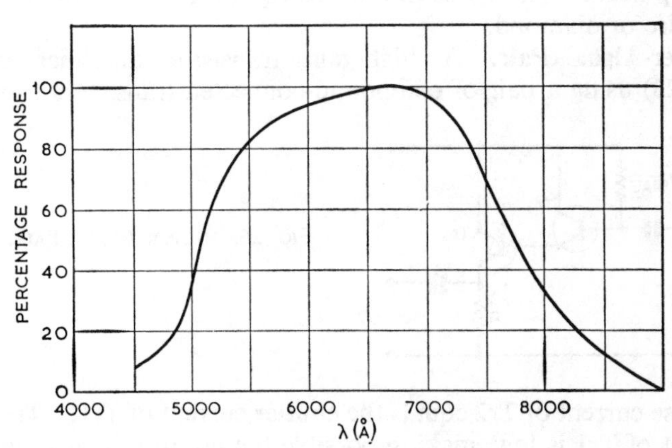

FIG. 25.—SPECIAL RESPONSE OF A CADMIUM SULPHIDE PHOTO-CONDUCTIVE CELL.

Addenda

Spot Limiter. See WHITE SPOT SUPPRESSOR[s].

Static Switching. System of switching based on the use of SEMICONDUCTOR devices. A TRANSISTOR, for example, when conducting corresponds to a closed switch and when non-conducting corresponds to an open switch.

Steering Diode. Diode used when a BISTABLE[s] MULTI-VIBRATOR is triggered on and off repeatedly with input pulses of the same polarity. The steering diode directs the input pulse to the appropriate valve or transistor.

Steering Magnet. Magnet used with a television picture tube to ensure that the electron beam is central within the final aperture of the gun so that the beam is correctly focused. Also known as beam-centring magnet.

Storage Time. Time taken for the output current or voltage of a pulse to begin to decrease after the input or voltage has been removed.

Store. A device used in the electronic digital COMPUTER. Information can be inserted into the store and retained as long as it is required. In most stores the information can be recalled or READ OUT[s] without loss of the recorded information. See also MAGNETIC MEMORY[s] and MEMORY ELEMENT[s].

Stylus. The correct name for the " needle " in a gramophone pick-up head. The stylus in modern equipment is usually made of sapphire or diamond.

Super-Alpha Pair. A high-gain transistor amplifier circuit (Fig. 26) using a pair of compound-connected transistors in which

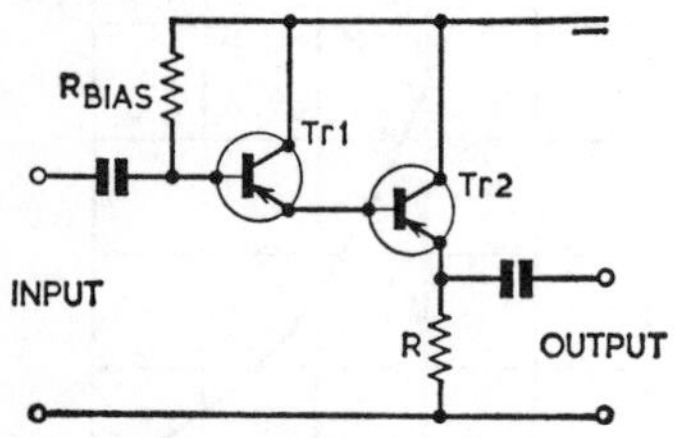

FIG. 26.—SUPER-ALPHA PAIR.

the base current of Tr2 equals the emitter current of Tr1. The base current of Tr1 is low, making possible the use of a high value bias resistor; input impedance may exceed one megohm. The circuit is unsuitable for use at high ambient temperatures because of leakage currents.

Super-regenerative Receiver. Radio receiver incorporating a detector to which sufficient POSITIVE FEEDBACK is applied to bring the circuit into a condition of oscillation at signal frequency. The grid capacitor and grid resistor are so dimensioned, however, that the oscillations are periodically quenched or suppressed, the interruption frequency being well above the audio-frequency range. Although possessing a high degree of sensitivity, the super-regenerative system is prone to troublesome re-radiation unless special precautions as regards screening are taken. The quality of reproduction is also poor.

Susceptance. Just as CONDUCTANCE is the reciprocal of RESISTANCE, and ADMITTANCE the reciprocal of IMPEDANCE, so susceptance is the reciprocal of REACTANCE. Symbol *B*, unit the MHO. It is numerically equal to the ratio of the reactance of a circuit to the square of its impedance.

Swinging Choke. A CHOKE of special construction used in power units where the output current variations are severe. The iron core of the choke has a small air-gap across which the MAGNETIC FLUX must flow. This results in magnetic SATURATION at high currents.

Symmetrical Transistor. A type of JUNCTION TRANSISTOR in which the collector-base and emitter-base junctions are identical. Such transistors can be used bi-directionally, i.e. the roles of the collector and emitter can be exchanged.

Sync.-cancelled A.G.C. Television receiver A.G.C. system in which the bias voltage is based on the back level of the television waveform. The positive sync. pulses at the grid of the sync. separator are cancelled by negative sync. pulses fed back from the sync. separator anode. The grid circuit acts as a peak detector providing the A.G.C. bias used to control the receiver gain.

Synchro. See SELSYN.

Sychronous Detector. A DETECTOR (demodulator) which receives two signals having a phase difference of 90°. Two such demodulators are required in receivers for the N.T.S.C. system of colour television.

Synchrotron. Apparatus designed for the production of very high energy X-RAYS. See also LINEAR ACCELERATOR.

Tachometer. A device used for measuring the rate of rotation of shafts and axles, etc. Electronic tachometers produce pulses, which may be electrical or optical, one or more times per shaft revolution, and these pulses are then counted electronically or used to operate a frequency meter.

Tandem Amplifier. A circuit configuration using two transistors connected in such a way that the current through one of the transistors is controlled by the current through the other. Fig. 27 shows a simplified tandem circuit.

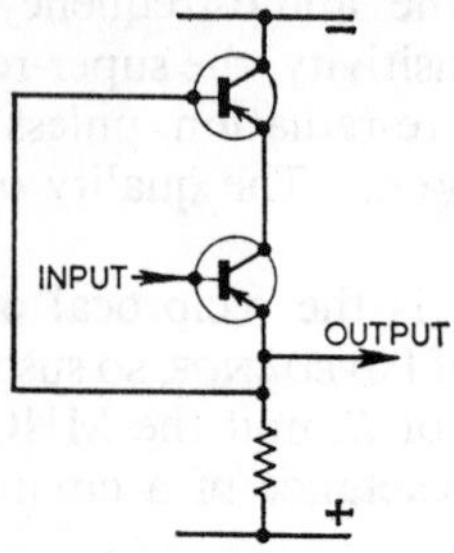

FIG. 27.—TANDEM AMPLIFIER.

Telemetry. The art of making measurements at a location beyond the reach of normal instrumentation—for example measurement of gamma radiation in the stratosphere by means of rockets fitted with measuring instruments together with communication devices which transmit the instrument readings to the ground.

Tesla Transformer. The normal device employed for generating high-voltage for X-ray tubes before the time when high power RECTIFIERS came into general use. The system is still used by neurologists for electric shock treatment. A typical circuit is shown in Fig. 28. The capacitors C and C are charged to a high

FIG. 28.—TESLA TRANSFORMER.

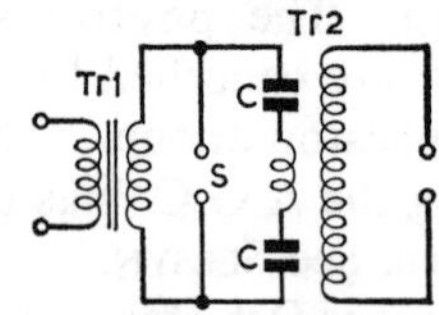

voltage by means of a step-up mains transformer TR1 until a momentary discharge takes place across the spark-gap S, setting up a high-frequency current in a few turns of wire forming the primary winding of the Tesla transformer TR2. The secondary of this transformer consists of many thousands of turns of wire and thus produces bursts of very high voltage.

Thermal Stability. The values of most electronic components, (e.g. their resistance) changes with changing temperature. In a well-designed and laid out system, however, after switching on, a state is eventually reached at which the rate of heat dissipation is equal to the rate at which heat is produced in the circuits, and this is termed thermal stability.

Addenda

Thomson Effect (Kelvin effect). A temperature gradient existing along a conducting wire gives rise to a small electric potential gradient.

Threshold Voltage. See PLATEAU[s].

Thyristor. Proprietary name for a SILICON CONTROLLED RECTIFIER[s].

Transductor. See SATURABLE REACTOR.

Trigatron. Name sometimes applied to a TRIGGER TUBE.

Trigger Circuit. Any circuit which remains in a state of equilibrium (usually cut off) until it has been stimulated by an increasing pulse is a trigger circuit. Usually, however, the term is applied to " flip–flop " circuits as described under MULTIVIBRATORS.

Trinister. Proprietary name for a SILICON CONTROLLED RECTIFIER[s].

Trochotron. A multi-electrode counting tube somewhat similar to the DEKATRON but capable of operating at speeds up to 1Mc/s.

True Temperature. The actual temperature, preferably expressed in °K, of a particular body at a particular time. See also COLOUR TEMPERATURE[s].

Tweeter. A small LOUDSPEAKER used to reproduce the higher range of audio frequencies. See also DUPLEX[s].

Twin Feeder. Cable consisting of two parallel conductors separated by insulating supports, and often used for making a balanced connexion between a DIPOLE aerial and a transmitter or receiver.

Twisted Pair. If a high-frequency alternating current is to be fed from one location to another with the minimum of induction effects in adjacent conductors, the two wires may be twisted together to form a " twisted pair ". Such a system can be used to connect a transmitter or receiver to a DIPOLE aerial. See also TWIN FEEDER[s] and CO-AXIAL CABLE.

Unilateralization. See NEUTRALIZATION.

Valence Band. The highest ENERGY BAND normally occupied by electrons in a neutral atom. Electrons in this band are termed VALENCE ELECTRONS. See also ATOM, STRUCTURE OF, and OCTET[s].

Varactor Diode. A silicon diode of special construction used in certain FREQUENCY DOUBLER circuits.

Varistor. A trade name for a type of THERMISTOR.

Addenda

Varite. Proprietary name for a range of non-linear silicon carbide devices similar to the METROSIL.

Video Tape. See MAGNETIC TAPE RECORDER.

Villard Circuit. A VOLTAGE DOUBLER RECTIFIER circuit employing a single diode and two capacitors as shown in Fig. 29 and giving a pulsed output.

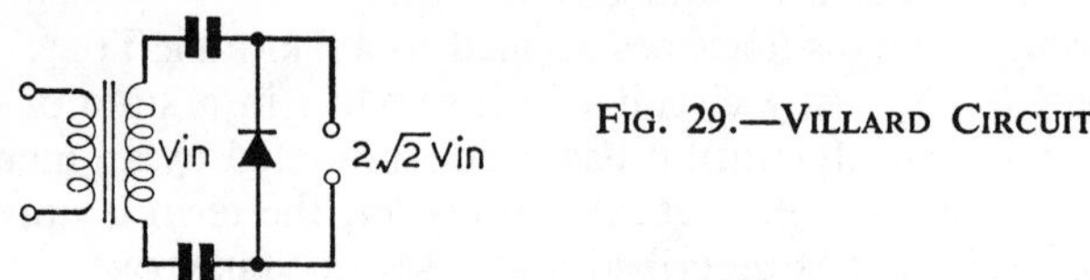

FIG. 29.—VILLARD CIRCUIT.

Voltage-dependent Resistor (V.D.R.). A silicon carbide resistor, such as the METROSIL, the resistance of which varies with the applied voltage.

Walkie-Talkie. A small, light-weight combined radio transmitter and receiver which can be carried on the person. Used to maintain audio contact between the wearer and one or more fixed or mobile stations such as a control post. In addition to their military applications, walkie-talkie sets are used by fire-brigades, the police, rescue parties, and on large building and constructional sites, etc.

White Spot Suppressor. A circuit incorporated in most television receivers to inhibit the effects of local ignition and other spark-

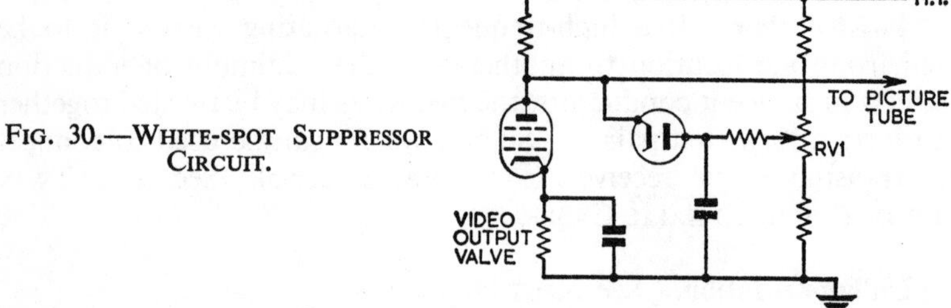

FIG. 30.—WHITE-SPOT SUPPRESSOR CIRCUIT.

produced interference on the picture. A frequently used circuit consists of a diode located between the VIDEO AMPLIFIER and the picture tube as shown in Fig. 30. The control RV1 is adjusted so that the normal negative-going pulses to the tube are just insufficient to render the cathode of the suppressor diode negative with respect to the anode. The diode is then non-conductive. Any bursts of interference, however, increase the amplitude of the negative pulses, causing the diode to conduct to chassis, thus preventing the excess (interfering) voltage from reaching the picture tube.

Wien Bridge. A useful form of resistance—capacity OSCILLATOR producing a near sine wave ouptut, using two triodes with frequency–selective POSITIVE FEEDBACK from the output of the second valve to the input of the first valve. The basic circuit is shown in Fig. 31. R1, C1 form the frequency–selective feedback loop in

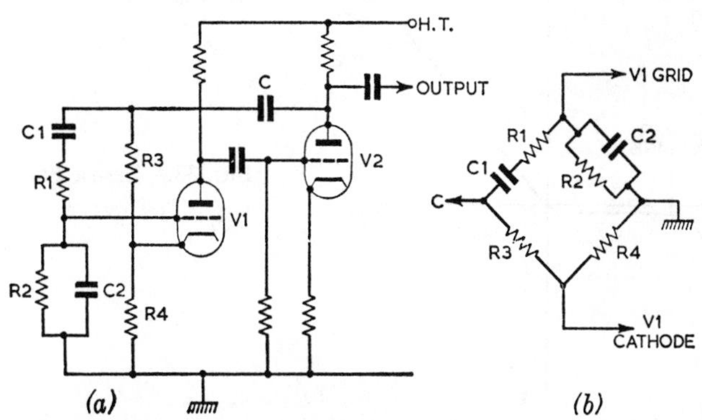

FIG. 31.—WIEN-BRIDGE OSCILLATOR CIRCUIT. DRAWN (*a*) TO SHOW THE FEEDBACK PATHS. NEGATIVE FEEDBACK IS PROVIDED BY THE VOLTAGE DIVIDER R3, R4, POSITIVE FEEDBACK BY C1, R1, C2, R2. PART OF CIRCUIT REARRANGED AT (*b*) TO SHOW BRIDGE NETWORK.

conjunction with R2, C2. The natural frequency is $f = 1/2\pi$ RC where R = R1 = R2 and C = C1 = C2.

Witka Circuit. A voltage tripler circuit using two diodes and two capacitors, the circuit being as shown in Fig. 32. The output

FIG. 32.—WITKA CIRCUIT.

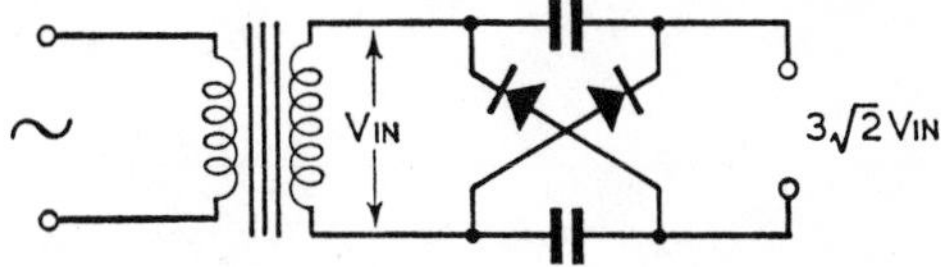

voltage is approximately $3\sqrt{2}$ times the input voltage. See also VOLTAGE DOUBLER RECTIFIER.

Write or Write in. The process of recording information in a MEMORY[s] or STORE[s].

y-parameters. A set of FOUR POLE[s] characteristics based on the ADMITTANCES of the network. See also h-PARAMETERS[s].

Yield. The ratio of the number of electrons emitted by a PHOTO-EMISSIVE CELL to the number of PHOTONS striking the cathode.

z-parameters. A set of FOUR POLE[s] characteristics based on the IMPEDANCES of the network. See also h-PARAMETER[s].

Zener Voltage. The reverse current of a SEMICONDUCTOR DIODE is of small magnitude and is very nearly constant over a range of

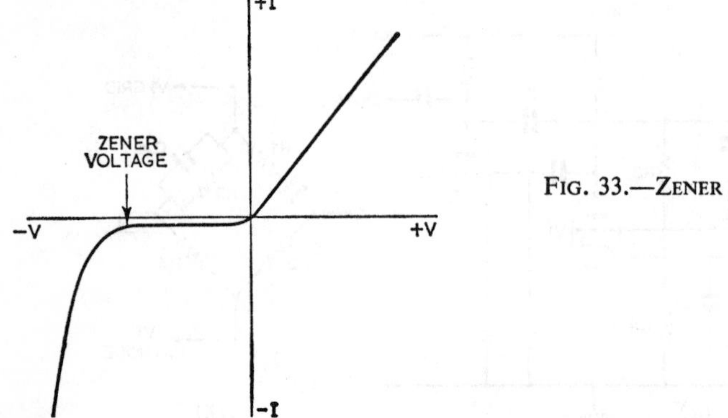

FIG. 33.—ZENER EFFECT.

applied voltages up to a certain maximum value—the Zener voltage. Beyond this critical voltage, as shown in Fig. 33, the reverse current increases very steeply for small increases in voltage. See also ZENER DIODE.

UNITS AND ABBREVIATIONS

A

a	Anode.
A	Ampere.
Å	Ångström unit.
ac	Alternating current.
ACR	Approach Control Radar.
af	Audio frequency.
afc	Automatic frequency control.
agc	Automatic gain control.
Ah	Ampere-hour.
am	Amplitude modulation.
amp	Ampere; amplitude; amplification.
ant.	Antenna (Amer.).
apc	Automatic picture control; automatic phase control.
AT	Ampere turn.
avc	Automatic volume control.

B

b	Battery.
B	Magnetic induction; brightness, negative feedback; bel.
Babs	Beam approach beacon system (Radar).
bfo	Beat frequency oscillator.
B.S.	British Standard Specification.

C

c	Inter-electrode capacitance; cycle; cathode; curie; centi-.
c	Velocity of light; speed of electromagnetic waves *in vacuo*.
C	Coulomb; Centigrade; capacitance.
cal	Calorie.
C.C.I.F.	Comité Consultatif International Fernsprecht.

C.C.I.R.	Comité Consultatif International des Radio-communications.
cgs	Centimetre-gram(me)-second system of units.
co	Crystal oscillator.
cro	Cathode-ray oscilloscope.
crt	Cathode-ray tube.
c/s	Cycles per second.
cu	Cubic.
cw	Continuous wave.

D

d	Diode; deci-.
D	Electric flux density; distortion.
Dag	A colloidal form of graphite, deflocculated Acheson graphite.
dagc	Delayed automatic gain control.
davc	Delayed automatic volume control.
dB	Decibel.
dc	Direct current.
DEW	Distant early warning (Amer.).
dcc	Double cotton covered.
dsb	Double sideband.
D.S.I.R.	Department of Scientific and Industrial Research.
dyn	Dyne.

E

e	Base of Naperian logarithms; emitter; ($-e$ is the charge on an electron).
E	Electric field strength; Earth.
ehf	Extremely high frequency.
eht	Extra high tension.
emf	Electro-motive force.
emu	Electromagnetic unit.
esu	Electrostatic unit.
eV	Electron-volt.

F

f	Frequency.
F	Farad; Fahrenheit.
F	Magneto-motive force.

fc	Frequency-changer.
fd	Frequency doubler.
fm	Frequency modulation.
ft	Foot.
fsd	Full-scale deflexion (of a meter).

G

g	Grid; gram(me); or g_c,g_m, conductance in a valve.
g	Gravitational acceleration.
G	Gauss; conductance.
gb	Grid bias; gain bandwidth product.
G.C.A.	Ground-controlled approach (radar).
grf	Group repetition frequency.

H

h	Heater; hexode; heptode.
h	Planck's constant.
H	Magnetizing force; henry.
hf	High frequency.
hp	Horse-power; high-pass (filter).
h	Hour.
ht	High tension.
hv	High voltage.
hw	Half-wave.
Hz	Hertz or cycle per second.

I

i	Instantaneous value of current; or the operator $\sqrt{-1}$.
I	Current.
icw	Interrupted continuous wave.
isb	Independent sideband.
if	Intermediate frequency.

J

j	Operator $\sqrt{-1}$.
J	Joule.

K

k	Cathode; kilo-.
k	Boltzmann's constant.
K	Kelvin (absolute) temperature.

L

l	Litre.
L	Inductance.
lf	Low frequency.
lp	Low pass (filter).
LS	Loudspeaker.
lt	Low tension.
luhf	Lowest usable high frequency.
lw	Long wave.

M

m	Metre; milli-.
m	Mass of electron.
M	Mutual inductance; intensity of magnetization; mega-.
mks	Metre-kilogram(me)-second system of units.
mmf	Magneto-motive force.
mw	Medium wave.

N

n	Neutron; nano-.
N	Number of turns.
nbc	Noise balancing circuit.
nf	Noise factor.
ntp	Normal temperature and pressure

O

owf	Optimum working frequency.
oz	Ounce.

P

p	Pentode; plate; power; pico-.
P	Power.

pa Pre-amplifier; power amplifier; public address.
PA Public address.
pam Pulse amplitude modulation.
pd Potential difference.
pfm Pulse-frequency modulation.
pH Hydrogen-ion exponent.
piv Peak inverse voltage.
PPI Plan-position indicator (Radar).
pm Permanent magnet.
Pot. Potentiometer.
pp Push–pull.
ppm Pulse position modulation; parts per million.
prf Pulse repetition frequency.
ptfe Polytetrafluoroethylene.
P.U. Pick-up, for leads from.

Q

q Tetrode.
q Quantity of heat.
Q Q-factor; electric charge quantity; quantity of heat.
qpp Quiescent push–pull.

R

r Röntgen; resistance; rectifier.
R Resistance.
rf Radio frequency.
rfc Radio-frequency choke.
rms Root mean square.
R/T Radio telephony.

S

s Second (also **sec**).
S Sensitivity.
s/c Short-circuit.
ssb Single sideband.

T

t Time; triode; target.
T Absolute temperature.

trf	Tuned radio frequency.
twt	Travelling-wave tube.

U

uhf	Ultra high frequency.
usw	Ultra short wave.

V

v	Valve.
v	Velocity.
V	Volt.
vhf	Very high frequency.
vvm	Valve voltmeter.

W

W	Watt.
W/T	Wireless telegraphy.

X

X's	Atmospherics.

Y

Y	Admittance.

Z

Z	Impedance.

GREEK LETTERS USED IN ELECTRONICS

α Current gain in a transistor.

ε Base of Naperian logarithms; permittivity; dielectric constant.

η Efficiency.

κ Conductivity.

λ Wavelength.

μ Permeability; amplification factor of a valve. Also micron and micro-.

Greek Letters used in Electronics

ν Frequency.
π Ratio of circumference to diameter of a circle; also symbol for certain circuit layouts.
ρ Charge density.
χ Susceptibility.
Ψ Flux.
Ω Ohms.
ω Angular frequency.

LIST OF SYMBOLS

These symbols are based on British Standard Specification No. 1409: 1950, " Letter Symbols for Electronic Valves ".

1. Symbols for Electrodes

Anode	a
Cathode	k
Grid	g
Heater	h
Filament	f
Beam Plates	bp
Fluorescent Screen or Target	t
External Metallization	M
Internal Metallization	m
Deflector Electrodes	x or y
Internal Shield	s
Resonator	Res

Note 1 In valves having more than one grid, the grids are distinguished by numbers g_1, g_2, etc., g_1 being the grid nearest the cathode.

Note 2 In multiple valves electrodes of the different sections may be distinguished by adding one of the following letters:

Diode	d
Triode	t
Tetrode	q
Pentode	p

Hexode	h
Heptode	h
Octode	h
Rectifier	r

Thus the grid of the triode section of a triode-hexode is denoted by g_t.

Note 3 Two or more similar electrodes which cannot be distinguished by any of the above means may be denoted by adding one or more primes to indicate which electrode system the electrode forms part of.

Thus, the anode of the first diode in a double diode valve is denoted a′.

2. Symbols for Electric Magnitudes

Voltages

Direct voltage	V
Alternating voltage (r.m.s.)	$V_{r.m.s.}$
Alternating voltage (mean)	V_{av}
Alternating voltage (peak)	V_{pk}
Peak Inverse voltage	P.I.V.

Current

Direct current	I
Alternating current (r.m.s.)	$I_{r.m.s.}$
Alternating current (mean)	I_{av}
Alternating current (peak)	I_{pk}
No Signal current	I_0

Miscellaneous

Frequency	f
Amplification Factor	μ
Mutual Conductance	g_m
Conversion Conductance	g_c
Distortion	D
Anode Efficiency	η
Sensitivity	S
Brightness	B
Temperature	T
Time	t

List of Symbols

	Inside Valve	Outside Valve
Resistance	r	R
Reactance	x	X
Impedance	z	Z
Admittance	y	Y
Mutual Inductance	m	M
Capacitance	c	C
Capacitance at working temperature	c_w	—
Power	p	P

3. Auxiliary Symbols

Battery or other source of supply	b
Inverse (voltage or current)	inv
Ignition (Voltage)	ign
Extinction (voltage)	ext
No signal	0
Input	in
Output	out
Total	tot
Centre tap	ct

4. Complex Symbols

Symbols in Sections 1 and 3 above may be used as subscripts to symbols in Section 2, to denote such magnitudes as Anode Current, Grid Volts, etc., e.g.:

Anode Voltage	V_a
Control-grid voltage	V_{g1}
Anode supply voltage	$V_{a(b)}$
Filament voltage	V_f
Heater voltage	V_h
Anode dissipation	p_a
Output power	P_{out}
Drive power	P_{drive}
Anode current (d.c.)	I_a
Anode current (a.c.r.m.s.)	$I_{a(r.m.s.)}$
No signal anode current	$I_{a(o)}$
Control-grid current	I_{g1}
Total distortion	D_{tot}

List of Symbols

	Internal	External
3rd-harmonic distortion	D_3	
Equivalent noise resistance	R_{eq}	
Limiting resistor	R_{lim}	
Cathode bias resistor	R_k	
Anode resistance	r_a	R_a
Insulating resistance (heater to cathode)	r_{h-k}	
Resistance between control-grid and cathode	r_{g1-k}	R_{g1-k}
Capacitance (cold)		
Anode to all other electrodes	c_{a-all}	
Anode to control-grid	c_{a-g1}	
Control grid to cathode at working temperature	$c_{g1-k(w)}$	
Control-grid to all other electrodes except anode (input capacitance)	c_{in}	
Anode to all other electrodes except control-grid (output capacitance)	c_{out}	
Inner amplification factor	μ_{g1-g2}	

APPENDIX 1

GRAPHICAL SYMBOLS USED IN CIRCUIT DIAGRAMS

In the following pages are reproduced a number of the graphical symbols most frequently encountered in circuit diagrams of electronic equipment, to represent various circuit elements and devices. They have been selected from B.S. 530, " British Standard Graphical Symbols for Telecommunications " and its various Supplements, to which the reader is referred for a more comprehensive presentation. It is assumed that the reader will already be familiar with the symbols employed in conventional light and heavy current electrical engineering diagrams.

GENERAL CIRCUIT ELEMENTS

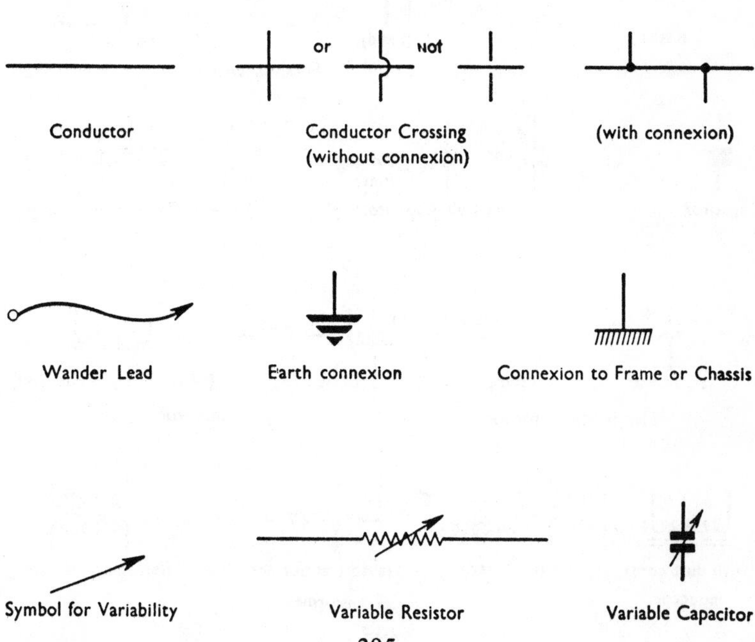

Appendix 1

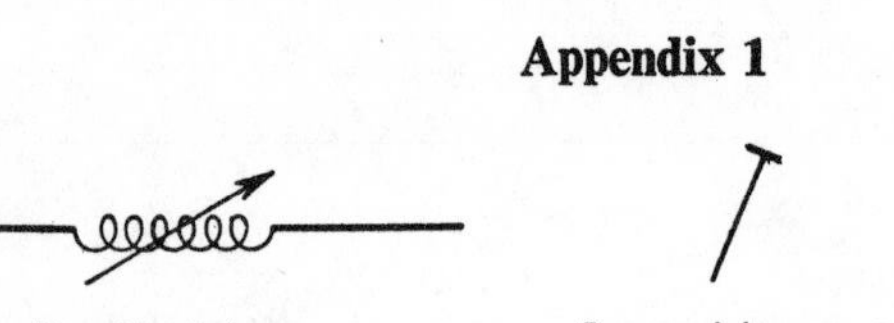

Variable Inductor Pre-set Adjustment Ganged Controls

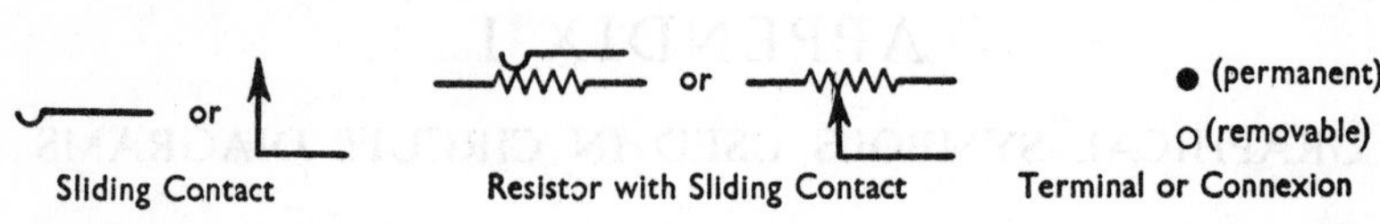

Sliding Contact Resistor with Sliding Contact Terminal or Connexion

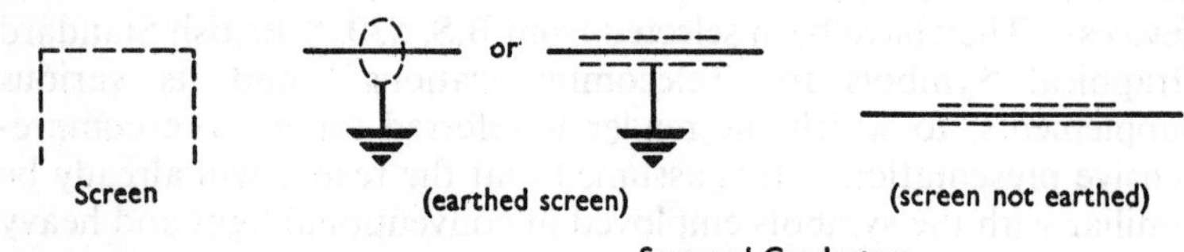

Screen (earthed screen) (screen not earthed)

Screened Conductors

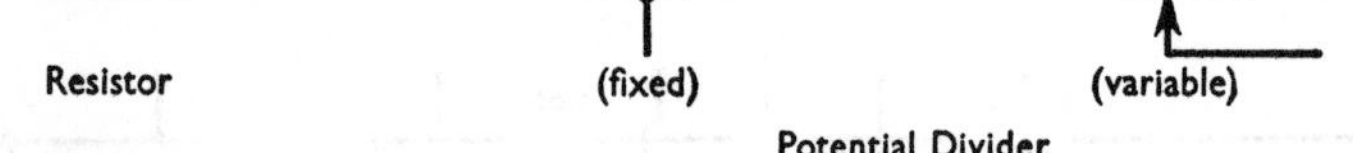

Resistor (fixed) (variable)

Potential Divider

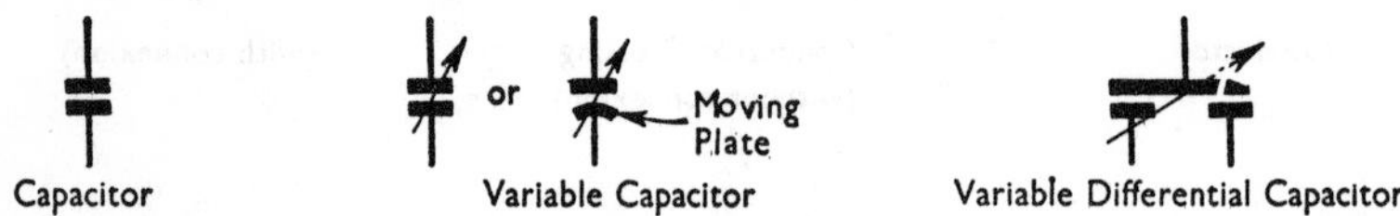

Capacitor Variable Capacitor Variable Differential Capacitor

(polarized) (non-polarized) (air-cored); (with ferromagnetic core)

Electrolytic Capacitor Inductor

(with dust core) (air-cored) (auto transformer) (ferromagnetic core)

Inductor Transformer

Appendix 1

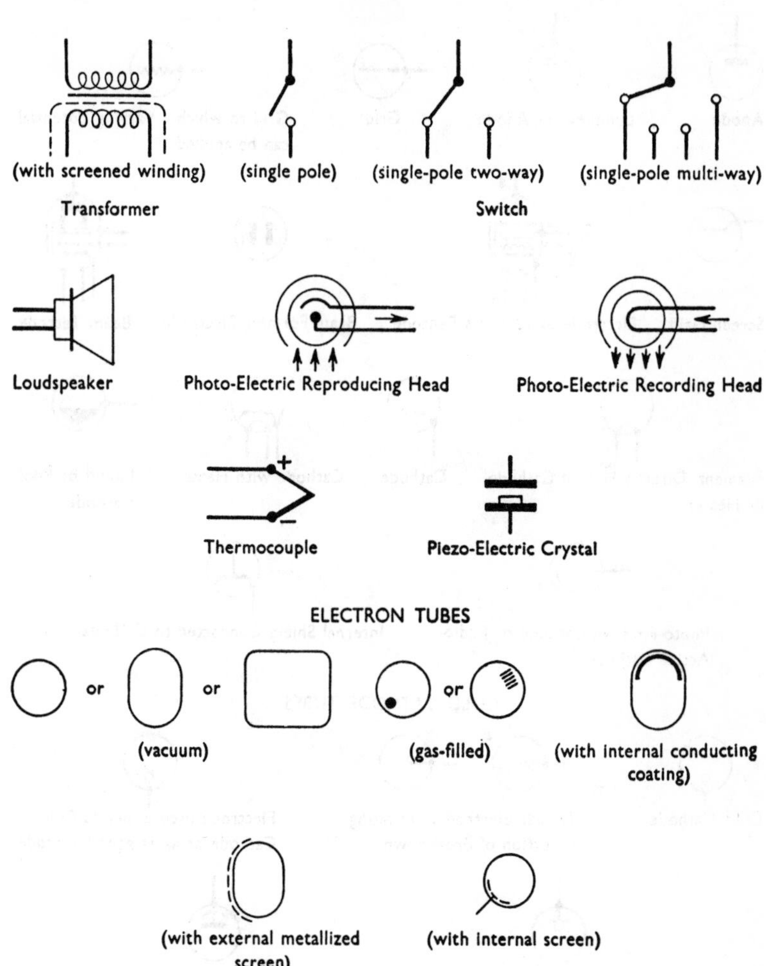

Valve Envelopes

Appendix 1

VALVE ELECTRODES

Anode

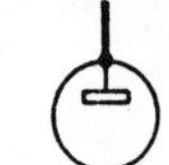
Luminescent Anode

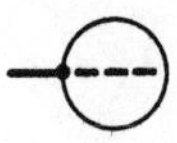
Grid

Grid to which a Varying Potential can be applied

Screen Grid

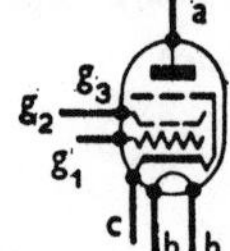

Electrode System of a Pentode

Beam Forming Electrode

Beam Tetrode

Filament, Directly-Heated Cathode, or Heater

Cathode

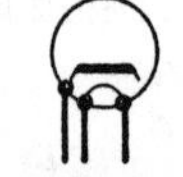
Cathode with Heater

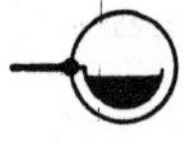
Liquid or Pool Cathode

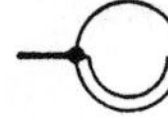
Photo-Emissive Cathode or Radio-Active Cathode

Internal Shield Connected to Cathode

COLD CATHODE TUBES

Cold Cathode

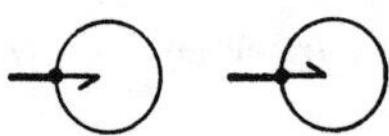
Trigger Electrode, Indicating Direction of Breakdown

Electrode used either as Cold Cathode or as Trigger Electrode

Electrode used either as Anode or as Cold Cathode

Dynode or Secondary Emission Electrode

Electrode with special function not covered in previous Symbols

Appendix 1

HIGH VACUUM TUBES

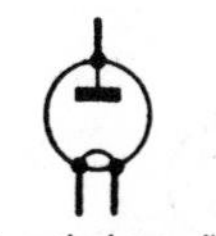

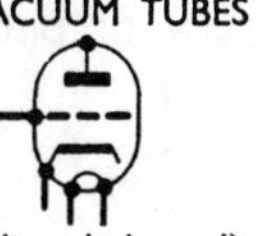

(directly-heated) Diode

(directly-heated) (indirectly-heated) Triode

Indirectly-Heated Triode with Metallized Envelope

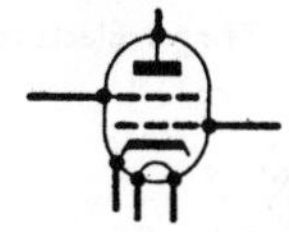

Indirectly-Heated Tetrode

Tetrode, Directly Heated

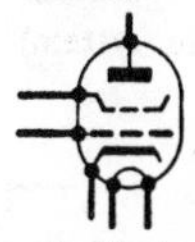

Indirectly-Heated Screen Grid Valve

Variable-Mu Indirectly-Heated Screen Grid Valve

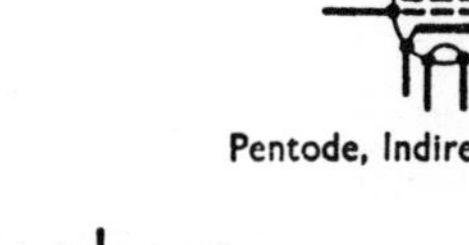

Pentode, Indirectly Heated

Pentode, Indirectly Heated with Suppressor Grid Connected Internally to Cathode

Heptode, Variable-Mu, Indirectly Heated

Half-Wave Rectifier Indirectly Heated

Full-Wave Rectifier, Indirectly Heated

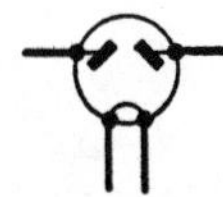

Full-Wave Rectifier, Directly Heated

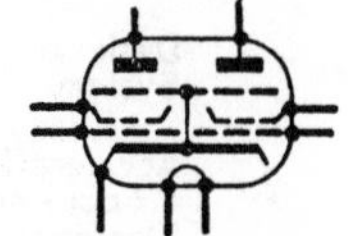

Double Pentode Indirectly Heated

Cathode-Ray Tuning Indicator

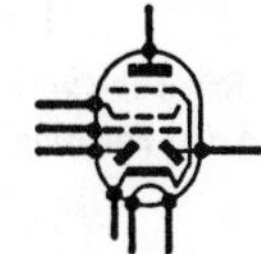

Double-Diode-Pentode, Indirectly Heated

Photo-Emissive Cell

Photo-Conductive Cell (arrows show direction of incidence of the radiation)

Appendix 1

COLD CATHODE DISCHARGE TUBES

(with symmetrical electrode system)

(with asymmetrical electrodes)

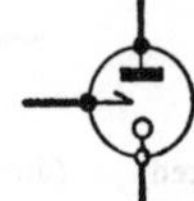

Trigger Tube striking between Anode and Trigger Electrode

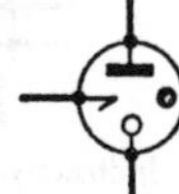

Trigger Tube striking between Cathode and Trigger Electrode

Trigger Tube in which Cathode and Trigger Electrode are Interchangeable

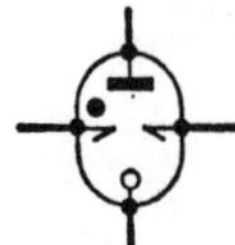

Trigger Tube with Two Trigger Electrodes

CATHODE-RAY TUBES ETC.

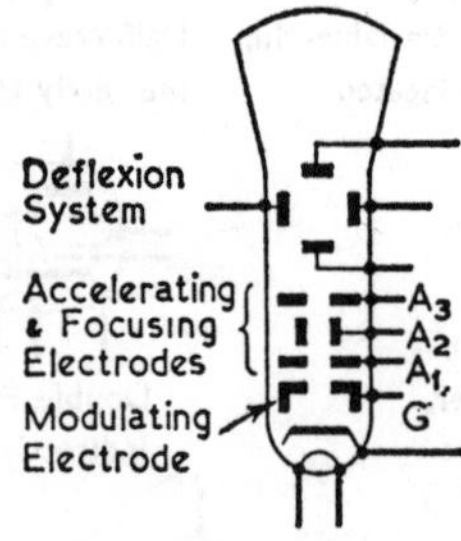

Cathode-Ray Tube with Electrostatic Deflexion and Focusing Systems

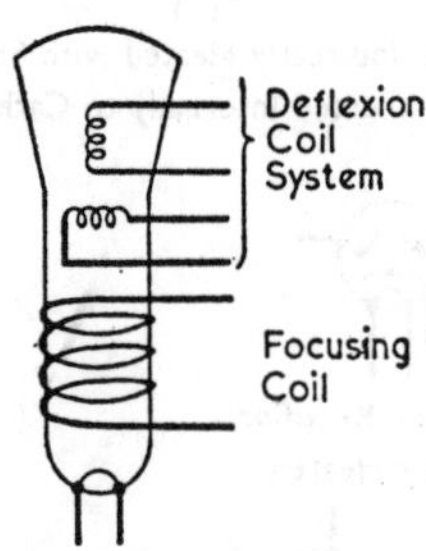

Cathode-Ray Tube with Magnetic Deflexion and Focusing Systems (electron gun system can be included if desired)

Vision Pick-up Tube (TV Camera Tube) —(Details of Electron Gun may be added if desired)

Appendix 1

MICROWAVE TUBES

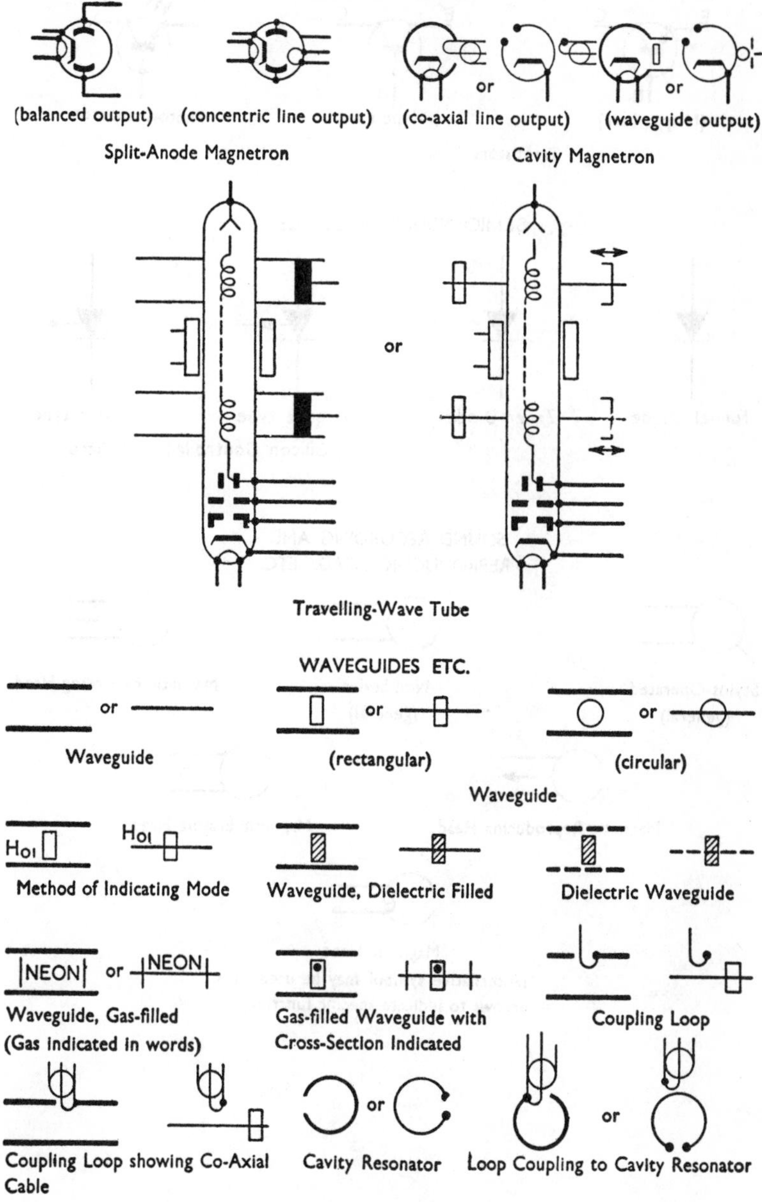

Appendix 1

TRANSISTORS

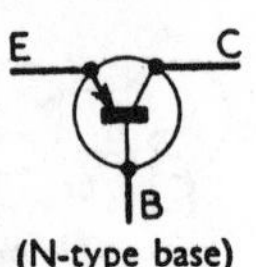

(N-type base)

E C B

(P-type base)

Photo-Transistor

Transistors

SEMICONDUCTOR DEVICES

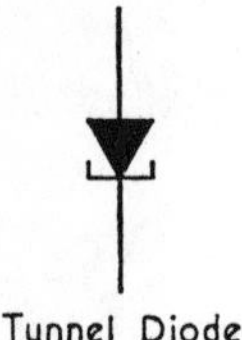

Tunnel Diode

Zener Diode

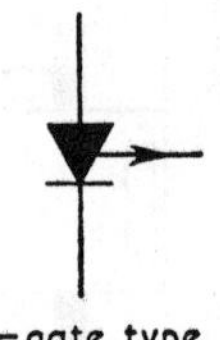

N—gate type

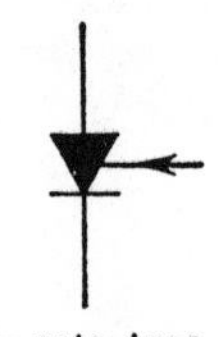

P—gate type

Silicon Controlled Rectifiers

SOUND RECORDING AND REPRODUCING HEADS ETC.

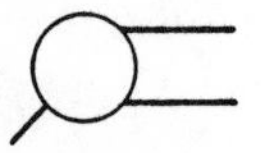

Stylus-Operated (general)

Non-Stylus (general)

Magnetic Recording Head

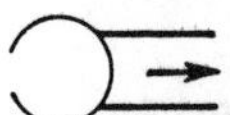

Magnetic Reproducing Head

Magnetic Erasing Head

Magnetic Head (Alternative symbol may be used with arrows to indicate specific function)

APPENDIX 2

COLOUR CODES FOR COMPONENTS

Fixed-value resistors and ceramic capacitors, and also cartridge-type safety fuses of the types used in large numbers in electronic equipment, are of small physical dimensions and for this reason, and also because of their shape, it is not always easy to mark them with their values in clear figures. Codes have therefore been devised whereby the values can be indicated by arrangements of coloured markings on the body of the component.

Fixed-value resistors

The code consists of four colour bands arranged as shown in the illustration below.

The indications are as follows:

First colour, " A " . .	First digit of resistance in ohms
Second colour, " B " . .	Second digit of resistance value
Third colour, " C " . .	Multiplier
Fourth colour, " D " . .	Tolerance on value

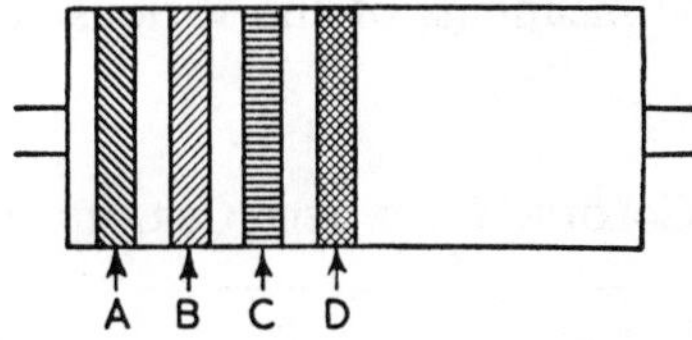

COLOUR BANDS ON A RESISTOR

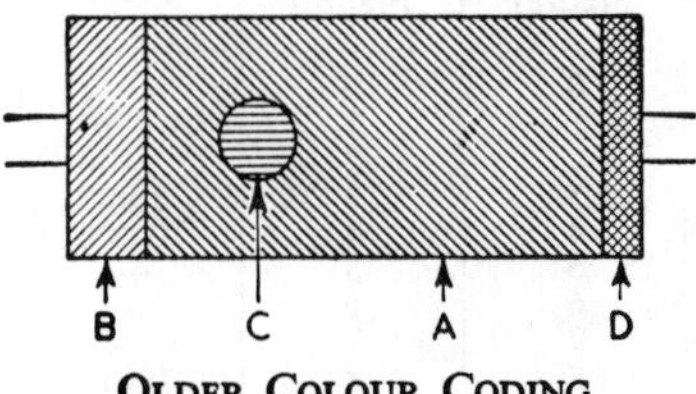

OLDER COLOUR CODING

The significance of the different colours is given in Table 1.

Appendix 2

TABLE 1.—FOUR-BAND COLOUR CODE FOR FIXED RESISTORS

Colour	1st Figure "A"	2nd Figure "B"	Multiplying Value "C"	Tolerance "D" (%)
Silver . . .	—	—	10^{-2}	±10
Gold . . .	—	—	10^{-1}	± 5
Black . . .	—	0	1	—
Brown . . .	1	1	10	± 1
Red . . .	2	2	10^{2}	± 2
Orange . . .	3	3	10^{3}	—
Yellow . . .	4	4	10^{4}	—
Green . . .	5	5	10^{5}	—
Blue . . .	6	6	10^{6}	—
Violet . . .	7	7	10^{7}	—
Grey . . .	8	8	10^{8}	—
White . . .	9	9	10^{9}	—
None . . .	—	—	—	±20

Fixed-value ceramic capacitors

The code consists of an " end colour " indicating the temperature coefficient in parts per million per °C, " N " signifying negative and " P " signifying positive; and four coloured dots indicating respectively the first and second significant figures, the multiplier and the tolerance. The meanings of the various colours are given in Table 2.

TABLE 2.—COLOUR CODE FOR CERAMIC CAPACITORS

Colour	End Colour (Temperature Coefficient)	1st Dot (1st Significant Figure)	2nd Dot (2nd Significant Figure)	3rd Dot (Multiplier)	4th Dot (Tolerance)	
					10 pF or Less	More than 10 pF
Black .	NP0	0	0	1	±2·0 pF	±20%
Brown .	N030	1	1	10	±0·1 pF	± 1%
Red .	N080	2	2	100	—	± 2%
Orange .	N150	3	3	1,000	—	± 2·5%
Yellow .	N220	4	4	10,000	—	—
Green .	N330	5	5	—	±0·5 pF	± 5%
Blue .	N470	6	6	—	—	—
Violet .	N750	7	7	—	—	—
Grey .	P030	8	8	0·01	±0·25 pF	—
White .	P100	9	9	0·1	±1·0 pF	±10%

Appendix 3

Current-operated cartridge fuses

The colour coding for ratings between 0·01 A and 10·0 A is as follows:

TABLE 3.—COLOUR CODE FOR CURRENT-OPERATED FUSES

Colour	Rating (A)	Colour	Rating (A)
Green and yellow .	0·010	Green . . .	0·750
Red and turquoise .	0·015	Blue . . .	1·0
Eau-de-Nil . .	0·025	Light blue . .	1·5
Salmon pink . .	0·050	Purple . . .	2·0
Black . . .	0·060	Yellow and purple.	2·5
Grey . . .	0·100	White . . .	3·0
Red . . .	0·150	Black and white .	5·0
Brown . . .	0·250	Orange . . .	10·0
Yellow . . .	0·500		

(*British Standards Institution*)

APPENDIX 3

DECIBEL CONVERSION TABLES

The ratio of two powers (P_2/P_1) or of two voltages (E_2/E_1) or of two currents (I_2/I_1) can be expressed in decibels in accordance with the following formulae in which N stands for the number of decibels:

$$\text{Power ratio } N = 10 \log_{10} (P_2/P_1)$$
$$\text{Voltage ratio } N = 20 \log_{10} (E_2/E_1)$$
$$\text{Current ratio } N = 20 \log_{10} (I_2/I_1)$$

The tables below enable simple ratios to be converted into decibels, and vice versa, without recourse to tables of logarithms and antilogarithms.

Appendix 3

TABLE 4.—CONVERSION OF POWER, VOLTAGE OR CURRENT RATIOS TO DECIBELS

Power Ratio	dB	Power Ratio	dB	Power Ratio	dB	Power Ratio	dB
1·0	0·000	3·3	5·185	5·6	7·482	7·9	8·976
1·1	0·414	3·4	5·315	5·7	7·559	8·0	9·031
1·2	0·792	3·5	5·441	5·8	7·634	8·1	9·085
1·3	1·139	3·6	5·563	5·9	7·709	8·2	9·138
1·4	1·461	3·7	5·682	6·0	7·782	8·3	9·191
1·5	1·761	3·8	5·798	6·1	7·853	8·4	9·243
1·6	2·041	3·9	5·911	6·2	7·924	8·5	9·294
1·7	2·304	4·0	6·021	6·3	7·993	8·6	9·345
1·8	2·553	4·1	6·128	6·4	8·062	8·7	9·395
1·9	2·788	4·2	6·232	6·5	8·129	8·8	9·445
2·0	3·010	4·3	6·335	6·6	8·195	8·9	9·494
2·1	3·222	4·4	6·435	6·7	8·261	9·0	9·542
2·2	3·424	4·5	6·532	6·8	8·325	9·1	9·590
2·3	3·617	4·6	6·628	6·9	8·388	9·2	9·638
2·4	3·802	4·7	6·721	7·0	8·451	9·3	9·685
2·5	3·979	4·8	6·812	7·1	8·513	9·4	9·731
2·6	4·150	4·9	6·902	7·2	8·573	9·5	9·777
2·7	4·314	5·0	6·990	7·3	8·633	9·6	9·823
2·8	4·472	5·1	7·076	7·4	8·692	9·7	9·868
2·9	4·624	5·2	7·160	7·5	8·751	9·8	9·912
3·0	4·771	5·3	7·243	7·6	8·808	9·9	9·956
3·1	4·914	5·4	7·324	7·7	8·865	10·0	10·000
3·2	5·051	5·5	7·404	7·8	8·921		

Notes

(1) The above table gives conversions for power ratios only. For voltage or current ratios treat figures in the " power ratio " column as voltage or current ratios and double the corresponding number of decibels.

(2) For ratios greater than 10, divide the given ratio by 10 a sufficient number of times to produce a final quotient less than 10, and add 10 dB (power) or 20 dB (voltage or current) for each such division by 10.

(3) If the input and output impedances are not equal, voltage current gains or losses must be specified with reference to input and output impedances.

TABLE 5.—CONVERSION OF DECIBELS TO POWER, VOLTAGE OR CURRENT RATIOS

Gain			Loss	
Power Ratio	Voltage or Current Ratio	+dB-	Power Ratio	Voltage or Current Ratio
1·000	1·000	0	1·0000	1·0000
1·259	1·122	1	0·7943	0·8193
1·585	1·259	2	0·6310	0·7943
1·995	1·413	3	0·5012	0·7079
2·512	1·585	4	0·3981	0·6310
3·162	1·778	5	0·3162	0·5623
3·981	1·995	6	0·2512	0·5012
5·012	2·239	7	0·1995	0·4467
6·310	2·512	8	0·1585	0·3981
7·943	2·818	9	0·1259	0·3548
10	$3{\cdot}162$	10	10^{-1}	$3{\cdot}162 \times 10$
10^2	10	20	10^{-2}	10^{-1}
10^3	$3{\cdot}162 \times 10$	30	10^{-3}	$3{\cdot}162 \times 10^{-1}$
10^4	10^2	40	10^{-4}	10^{-2}
10^5	$3{\cdot}162 \times 10^2$	50	10^{-5}	$3{\cdot}162 \times 10^{-2}$
10^6	10^3	60	10^{-6}	10^{-3}
10^7	$3{\cdot}162 \times 10^3$	70	10^{-7}	$3{\cdot}162 \times 10^{-3}$
10^8	10^4	80	10^{-8}	10^{-4}
10^9	$3{\cdot}162 \times 10^4$	90	10^{-9}	$3{\cdot}162 \times 10^{-4}$
10^{10}	10^5	100	10^{-10}	10^{-5}

APPENDIX 4

THE ELECTROMAGNETIC SPECTRUM

The frequency (or wavelength) range of explored electromagnetic radiation extends from about 10^{20} cycles per second down to about 10,000 cycles per second (wavelengths from about 0·03 Å to 3×10^{14} Å or 30 km). This spectrum can be conveniently divided into six principal bands according to the behaviour and effects of the waves. This primary classification is given overleaf:

Appendix 4

Frequency (c/s)	Wavelength (Å)	Type of Wave
6×10^{21}–3×10^{19}	0·005–0·1	Gamma waves
6×10^{19}–6×10^{16}	0·05–50	X-rays
10^{17}–8×10^{14}	25–4000	Ultra-violet light
8×10^{15}–4×10^{15}	4000–8000	Visible light
4×10^{15}–7×10^{11}	8000–4,000,000	Infra red
3×10^{12}–10,000	10^{6}–3×10^{14} (0·1 mm–30 km)	" Radio " waves

Radio-frequency spectrum

" Radio " waves are classified in terms of their frequency band or wavelength range as follows:

Frequency	Wavelength	Classification
Less than 30 kc/s	Above 10,000 m	Very low frequency or Myriametric
30–300 kc/s	10,000–1000 m	Low frequency or Kilometric
300 kc/s–3 Mc/s	1000–100 m	Medium frequency or Hectometric
3–30 Mc/s	100–10 m	High frequency or Decametric
30–300 Mc/s	10–1·0 m	Very high frequency or Metric
300–3000 Mc/s	1·0–0·1 m	Ultra high frequency or Decimetric
3–30 Gc/s	0·1–0·01 m	Super high frequency or Centimetric
30–300 Gc/s	0·01–0·001 m	Extra high frequency or Millimetric
300–3000 Gc/s	0·001–0·0001 m	Decimillimetric

APPENDIX 5

VALVE BASES

The drawings show the principal standard arrangements of the connexions, usually metal pins, on the bases of electron tubes, and of the mating contacts in the corresponding valve sockets (valve holders). The connexions are shown *as viewed from the pin-end of the tube.*

Correct location of the tube in the socket is ensured by the irregular arrangement of the pins and sockets (e.g. B7G) or by the use of pins of two different diameters (e.g. UX-7-Pin) or by locating devices such as mating indentations and projections (e.g. B12A) or in some cases by coloured spots or bands (e.g. B5A).

Manufacturers' published data always indicates the type of base for each type of tube, and includes a diagram showing to which pin each electrode is connected.

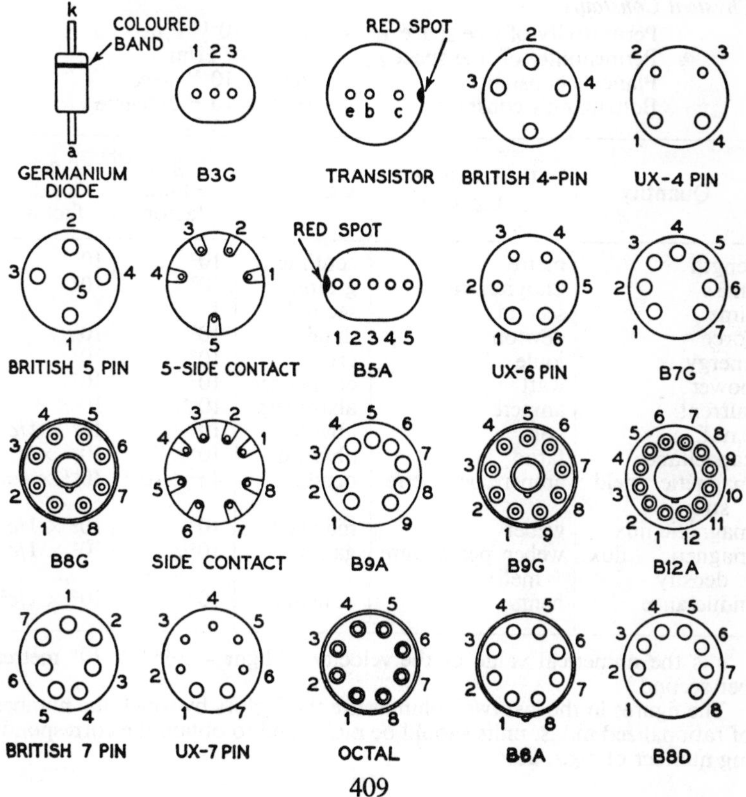

APPENDIX 6

RATIONALIZED M.K.S. UNITS

For the assistance of scientists and technicians who are as yet unfamiliar with these units, the table which follows shows how the general and basic electronic units in the rationalized metre-kilogramme-second system are related to the corresponding electromagnetic and electrostatic units in the centimetre-gramme-second (c.g.s.) system. For the purposes of electronics it is necessary to introduce the concept of charge in order to define electrical phenomena, and the properties of free space are chosen as reference. Thus the permittivity and the permeability of free space, each arbitrarily unity in the c.g.s. system, have distinct values chosen so that the units of electricity so derived are close to the practical units in common use, e.g. ampere, watt. Rationalized m.k.s. units may be converted one into another without the use of a conversion factor, i.e. they are in one to one ratio.

Physical Constants

Permittivity of free space $\chi_0 = 8{\cdot}854 \times 10^{-12}$ F/m
Permeability of free space $\mu_0 = 4\pi \times 10^{-7}$ H/m
Planck's constant $= 6{\cdot}624 \times 10^{-34}$ J-sec
Boltzmann's constant $= 1{\cdot}380 \times 10^{-23}$ J/degree

Quantity	Rationalized m.k.s. unit	c.g.s. unit	c.g.s. e.m.u. factor	c.g.s. e.s.u. factor
length	metre	centimetre	10^2	10^2
mass	kilogramme	gramme	10^3	10^3
time	second	second	1	1
force	newton	dyne	10^5	10^5
energy	joule	erg	10^7	10^7
power	watt	erg per sec	10^7	10^7
current	ampere	abampere	10^{-1}	$10 \times c$
e.m.f.	volt	abvolt	10^8	$10^6 \times 1/c$
capacitance	farad	abfarad	10^{-9}	$10^{-5} \times c^2$
magnetic field strength	ampere per metre	oersted	$4\pi \times 10^{-3}$	$10^{-1} \times 4\pi c$
magnetic flux	weber	maxwell	10^8	$10^6 \times 1/c$
magnetic flux density	weber per square metre	gauss	10^4	$10^2 \times 1/c$
inductance	henry	abhenry	10^9	$10^5 \times 1/c^2$

c is the numerical value of the velocity of light $= 2{\cdot}998 \times 10^8$ metres per second.

The figures in the last two columns are the factors by which the number of rationalized m.k.s. units should be multiplied to obtain the corresponding number of c.g.s. units.

WITHDRAWAL